John Alan Maxwell

VAIN SHADOW

VAIN SHADOW

BY HARTZELL SPENCE

PEOPLES BOOK CLUB, CHICAGO

This is a special edition published exclusively for the members of the PEOPLES BOOK CLUB, P.O. BOX 6570A, Chicago, Illinois. It was originally published by Whittlesey House, a division of McGraw Hill, Inc.

To
PAUL FEJOS
*Who might have written this book
so much better*

Introduction

IN THE year 1541 a one-eyed Spaniard, Don Francisco Orellana, crossed over from what is now Ecuador into the headwaters of the Amazon, and discovered the mightiest river in the world.

Vast stretches of that river remain today exactly as they were four hundred years ago, when Orellana first saw them. The descriptions of the river in this book are as I myself saw it in 1941, and as you may see it if you will go there now. Within the past decade, a scientific expedition into the upper basin, bearing the most modern equipment known to civilized man, was forced by fierce savages and fiercer sicknesses, to flee the jungle.

Yet Francisco Orellana, without medicines, maps, or scientific data, without even knowing where he was, transiently mastered the river four hundred years ago, an incredible achievement in the light of modern knowledge.

When Orellana set out upon the river, he was a Spanish conquistador, ambitious to become a colonial governor. He emerged completely changed in character. His charter for the colonization of New Andalusia, a land without slavery, without racial or social discrimination, might well serve as a model today, since no nation has achieved its lofty concepts.

Oddly enough, Orellana has failed to reach the historical stature to which his life entitles him. As careful a scholar as William H. Prescott established the myth that Orellana was a scoundrel, and for the last one hundred years Prescott's estimate has been the standard reference. After more than three years of research, I am convinced that my present version of Orellana's conduct is the true one, and that he was unusually enlightened not only for his own dark age, but for any period in history.

This book might have been written either as a biography or as a novel. In the process of its development it turned out to be what, for lack of better definition, I call a romantic biography.

As such it is a reconstruction of the life of Orellana from available sources. Where provable facts are lacking, I have chosen to do in words what the architects did in masonry at the restoration of Colonial Williamsburg, Virginia: augment the existing materials with colorful authenticities of the period, in order that the whole impression be at once true and vivid.

I have deviated from known fact in very few particulars. Two villainous priests, Friar de Vera in the New World and Friar de Torres in Spain, have been incorporated into a single character. I have employed the same device to team several other personalities, to prevent the narrative from becoming cluttered with characters, and to give story continuity to events that took place in both the Old World and the New.

It is necessary to add that I turned to the life of Francisco Orellana at the suggestion of Dr. Paul Fejos, the archeologist, and that he, and his Viking Fund colleagues, greatly assisted me in my researches.

HARTZELL SPENCE

I

THE LITTLE city of Quito lay deep in the shadows of the setting sun, as though crouching against the hard wind that blew across the Andean plain. The day had been warm, as it is even in midwinter in a land so close to the sun, but now the cold returned to the city from the high mountains, and the women wrapped llama scarves across their mouths to keep out the dampness.

Only three women were in the streets, hurrying past the granite edifices the Incas had built, and the white stucco cottages of the conquerors. There were no men anywhere except an aged chaperone of the women, and no dogs, either, which was strange for a city of many dogs.

Out of the sunset, and through the central square, filed a weary body of Spanish soldiers, richly clad. Twenty-four men there were, fourteen ahorse, trailed by fifty Indians bearing luxurious luggage. At their head, on a black Basque stallion, rode an illustriously caparisoned knight.

The three women of Quito turned on him the sharp eye women always have for strangers. That he was rich was beyond doubt. The trappings of his party were magnificent, and equipment was expensive in the new world: twelve thousand dollars for a horse, eight hundred dollars for a pair of high boots, two thousand dollars for a cloak. Mother of God! Here was a man whose detachment represented an outlay of four hundred thousand dollars at least. Beyond doubt he was one of the conquerors of Peru. They alone had so much gold.

He was not a large man, perhaps five feet eight or nine, but he was lithe, hard as a Portuguese nail, and steel muscles in his wrists curbed his fretful stallion. His gauntleted hands were huge, and his legs handsome. He was young, too; not over thirty. The women began to primp. But their hands froze to their hair as the gentleman turned his head and looked down at them.

In his face was a gaping, jagged scar where the left eye should have been, such a scar as eclipsed completely his good bronzed forehead, his long Roman nose, and a jaw so sharp and chiseled that not even a full black beard screened it. He looked at them, and from his right eye shot the hypnotic flash of ten devils.

The women instinctively crossed themselves. The knight frowned, turned away, and rode on.

He dismissed his troop at the edge of the square, gave his horse to an Indian page, walked strongly down a little street to a new house and knocked. The door was opened by a white-haired old warrior of Castile.

"By all the Saints," he exclaimed. "Francisco, my lad, come in."

Don Francisco Orellana, a captain general of Peru, lieutenant governor of La Culata and Puerto Viejo on the Ecuadorian coast, founder and mayor of the city of Guayaquil, entered, threw off his cloak and gloves, and sank wearily upon a bed.

García Tapia helped him unstrap his surcoat and unbuckle his sword and dagger.

"You are a week too late," Tapia said. "His Excellency has gone."

Orellana nodded. "It is evident," he said.

Tapia stroked his rough beard for a moment, looking down at his dejected young friend, then quickly brought from the cupboard a bottle of precious brandy. Orellana brightened, strode to his luggage and returned with a great gold cup. Much honored, Tapia poured.

"The Saints still look after you, Francisco," the old man said. "Now you do not have to go."

The gold cup was rich and warm under Orellana's hand, and he caressed it with his thumb. Brandy, he thought, tastes better in glass, but warms the heart more in gold. The cup was honest, straightforward in design, and meant to quench a thirst. It held all of an azumbre —two quarts—if García had enough liquor to fill it. Its double handles were condor heads, and the wings spread back along the rim of the

2

cup until they touched in the center. Below the outstretched wings were intaglio mountains, with vicuña grazing in a valley, and a lookout in a tall knit cap scanning the valley from behind a masonry wall.

"It is beautiful," Tapia murmured. "I remember when you won it at Cuzco. But why did you bring it with you? An expedition is no place for such treasures."

"Everything I own I have brought along," Orellana said. "All my possessions in Guayaquil went to furnish my men."

"Everything! Nombre de Dios, Francisco. Was that wise?"

"Once in a man's life he must risk everything he has. This is the moment."

"And if you fail?"

Orellana drank deeply of the brandy, holding the cup by both its handles. "If I fail," he replied, "I still have the cup—and this."

He reached inside his shirt, withdrew a vicuña sack, opened its draw string and spread out a fortune in emeralds. Tapia gasped.

"Enough for a new start," Orellana said, and put the sack away hurriedly. "But I shall not fail."

"My boy," Tapia said, shaking his head, "not even the help of all the Saints can bring Don Gonzalo Pizarro back alive. Of all the foolhardy undertakings, this of Gonzalo is the worst. Believe me—I have been over the mountains."

"You came back," Orellana said. He was fond of Tapia, with the gentle affection born of perspective and separation. Once they had been companions in Panama. That had been long ago, and Tapia had changed. No longer did the woman-quest flash in his black eyes, and his hair was muddy white. He had a fine house, built upon the foundation of an Inca palace, and he was comfortable, surrounded by Indian slaves and self-importance. His share of the Inca gold was enough to keep him the rest of his days which, Orellana thought, judging from the flabby cheeks, the flushed face, the red-veined nose, would not be many.

"Yes, I came back," Tapia said, sniffing his drink, "but it was a miracle of my patron, Saint Bartolomé. I thank him in my prayers to

3

this day." He looked up gloomily. "The mountains are purgatory, and so I shall go straight to heaven when I die. Return to Guayaquil!"

"No. I must go. I gave my word."

"What good can your two dozen men be in a field already too large?" Tapia asked irritably. "Ten men, without Indians or horses, might get to the land of Cinnamon, and five might return. But two hundred! Name of God, son, how will two hundred survive the jungle? Who will feed them? They had to leave Quito a week early because there was not enough here to fill their ravenous bellies. That's how you missed them. How will they, who travel like Knights of Calatrava, live off a few miserable Indian villages?"

"That's Don Gonzalo's problem," Orellana said, "not mine."

"All right then. How will you ever catch up to him? At least he has highland Indians, who are used to the mountains, and horses that have become acclimatized to these summits. Your Indians are from the seashore swamps, and your horses, too. They will die like flies before you have gone a hundred miles."

"You underestimate the stamina of our lowland animals," Orellana said.

"Indeed not! I have had the mountain sickness. It takes more than Spanish courage to survive it. It takes years of living in it. Gonzalo's Indians have lived here all their lives; yours have not, and yours will die."

"It is a risk I must run." He changed the subject abruptly. "How many went with His Excellency?"

Tapia shook his head sadly, and described Don Gonzalo's departure. A force larger than that with which the conquistadores had defeated the Inca Atahualpa had accompanied him on his journey. Two hundred thirty men, two hundred horses, four thousand Indians and a score of black slaves formed a procession five miles long. Gonzalo had carried with him a dining table, and six sets of armor. With llamas as beasts of burden, two thousand live hogs and many fowl, two thousand fierce dogs to keep the Indians in line, and two priests to do the same for the Christians, Don Gonzalo had marched from the square in

Quito a week before, after a dawn mass at the unfinished church of San Francisco. Trumpets, bugles, drums, and the shrill dissonance of native pipes and strings had sped him on his way. Almost the entire city had accompanied him the first half day's march northeastward across the windswept waste of Yaruqui which rolls into the Cordillera Oriente of the Andes at the Guamani and Pambamarca mountains. Now the city was devoid of men, except for a few cripples and the aged. The boys had gone along as pages; even Gonzalo's enemies were included in the party, for he dared not leave them behind. Every repartimiento had been stripped to provide Indian guides and porters. There was not even a dog left to scratch fleas beside the well in the public square. Some men, weary of conquest, had not wanted to go, but Gonzalo was firm. Their lands and slaves, which they held through the tolerance of Gonzalo's brother the Marquis, might be canceled unless the proper loyalty were shown to the Marquis' brother. Thus they went to protect what they had.

They were not a gay crowd, Tapia said. A few of them had been over the mountains before, with Benalcázar or Alvarado, and had no stomach for the mountain sickness, the freezing bitter cold, the snow-drifts, the declivities, and the great condors that would follow the party and feast upon the faint. Even fewer wished to penetrate the tropics that lay beyond the mountains, for they were weary now of conquest, and tales of cannibals with poisoned weapons tarnished the lure of gold. The Spaniards of Peru were surfeited with gold, but they went with Don Gonzalo, because there was nothing else to do.

Orellana listened, carefully wiping the dregs of brandy from the gold cup, lest a thousand ants invade its sweetness before morning.

"Look." Tapia became confidential. "No one is left here now. The strongest man in the province is yourself. The largest band is your own. Stay here. Then when Gonzalo does not return—" he paused, gazing sharply at the younger man, "—who better than yourself to take over? Eh, man? What a chance! Stay, and I will help you."

"You have had too much drink, amigo," Orellana said, rising and

5

replacing the gold cup in his baggage. "Don Gonzalo will come back, and I shall be with him. It is my big chance."

"You are still determined, then, to become a governor?"

Orellana sprawled again upon the bed and considered his reply seriously. "What other opportunity is there," he said finally, "for an ugly man in the new world? Today, entering Quito, three women crossed themselves when they saw my face. No, no, García. I must go. You do not know what it is like to be alone, to have women turn from you. I have had gold in Guayaquil. It is not enough. I must be great, too. Then I shall not look so ugly, and some woman will have me."

Obviously, Tapia was not convinced. He knew Orellana well enough to recognize a mask, but not to see behind it.

"Look you," Orellana said. "Before I left Guayaquil. . . ." He told Tapia what he had done. His last act, before setting out from the coast, had been to put through the court a Memorial, duly witnessed, of all his past services to His Majesty the King. There it all lay, in writing: his qualifications for government, his record as an hidalgo and horseman at arms, an enumeration of his losses, including one eye, in the royal service. This petition now was en route to Spain. The men on the Council of the Indies could not help but be impressed; and the man who bestowed governorships in Peru, Francisco Pizarro, now Marquis del Valle, would be justified by the written record in establishing Orellana as governor of Quito, in good time. First, however, he must assist the present governor, Francisco's bastard half-brother, in a perilous enterprise. Then Gonzalo, surfeited, would step down, and Orellana would step up.

"But are you sure this will happen?"

"As certain as one can ever be of Spanish honor," Orellana replied. "I promised Gonzalo sixteen men and twelve horses, and I have more than kept my word. He promised me the governorship, and he will answer to me for it, even though my sword must remind him."

"Then nothing can stop you?"

"Nothing. I have given my word."

6

Tapia yawned and removed his shoes.

"In that case, I speak no more," he said. "In a world of liars, your word is still good. Goodnight, my friend. Sleep well. It is the last rest you will have for many months."

ORELLANA set out toward the mountains the next day at dawn. He was excited, as he had not been since the day in Panama, nine years before, when he had first seen the great Francisco Pizarro, and knew that he was setting out to conquer an unknown land. For the past two years he had stagnated in Guayaquil, and now he was off again, upon an adventure into the unknown, pursuing the rainbow that led to gold.

This time, however, he sought more than gold, and knew that he must find it. It was all very well to tell Tapia that his quest was for a woman. The simple old soldier could understand that. There was more, however, a great deal more, before him; more even, he thought, than he himself could see. Rather, he felt it, and that was the reason for his great excitement this morning.

Peru now was conquered. The Marquis Pizarro was building a costly city at Lima, where the conquerors would be grandees. Soon Peru would be like Spain, and he who had gold and position would be as illustrious as was the Marquis of Priego in Orellana's native province of Estramadura. Even in little Guayaquil, on the banks of the stinking Guayas river, Orellana could see the approach of Spanish civilization. For two years, living in his great house, he had seen it coming. Unlike his companions among the conquerors, however, Orellana did not welcome the encroachment of civilized Spain upon the New World. It brought with it all the old questions from which Orellana had run away.

He had not been impelled by excitement to the New World. He had been too young for war. He had run away from home, urged by an impulse that came over him like a clean breeze while he sat before his parish church listening to a story from the New World, where everything was fresh. At home there were too many questions that no one ever answered. He remembered his longing to read, and the parish priest's answer: "The Word is the Word of God and may be read only by God's vicars. They will interpret for you all that you need to know." And he recalled the sermons he had heard, telling him to believe blindly and not ask questions, when the whole world about him was a question that begged an answer.

Now all that was coming to Peru. Of course it had never been far away. He had seen slaves in Panama, had owned five hundred of them in Guayaquil. He had seen holy zeal burn so brightly that the Indians were burned for resisting Christians. He had seen Friar Valverde, standing in the square at Caxamarca, rage mad and foaming at the lips when a savage who could not read had thrown the missal of the church unheedingly to the ground. For what he considered an insult to Holy Writ, Valverde had caused a massacre with the angry words to Pizarro: "Do you not see that while we stand here wasting our breath talking to this dog, full of pride as he is, the fields are filling with Indians? Set on at once; I absolve you!" The Indians had died, caught like rabbits in a corral in their own walled square; men who knew no steel and no Christianity, cut down by Christians with cold steel and cannon.

He looked back along the trail. In perfect order his troop was following. Ahead, the slope was gentle, with only the giant peaks beyond hinting at the trial that was to come. He settled into his saddle for another long hour.

Wherever there were Spaniards, he thought, turning his mind to its own trail, there would be questions from which he could not run away. The Spaniard himself was a contradiction to the very questions that he raised. The Spaniard could, in perfect honesty, offer a living sacrifice like the Inca to his Christian God, and hurl an entire nation into slavery that its children might adopt the True Cross. He could invoke the Holy Mother's intercession to bend an innocent girl to his will. With a prayer on his lips he could cheat the crown of its share of plunder. He was a contradiction also in another way. In the field,

9

dogging his prey, he was alert, canny, indefatigable, disciplined, unbeatable; but with his battle won, he sought a girl, a guitar, a pair of dice, a cup of wine, and became God's most indolent, dull-witted, degenerate mortal.

These contradictions were easily enough explained. They had emerged through eight hundred years of turbulent warfare against the Moors for possession of Spain itself. Generations of men had left the flocks to fight, and the plunder was their only livelihood. The wars against the Moors were holy crusades, and God's help logically was invoked against the infidel, whether afield or abed. The dissolute example of the clergy had forced even the unthinking Spaniard to observe the form of his religion rather than its essence, and Grace was assured if the form was observed to the letter. Nowhere was it observed more to the letter than in Spain. But the Spaniard had been so long at the wars, that between battles he must relax if he were to have any life of his own; and from the Moors he had learned to relax amid glittering luxury. So, though unbeatable in war, he was a poor administrator of the peace.

Orellana had often pondered the peculiar temperament of his people, wondering whether an industrious administration might lead them out of indolence into industry, out of warfare into fruitful peace. In Guayaquil his government had been a success, though not on the Spanish model. In all his commands, he had lived by four rules of government, and he had never once been false to them. His friends called them his weaknesses; his enemies said that in them lay his strength. They were simple enough rules: never to ask anyone to follow him blindly, but to speak his mind as a comrade; never to impose his will when a majority were contrary minded; never to treat an Indian, or even a black slave, as other than a human being; and never to treat any man as less than an hidalgo, worthy by birth to respect. The rules had always worked well until a higher government intervened, usually the Marquis Pizarro or the clergy. Could a new world be ordained in which there were neither Pizarros nor priests? Orellana stirred

restlessly. The prospect was not consoling, especially with a cold mountain wind cutting across his face.

He thought of his friend García Tapia, who had been his companion
in many adventures. No, he could never tell Tapia that the real reason
he was joining Gonzalo Pizarro was to acquire a governorship and
then test his dream of authority. It was something he must hold hidden,
like his vicuña sack of emeralds. He had set out upon his great chance,
and he was prepared for it. The cost of outfitting his men had been
fantastic, but the expense was as nothing to his dream.

Sprawled now across the plain, approaching the great mountains,
his men were magnificent. Even Gonzalo Pizarro, who had seen
Spanish troops pass through Truxillo in his boyhood, would be impressed. And Orellana relied heavily upon this impression. The patronage of the Pizarros was, after God's grace, the most important
consideration in Peru.

So far, Gonzalo's brother, the Marquis Pizarro, favored him. His
record was clear. He congratulated himself on his foresight in putting
his achievements on file with the Council of the Indies. His deeds
were written down now, for all to see. Orellana could not read it, but
he had seen it written and witnessed by the magistrates. The scrivener
had read it back slowly to him—for a price of two gold ducats. Because he could not read, Orellana's memory was long. He remembered
the petition almost word for word: how he had participated in the
conquests of Caxamarca, Lima, and Cuzco with Pizarro, and then
on his own initiative had founded Guayaquil. In all this he had served
at his own expense, maintained his own horse and equipment, and
fought Pizarro's rebellious partners as well as Indians. Yes, the record
was there. Not too little, or too much. The magistrates had added, on
their own initiative, some mention of his services in providing haven
in his own house to all who were in distress. Not that this would make
any impression upon the Council of the Indies, but it was a nice touch.

He wished he knew Gonzalo Pizarro better. In all the battles for
Peru, Gonzalo had been cool, because Orellana was his cousin and

knew him to be an illegitimate child. He must watch himself, he thought; trust no one, confide in no one. Rashness was the lure to death, unless one were alone. There might be hardship in the mountains ahead, as there was in the jag-toothed peaks of Estramadura, but alone in man was there danger. Everything in nature was predictable and its perils circumventable; only man was unpredictable. Nature was aptly named *natural*, in the sense of being wholesome and dependable; only man was unwholesome and unreliable. And only man was uncivilized enough to hate, as the Pizarros hated, and vengeful, as the Pizarros were vengeful. He remembered the first time this truth had struck him. He had been in Spain then. Now here, on the slope of the Andes, riding along the equator twelve hundred leagues from Spain, that truth was the same.

Juan de Illanes drew alongside.

"There is no doubt Don Gonzalo passed this way," he said. Not so much as a petal of fuschia had been overlooked by the voracious caravan. What the Spaniard had thrown down the Indian had eaten, and what the Indian had left, the blacks, the pigs and the fowl had devoured.

Illanes, a tall Asturian, young, with the stride of the professional soldier and the quick, greedy eyes of a rogue, drew his cape close against the mountain wind. He was Orellana's lieutenant. A gambler, he possessed the gambler's two strong qualifications for leadership: he could make rapid decisions, and he understood men.

Illanes had been reluctant to leave Guayaquil with Orellana. He had a good thing there. Orellana's city was the port of northern Peru. Every passing ship touched there. New arrivals from Spain came ashore. Money was easy, and Juan de Illanes' dice were unusual. Now, after accompanying Orellana on the hard march from Guayaquil to Quito and on into the bitter mountains, Illanes was beginning to feel that perhaps he had a good thing here, too.

Orellana was too easy going, too soft of speech, too reluctant to use the whip, to be a great leader. In gambler's words, Orellana was soft. Illanes had suspected this long ago in Guayaquil, but had paid no attention then. Now little incidents assumed new significance, such as the time an Indian boy came down with typhus. Spaniards had an effective remedy for the plague—they took the infected body by the corners of the blanket on which it lay, and dumped it in the river when the tide was moving out. Orellana, however, had sat beside the child, bathing his fevered head with oil, forcing water down his throat, with his own hands plunging the frail body into a vat of cold water day after day, until the fever died and the boy was on his feet again.

Yes, Orellana was soft, and therein, Illanes thought, lay hope for himself. The price was high, but the gamble was worth it, for Gonzalo Pizarro was headed for the jungle, in search of El Dorado, the man of gold. For years the Spaniards had sought this Indian monarch who covered himself each morning with gold dust and at night washed it off in a ceremonial pool. El Dorado's lords wore clothing stamped with gold and put on the same garments every day; but such parsimony was beneath the man of gold. A fresh coat of gold dust each day set him apart from all men everywhere. To find that pool, now, Illanes thought, there would be a discovery! El Dorado's house was described as sheeted with hammered gold, and his wives possessed so many emeralds that they could cover themselves daily with a different selection for an entire year, without once repeating a single stone.

Yes, it was worth the gamble. And there was even more. Over the mountains somewhere lay a land teeming with cinnamon, which might become a new Spanish colony as rich as Quito province. Everyone knew that this land was Orellana's goal. And when a soft man dreamed of empire, gold went begging. Juan de Illanes smiled.

But not for long. At his feet he saw the skeleton of one of Don Gonzalo's horses, its bones picked clean. A giant condor circled overhead. The sight of the vulture, waiting to pounce upon the unsuspecting, reacted harshly upon the gambler, who waited for richer prey.

"Carrion dog!" Illanes shouted, shaking his fist. "Pick your bones elsewhere, but stay away from me."

T HREE days later, Illanes saw the condor again.

After two days of bitter cold and ruthless altitude, the men
were climbing a granite summit, and there was no heart
left in them. A drop of eight hundred feet was on their left hand and
a snow sheet on their right. A few scrub cedars clung to the cliffs.
Ahead they could see a dense forest of pigmy pine. A screaming wind
whipped the snow around their faces like clammy sawdust, blinding
them and causing the horses to stumble. To ascend the mountain directly was impossible. The men wound in almost looping circles around
great boulders, across hummocks of slippery shale, over treacherous
icy brooks. The nostrils of the horses were white with frost, and the
Spaniards' beards were frozen to their lips. The Indians, accustomed to
the lowlands, coughed blood, leaving a splotched red trail behind them.

Overhead the sky was emerald color, and as cold. Out of it suddenly, without a sound, circled the condor. He was a great vulture,
with a wing span of fully twenty feet. He hovered, his eyes darting
down the line of men, horses, and coughing Indians. His black wings
striped with white were motionless, but his white-ruffed neck darted
alternately right and left, out and in, like a striking rattlesnake. His
sharp, clawed feet were thrust down, talons extended like knife
blades, waiting to rip the first living thing that faltered.

"Oye!" Illanes shouted, pointing down the mountain. A thousand
feet below, on a snow-white field thick with boulders, lay a tangled
mass of horses and men, their stiff-frozen arms and legs pointing like
spires to heaven.

"Look sharp," Illanes said. He drew up his horse, for the trail ended
suddenly. A fissure had opened in the ice under the weight of Don
Gonzalo's party, and had carried a hundred men and horses to their

deaths. Quickly, to keep his own party from dwelling on the sight, Orellana wheeled, broke a new path around the fissure, and commanded his men sharply to follow him.

"Do you want to freeze to death?" he shouted. "There is no standing idle here. Push on." To keep himself warm, he leaped from his horse and led it across the snow.

He acted more wisely than he knew, for after a few paces the black stallion neighed, clambered for footing on the icy slope, broke rein and skidded screaming into the abyss. A tinkle of shale sounded a requiem behind. The condor followed like a thundercloud.

Immediately Illanes offered his own mount to his chief, but Orellana declined.

"We are all safer afoot, Señor," he said. "Let the Indians lead the horses, and we shall walk. We can't afford to give that carrion son of Satan any more horsemeat; it is too expensive."

They dug into the wind and plodded on. The beautiful capes, bought with such pride in Guayaquil, were next to go. They acted as sails, almost blowing their wearers into the void. An Indian slipped from the trail; another, wracked by a coughing fit, lay down his burden and died of frozen lungs. His pack was thrown across a horse. The Indian was left to the condor.

At noon they halted in the lee of an immense granite boulder and chewed a few kernels of corn—but the pause was for rest, not for food. The horses particularly showed signs of failing, their nostrils distending with swollen veins, their diaphragms sucking in and out as though powered by leather bellows. Orellana commanded the brilliant harness to be cut away. The trappings of knighthood, purchased to impress Gonzalo Pizarro, were worthless in a battle against wind and sky. A few of the Spaniards, unaccustomed to walking at such altitude, retched up their Indian corn and tore the heavy mail from their throbbing chests. Thus lightened, they were able to walk more surely across the ice field. Within an hour, Orellana was the only man who still had his chainmail on his bent frame. By mid-afternoon, two horses lay their wasted bodies upon the snow and begged with ter-.

rified eyes for merciful death. The party pressed on, not stopping to redistribute the packs the horses had carried, or to salvage the priceless saddles, for none of them, Spaniard or Indian, could carry another libra upon his back.

One of the companions, a knight named Blas de Medina, possessed a heavy scabbard, encrusted with gems. Twice he tripped over it and fell to the snow. Tripped again, he cursed bitterly, tore the scabbard from him, and left it in the path. Gleefully Alonso Marquez, a poor man, claimed it; but after a half mile he, too, discarded it, and another soldier took it up. Soon it was abandoned again, despite its great value and this time none retrieved it, for by now not a scabbard remained among the company. The riflemen would have thrown away even their precious arquebuses had not Orellana decreed the death penalty to any man who cast off his weapons.

The gauntlets were next to go. The steel froze to the fingers, and several men lost fingernails attempting their removal.

Now the trail behind them bore their own marks as well as Gonzalo's, baules and cases and bits of leather, scabbards and cuirasses and fine brocaded shirts, blood from the feet and lips of Indians, and here and there a poncho-covered hutch in the snow, where an Indian lay in his own shroud. Orellana's nose and ears were deeply frostbitten, and his fingers were numb in his heavy gauntlets. Mercifully, toward sundown, the men came to a cavernous boulder field, providing some shelter from the wind. They sank stupidly to sleep without prayer.

Orellana shook them awake before midnight. They could not stay, he said; by morning they would be frozen.

They stumbled through the blackness, and before dawn felt the wind die on their backs. Thus they knew that they had encompassed the mountain and were moving downward at last. To a cavelike gouge in the rocky cliff they stumbled, more numb than alive, commended their souls to heaven, and sank to sleep. The sun was far over the mountain before any of them awoke. Three of the Indians did not waken, and all the horses were dead.

In the shelter of the cliff, Francisco Orellana considered his position. The splendid detachment that had left Guayaquil was proud no longer. The twenty-four Spaniards were still alive, thanks only to God's mercy, but less than half of the fifty Indians, and these were huddled, facing the fire, wrapped motionless in their heavy ponchos, unable to carry baggage farther. The trappings of the expedition, which he had bought at the cost of his entire fortune to impress His Excellency the Governor, were gone. The men had their swords and shields, daggers in their belts, their arquebuses and crossbows, a sack of personal belongings across their shoulders, a small pouch of food dangling at their waists. That was all. Some had even discarded their helmets, preferring the wind in their matted hair to cold sweat that froze to the flesh inside a steel icecap and then ripped away the skin when it was taken off. The fine boots, meant to show form in the saddle, were rags of worthless cowhide.

Orellana was tempted to turn back. Under the inspiration of going home, the men and Indians would rally sufficiently to return to Quito. At least they knew what measure would be taken of their strength on the road back. Ahead lay nothing but death. What good, Orellana asked himself, to push on, ragged beggars that they were, to receive the contemptuous charity of Don Gonzalo, rather than his admiration and esteem? Old Tapia was right. Ten men without horses or Indians might make it.

"Water!"

The plea was feeble, from one of the miserable men. But there was no water. For days, now, there had been none. At first they had tried to quench their thirst with the snow, but in such intense cold the snow had frozen to the tongue. And Orellana did not know how many days yet remained before they found anything to drink.

Again he looked at his men. Not one looked at him. Not one wanted to go on.

Yet he could not give the order to turn back. Like Cortez, who had burned his ships behind him on the shores of Mexico, he must go on. He must see this quest to its conclusion, like Francisco Pizarro at Tumbez, drawing with his sword a line in the sand and shouting,

17

"Across this line lies death or greatness; who will share it with me?" Once embarked upon a dream, man must follow to its end; dreams never retreat.

Orellana shook cold numbness from his brain, and summoned Juan de Illanes.

"Of the men," he said, "who are most trustworthy?"

Illanes considered the question carefully. Trustworthiness, even on an eighteen-thousand foot summit in midwinter, must be weighed on the most precise scales. Orellana bored through him with his one devilish eye.

"I would pick first Antonio Hernández," Illanes said. "He is a Portuguese, small but strong, and he is resourceful. He was with Benalcázar in Popayán, Captain, and led a detachment at Timana. He limps a little from on old leg break, but is not inconvenienced by it."

"Yes," Orellana said, looking at the wizened little outcast. He had noticed this limping man before. By law, no Portuguese were allowed in Spanish dominions in the New World. The edict, like many another, was ignored by colonial governors, but no Portuguese ever came to Peru without a murderous past. He took careful stock then of the gambler's first choice. Hernández was a small man, not fifteen hands in height, so dark complexioned as to be almost negroid except that his nose and mouth were small and shrewd. He wore a mat of black hair straight back from his low forehead, tied with a shabby red ribbon in back at the neckline. He had no armor of any kind, having been among the first to discard it; his doublet was loose upon him, his blouse too long of sleeve and open at the throat even in the bitter mountain cold. He was of uncertain age, Orellana thought, although tribulation rather than years might account for the deep-socketed seriousness of his black eyes and the curls of gray that ran unevenly through his coarse beard.

"All right," Orellana said.

"Next I would pick Hernán Gutiérrez de Celis, a small but wiry fellow, and solid—especially handy with the arquebus, if that's of any account now."

Orellana nodded. Gutiérrez, a mountain man in Spain, would bear up even in the Andes. He liked the look of Gutiérrez, the first man in Guayaquil to volunteer for this undertaking, chunky, olive-skinned, a full beard that complemented the great strength in his muscular arms and legs; all in all a man who could go far on a few kernels of grain. Seeing himself observed, Gutiérrez turned his pin-point brown eyes full on Orellana.

"I need one more," Orellana said.

The lieutenant surveyed his men again, sucked in his breath and spoke.

"If it were my decision, Captain," he said, "and thank the Lord and the blessed company of Saints that it is not, I would pick Antonio Carranza, although I probably ought not to do so."

"Why?" Orellana asked, looking quickly at the oldest man of the party, a grizzle of fifty who, in Guayaquil, had been almost rotund of flesh, but now was gaunt, his leanness accentuated by a flabby jowl to which clung the strings of a disreputable gray beard. He had lost his helmet but he needed no such protection, for a thicket of salt and pepper curls matted an unusually large head, the ringlets overflowing onto his high forehead and down over his eyes and ears. He, too, saw Orellana observing him, and he, too, returned the glance. His eyes were nubian, dashed with humor the least bit impudent and mocking.

"I hesitate," Illanes said, "because there are some who say he is a Jew. Myself, I don't ask questions."

"Nor I," Orellana said. "At least on this mountain we are one under heaven. Why do you nominate him?"

Illanes rubbed the icicles from his beard with a cold hand. "Because he is old and wise, and thinks before he speaks. Because he knows cures and conjures, and the stars and the seasons. He is a physician and it is whispered he also is a necromancer—but that I wouldn't know, but sometimes it would be handy. And he is cheerful. There is nothing he cannot laugh at."

Orellana nodded. "All right," he said. "Bring them here."

The summoned men approached slowly. All were breathing rap-

19

idly, sucking into their lungs what little oxygen could be distilled from the rare mountain air; and all were weary.

"Gentlemen," Orellana said, "I think it is time we organized our camp. I had hoped, before now, that we would have joined His Excellency the Governor, and no such organization would be necessary. Now we fight for our lives, and fighting requires leadership."

At any other time such honors would have swelled a Spaniard's heart, but not a man moved. They had no courage for leadership along the road to death.

"I do not want you to think that I have failed to organize a council sooner out of any arrogance of my own. I know our Castilian tradition as well as any of you."

He caught a mocking glint in the eyes of Antonio Carranza, but his brain was too numb to diagnose its meaning. His entire strength and will were marshaled for the job of speaking coherently. He did not want to talk. He wanted to lie down and sleep.

"It would be presumptuous of me to establish leaders in an expedition of which I am not the commander. Therefore such titles as I am going to give will be terminated upon our arrival in the governor's camp. That is clear, please?"

The four men nodded. Orellana was pleased to see that Illanes understood this delicate point, for he was not sure his lieutenant had appreciated the transiency of the cloak that was on his shoulders.

"Illanes, as you know, gentlemen," Orellana went on, "is our lieutenant. In my opinion he has done well. Now that we are in council, I shall entertain any comment upon his fitness."

He looked slowly at each of the four, but their eyes were as frozen as the ground.

"There being no objection, Señor Illanes is confirmed in his lieutenancy."

The formality of the council, high on the crest of the Andes in midwinter, for a moment appeared to Orellana a ridiculous vanity. Formality when men were freezing to death! But he knew that to Spaniards it was as necessary as warmth.

"You, Señor Hernández," he went on, "shall act as campmaster. Someone must husband our provision from now on, or we shall all be dead men."

Hernández rallied sufficiently to signify that he understood.

"Señor Gutiérrez, you I appoint leader of the advance guard. I have noticed that you press forward when all of us seem to falter. It is a trait we all might follow to advantage, and from now on, we shall."

Gutiérrez acknowledged this high praise from his captain with a nod of the head.

"And you, Carranza," Orellana said, at the end of his strength now from the long talking, "shall be master-at-arms. I count upon you to keep the line moving, to strengthen those who falter, and to encourage us all. . . . Are we all agreed?"

No one moved or spoke.

"You four, with myself, will serve as council. If at any time you have a suggestion, I am at your service."

The men assumed their new duties swiftly. Illanes whipped the Indians from their torpor. With two Indian guides, Gutiérrez moved swiftly down the mountain. Hernández, after a private council with Orellana, gathered together the maize in sacks, cut two large chunks of frozen meat from a mare's rump, and loaded the Indians for the day's journey. Everything but essential food was left behind. Orellana watched the departure in silence. Finally only he and Carranza were left.

"Do not pause if a man can go no farther," Orellana said. "Keep the line moving, but trouble yourself only with the living. The dead, with God's mercy, must fend for themselves."

Carranza's gray curls shook in the cold wind. "Trust me, Captain," he said, "to leave the dead behind."

Orellana pushed forward into the van. Occasionally he looked back, but not often. It seemed that every time he turned his head, Carranza was covering another dead Indian with a poncho.

4

FOUR days passed. To Hernán Gutiérrez de Celis, the advance guard, they were a torture imposed by God to sweeten the prospect of inevitable death. The lee side of the mountains was a vast snowdrift through which he bogged kneedeep, relieved occasionally by short stretches of cedar-sparsed boulder fields treacherous with shale.

Late in the day, Gutiérrez broke from the snow into one of these clear fields and turned to encourage his guides. Only one was standing. The other, an older man, lay face downward. He had fallen, and without strength to lift his head, he had smothered to death in the snow.

"Devil take it," Gutiérrez muttered, looting the body of its little sack of corn and adding the kernels to his own pouch. "Just like an Indian to die when you need him." To the other guide he said, "Well, let's go."

The younger man did not move. He squatted for a moment beside the corpse, arranging the coarse black hair, straightening the gay cotton shirt with its pattern of sun over grain fields, an embroidery woven with laborious pride by the younger Indian's mother for the older man, his father. The old man had worn his brightest uncu to make a good appearance for the Spaniards.

Unmindful of Gutiérrez, the son seated his dead father upright in a niche made by two granite boulders, and stepped back, his face a mask. Gutiérrez, lash in hand, turned toward the trail. The young man, however, had not yet finished with his father. He did not like the look of what he had done. After a moment's deliberation, he removed his own bright red and blue poncho of which nothing much was left except tatters, rearranged the corpse, and wound the tatters de-

liberately around his father's head and neck, then downward to pin
the old man's arms close to his dead frame. With much effort the
young man found a rock, rolled it to the niche and sealed his father
in the granite. He broke cedar twigs from a tree and with them dis-
guised the entrance to the crypt.

"Oye!" Gutiérrez said at last, "vamos ahora." The Indian took
the trail obediently, without looking at the Spaniard, and without
glancing back.

Another day passed. They followed the trail in agony, up and down,
over never-ending rocks, gradually dropping to lower altitude toward
the east. The snow had waned off behind, surrendering to thick
timber. This was worse than the snow, for at times the trail was
blocked by vines and fallen trees. The young Indian, hacking with a
broken sword, worked ever more slowly, and finally gave up. Gutiérrez watched him squat silently on the ground, sliding his bony but-
tocks down the backs of his legs until they touched his heels. Usually
the Indians could squat in this crouching position for hours without
moving. Today the guide, who had the frozen moon face of the
Quechuas and the short bowed legs of his tropical ancestors, lost balance and rolled over on his back, his sword falling from his hand.

He looked up, ashamed of his weakness, mutely staring at the
Spaniard with eyes that begged forgiveness for his failure and at the
same time reflected the fear of all Indians that when they can do no
more, the Spaniard will beat them.

Gutiérrez had had enough of beating. He too was at the end of
his strength. Obviously, the lad was dying, the last of fifty Indians
who had set out from Guayaquil.

Don Gonzalo, Gutiérrez reflected, had had better luck with his
porters. To a woodsman and guide, Gonzalo's progress was as clear
as a goat trail. The expedition had not lost many horses, but the
excreta indicated they were getting little to eat. The spoor of the
pigs was no longer prolific. The jumble of Indian tracks remained
vigorous, however. As Orellana's lowland Indians had died in the
mountains, Gutiérrez reflected, so Don Gonzalo's would evaporate

23

in the jungle swamps. And the only thing the Spaniards could do, in such a situation, was to take the Indians along as far as they could go, then shift without them when they died, or capture others along the way. Fortunately, Gutiérrez thought, Indians cost nothing but a little effort. Their loss does not come out of the pocket like the golden ducats required to buy a horse.

The result of losing his last guide was more work for Gutiérrez himself, and he was faint from hunger and long exertion. He could stand the mountains well. He was at home there. In his boyhood in the Spanish mountains he had liked to scale the cliffs, walk the hard mountain roads (for in his whole family connection there was not one horse), suck into his young lungs the rare mountain air. Now, however, he was descending so rapidly that his ears popped, and perspiration had begun to drip on his brow and run down his back. Each bead of sweat carried off a little of his strength. He could feel it leaving him, hour by hour. His stomach, strong on the mountains, now turned and made him retch when he passed one of Gonzalo's night camps to which clung the rotten smell of decay that unsanitary man leaves in his path.

Without Indians to help hack out the ever increasing vegetation, Gutiérrez could not long go on. He heard his companions dog pantingly behind him, and he took the Indian by one leg and hauled him off the path into the brush. No need for the company, starved for food, to feast their eyes on dying human flesh. Gutiérrez was standing, sword heavily in hand, in the middle of the track when Orellana came up with the little company. There were not many of them now. Twenty-four men, swords and shields in hand, eight with arquebuses, powder horns and shot bags weighting their drooped shoulders, six with crossbows clutched in the cuddle of their left arms and a quiver of arrows over their left shoulders. Food there was none, save for the leather sack each man carried. Of personal possessions there was no trace either, for by now such treasures as had not been thrown away were carried around the neck, inside the shirt. Only Orellana, Gutiérrez observed, still shouldered a large sack that was rumored to con-tain three changes of linen and a fabulous piece of some Inca treasure.

Orellana nodded to his scout, cast his one eye sharply about for signs of the Indian guide, and noted the swab on the ground where the body had been dragged away. He needed no explanation. The companions threw themselves down on their burdens, breathing heavily. Antonio Carranza padded quietly up from the rear, still strong, his curly hair more wild and windtossed than ever. On seeing the exhausted caravan, his eyes momentarily lit with a glint that Orellana thought, with a shocking jolt, was one of satisfaction. Carranza sank beside the Portuguese Hernández, and now only Gutiérrez and Orellana were on their feet, facing eastward toward the agony that lay before them.

They stood upon a long granite Roman nose that ran down the face of the mountain. Ahead, for the first time clearly, they could see a cobalt haze finger-tipped with tree tops that covered a vast expanse of jungle. As flat as the back of a hand the blue forest stretched away into infinity, overlaid with gossamer and rolled-up clouds from which radiated a turgid pall of steam. This vast and listless vista was no blood brother to the cheerful jungle of Guayaquil, with its flashy storks and gay mumuyu trees; it was a labyrinth of agony.

"How fresh is the track now, Señor Gutiérrez?" Orellana asked.

Gutiérrez felt the attention of all the comrades in his backbone, like dagger stabs. Should he admit that Gonzalo's trail was beginning to wander, to loop back on itself? Should he admit that, in his opinion, Gonzalo was either lost or beset by such indecisiveness that he lacked the power of forceful direction?

"How fresh is the track?" He repeated the question to give himself time to frame an answer. "I would say, Señor Captain, that it is now only from four to five days old, and they are traveling more slowly than formerly."

"You think, then," Orellana said, searching the jungle haze as though for signs of human life, "that we should come upon His Excellency in a week?"

"Much sooner, I would say," Gutiérrez responded. "Their llamas and horses have moved rapidly up to now, but in the jungle they will be a liability. We, on the other hand, will move faster. We are not heavily burdened."

Orellana almost smiled. "No," he admitted ruefully, "we are not heavily burdened. How long, then?"

"Five days at the outside, if we are not attacked by Indians."

Orellana pondered, then called, "Señor Illanes—do not get up, please. How much corn have we left?"

Juan de Illanes joined Orellana and Gutiérrez. "Not much," he said. "Since we divided the maize three days ago, I can only tell from what is in my own sack. I would say thirty kernels. Do you wish me to count?"

"No. That is about what I have myself. Thirty kernels of corn. That is three kernels a day for ten days." He paused, and looked again at the swab of his last Indian on the trail.

"We must send forward and ask His Excellency to wait for us."

Gutiérrez nodded. He was of the same opinion. Orellana noticed the gesture and capitalized quickly upon it.

"I would like two volunteers to go to Don Gonzalo."

Immediately Gutiérrez stepped forward. "I will go," he said, "if you can find another to go with me."

Everyone in the company heard his words, but not a man moved. After the mountains, none had stomach for new forms of torture: poisonous and constrictor reptiles, inedible fungus, swamps, quicksands, savages. Orellana waited. Gutiérrez looked about the company, but no man met his gaze. Enough was enough.

"We cannot go on like this much longer," Orellana said. "Our only chance is to reach Gonzalo's camp quickly."

There was a stir behind him, and Carranza rose wearily to his feet. "Well, then," Carranza said, "let's not waste any time."

"Thank you, Señor," Orellana replied. "As you say, let's not waste time. If the track followed by His Excellency becomes indistinct at any place, blaze a trail that we may follow. I assume Señor Carranza will carry along what passes for our machete?"

"I can manage it, I think," Carranza said, "but in the use of it I am unhandy."

He picked up the broken sword from the trail, where it had fallen from the Indian's hand, and flung it across his shoulder. "My father once told me," he said, trying to laugh, "that if I did not learn my letters he would make a woodchopper of me. I thought it was the worst thing that could befall me and now look—of a sudden it becomes the best. Fate has an ironic sense of humor, amigos. Shall we go?"

Gutiérrez began a rapid descent toward the jungle, without a word of farewell, his chunky legs digging into the shale for solid footing. Carranza followed, and after a few experimental hefts of the broken sword from shoulder to shoulder, he threw it away, and drew his own sword from his belt. He turned and waved.

"I shall reach drinking water, gentlemen," he called, "before you do. Adiós."

"Adiós," Orellana shouted. "Vaya con Dios."

As though lightened of a great weight, Francisco Orellana's men pushed forward rapidly. Hope to the Spaniard is like a kiss from the Virgin, all the strength he needs; and now Orellana's men had hope. Scrub timber gave way to taller and taller trees, shale disappeared before an ever thickening mass of close undergrowth; but they did not notice these encroachments of the jungle, for in their minds was only one thought: water. They found it at last, carefully quenched their thirst at a mucky stream and then, just at dusk, pressed on.

But night had fallen with great speed, as it does in the forest, and they plunged across the stream into the full, dark density of the jungle. As when entering a cathedral at night, at first they saw nothing. They felt the thick growth about them, and the thorns that seized them, yet heard nothing. Their nostrils shrank from the pungent layers of smell, without identifying any. They sensed the towering pillars of hardwood trees, the spiderweb windows, the flying buttresses of gigantic wood stumps, the interior timbers of immense vines. But they saw nothing. They were too awed to look up toward what must,

27

in the hidden mystery of the forest ahead of them, be the high altar.

The tropical verdure closed blackly about them and fingered their clothing. They heard the splash of water from the little stream, but it might easily have been a fountain in the cathedral close. They heard a repressed swish ahead of them, but it might have been a monk hurrying to the cloister after his evening prayers. Night had descended so fast that the companions could not even see each other.

Overcome, Illanes whispered the Ave Maria.

"Gloria patri," Orellana said, himself hushed into Latin by the sudden dark, "is that you, Illanes?"

"It is, Captain."

"Are we all here? Oye! Stand still and call your names."

"Alonso Marquez, Señor," came a quick reply at Orellana's right hand.

"Diego de Matamoros, first citizen of Badajos."

"Diego, not of Badajos, thank God, but of Medallín, and called Moreno."

"Cristóbal de Palacios, and why I left Ayamonte is for God to ponder."

So on down the line, rallying to the jests. The Spaniard likes to spit wit into the face of fear. Bringing up the rear, in a loud voice, "Blas de Medina, whose home is in his sword, gentlemen, and thus safe from thieving Spaniards."

They laughed into the darkness. In the night they could afford to laugh, for Orellana's eye was not upon them. Yet it seemed to all that their jokes were out of place in the cathedral, and they quieted suddenly.

"Let no man move until we can see better," Orellana said. "Our eyes will become accustomed to this dark."

"Whoever heard of a Spanish dog with the eyes of a cat?" someone called. This time no one laughed.

"You will need the strength of the lynx, too," Orellana said. "Illanes, be careful, but see if there is anything dry under your foot that we might touch a flint to."

"No, Captain," Illanes said after a moment. "I am up to my knees in muck."

"Señor Medina," Orellana called, "walk forward slowly. Make a chain with the others as you come, until we are all together."

The links gathered around Orellana. Hernández called, "Come here, one of you arquebusiers. The Saints are with me, as usual. My toes feel something dry through the shred of my left boot. Drop a little powder on it and flint it off."

A spark shot out, ignited a puff of shot powder, and Hernández, on his knees, blew life into the fire. Quickly it leaped up, scudding shadows up the trees like devils fleeing from a crucifix.

"Por Dios, that's something," Hernández said, looking up. "Companions, you look like ghosts!"

The men turned away quickly, disguising in a busy search for dry wood a knee-weakening fear of the shadowy murk. Orellana walked to the fire.

"God is merciful," he said. "We are on dry ground."

He saw at once, however, that the spot was not suitable for a camp. It was indefensible against surprise attack. He ordered Illanes to find safer quarters. But the men objected. Their fire was lit and already they sprawled around it, billeted for the night. Here there was dry land and fresh water. What more could a man ask?

Orellana pointed out the close-lying thicket, out of which jungle savages might pounce. The men were not in the least concerned. They were too weary. With misgivings, Orellana yielded. He could not impose his will upon them.

In the hush of dawn they were attacked. Screeching savages leaped from the thicket and were on them before they could move. Had they not slept in armor, with unsheathed swords beside them, none of the Spaniards would have survived. At the first rush, Orellana, Illanes, and Hernández were up, parrying the long spears, striking down the estoricas, thrusting blindly at the dim naked silhouettes that charged through the brake. As the attack developed, savages crept up from behind the river bank, others swung overhead on long vines to drop on the Spaniards' backs. Orellana never knew how many the attackers numbered. They occupied his men for a fierce hour before they fled, leaving eight of their number slain, and three Castilians wounded.

Illanes was the most seriously hurt. His cheek was laid open from mouth to eartip by a spear thrust, but he made light of it.

"The scar will remind me," he said, "that armed men should never expect to sleep in peace. I was a fool."

"I was the fool, Señor," Orellana said. "As your leader, I should have insisted on camping on a safer ground." He was bitterly chagrined. Listening to bad counsel, he admitted to himself, was his great weakness. In Guayaquil he thought it had been overcome; but that was leadership, not command—an entirely different talent.

However, this was no time to analyze his failings.

"Forward, gentlemen," he said, "and quickly. We must be out of their territory before they rally."

5

THEY came across an old camp of Don Gonzalo's which, in the dog bones surrounding a cold fire, revealed that like themselves, the governor had found little forage upon the land.

"With their hundreds of pigs eating every root for a quarter league on each hand," Illanes asked, "why do they eat their dogs?"

"Because," Orellana answered, "the pigs eat roots and survive, but dogs must have meat or become the meat themselves."

"By my conscience," young Blas de Medina exploded, "they'll get me to eat no dog meat in the camp of Gonzalo Pizarro. May God strike me dead if hunger ever brings me that low." He was a proud knight, this Medina, and never let anyone forget he was bred of the bluest blood in Spain.

"Softly, my worthy friend," Orellana said. "I have seen the day when a tender second joint from a well-appointed bitch was worthy even of the sons of the great Medinas. In this cursed selva, men are not nobles and vassals, just hungry mortals."

"Santa María forgive me if ever I stoop so low," Medina said. "I'd sooner be a dog than eat one."

The undeniable jungle enclosed them on all sides and from above. The gloom of twilight was the day, vanishing at night as swiftly as a puma in the dense forest. The little stream now was a stout river, a crossbow-shot wide, deep and swift, its surface punctured by the black sniffing noses of water-bogged logs, or triangled by the swift course of a crocodile. Shadows hung where vines did not among the mat of trees, and nowhere under foot was there a free causeway. Every step was a detour around a stump or over a log or under a high thicket. The murk of half-day, and the silence of half-night, clung to the

31

stinking air. Each yard was hacked by swords from the matted brush, by men knee-deep in slippery muck.

About four o'clock of the fifth day after Gutiérrez' departure, as Orellana was preparing to huddle his camp against the swift transition from gloom to night, a splash of sound broke out of the east. Every man's hand sought his weapon. No one moved. The clatter swelled and magnified in the reverberating echoes of the forest, drawing closer from the direction toward which Orellana faced. The six crossbowmen bent noiselessly to draw their arrows. Hunger was no longer with them.

Orellana, leading, gasped in disbelief, and stepped forward.

"Who's there?" he shouted.

"Praise to the Highest," came the reply in rich Castilian.

"Forever, Amen," Orellana said, and broke into a run, throwing himself a moment later into the arms of Antonio Carranza. Four Indians, their backs heavy with burden, halted to witness the reunion. Orellana's companions searched the baggage and gnawed greedily at the smoked pork they found. Bringing up the rear, haughty but filthy, was a captain, Gonzalo Diez de Pineda, of Pizarro's force. Carranza smiled as a man may only when his belly is full.

Pineda was big, bluff, and unkempt, his armor flashy but tarnished. His was the self-assurance of a man who has no enemies and many influential friends, a man of importance. He was a tradesman in the luxury merchandise of special favors, which he wheedled cheaply from the great and sold dear to the lowly. Today, however, his goods were free; he was paying Orellana something on an old account.

"By heaven," Orellana said, pounding Pineda on the shoulder, "I'm glad to see you. Even without the food you bring, you are a sight for my aching eye. But you should not have come yourself."

"I had to come," Pineda said quickly. "For the sight of you, you one-eyed devil, I would cross ten selvas."

"Gutiérrez—where is he?"

"He remained at camp, Captain," Carranza said, "to procure tents and establish a camp site befitting our captain."

"Good," Orellana replied. He had known that the quiet mountain man would not fail him. Gutiérrez might be so direct as to be blunt, and hurt men's feelings, but he got things done. In a tight shoe, he thought, Gutiérrez was a good man to be pinched. He must remember that.

The camp of Don Gonzalo Pizarro, brother of the Marquis del Valle, Governor of Quito province and captain general of the expedition in search of cinnamon and the man of gold, was a European pageant of shining armor, brilliant banners, gay tents, magnificent horses, and swaggering bluster. Most of the conquerors had learned to travel humbly in the new world, but not Don Gonzalo. His Excellency loved display above everything except the glitter of gold, the clash of arms, and the Virgin Mary.

Francisco Orellana was ashamed to enter the camp. Fatigued as he was, gaunt from hunger, ragged, bedraggled, he paused at the hem of the forest before a broad savanna on which for a distance of three miles rippled the banners of the expedition. This was not his carefully planned meeting with Don Gonzalo. The forty-thousand peso equipage, all those trappings that meet and convince the eye of the soldier and most especially the meticulously elegant eye of Don Gonzalo, were gone, victims of the mountains—the costly mail, the fine swords and daggers, the spotless bucklers, the fourteen expensive horses, the fifty Indian bearers of rich provision.

Orellana had in hand his sword and shield. There were no boots on his feet, nor did the cape that was as much a part of him as his long nose and prominent jawbone swing from his shoulders. Of his followers, none had as much as he, for he was still wearing his tarnished mail and mud-stained helmet, and over his left shoulder still hung the sack of intimate belongings with which he had left Guayaquil, and which he had carried himself along the entire weary march.

Now seeing the camp, Orellana wanted again to turn back. He could not approach Don Gonzalo as a beggar with a rabble at his back. He had pledged munitions, horses, strong fighting men richly equipped, and here he was without even a pair of boots. Ahead of him two hundred mosquito smudges marked the fires of a camp fit for a prince, or even for a duke.

Orellana cast a professional eye over the camp and found it in order. In neat semicircles the tents curled away into the distance, the fluttering pennons of captains above ostentatious canopies, stores piled high around the outer perimeter of the camp site to serve as fire steps in case of attack. Hemmed in the center of the oval, Orellana could see the horses, head-down grazing on the field, to the right of them the great droves of long-necked llamas with their Indian tenders, and to the left the lean red or black backs of hundreds of pigs guarded by Indians and dogs. Orellana could not in the vast stretches of the camp discern the location of Gonzalo's tent, but he knew that it must be somewhere directly down the avenue before him, for smartly shining soldiers, their armor neat despite suffocating humidity, patrolled this avenue and none other, and the traffic pattern of men afoot and ahorse converged upon this same camp street.

Under normal circumstances, Orellana would have joined the traffic confidently, with bold steps marched straight to the burnt orange and French blue standard of Pizarro, and shouted his name to the guards. Instead, he stepped back a pace into the shelter of the forest, to hide his nakedness.

Captain Pineda, anxious to report to Gonzalo his success in finding Orellana, pushed impetuously out of the pause and strode forward, but Antonio Carranza caught his sword arm and quietly shook his head, holding up one finger for silence. Surprised, Pineda whirled around, then stopped as though struck in the temple by a sling stone at the sight of Orellana and his men. In the jungle, with hostility and starvation and pestilence for companions, the ragged disorder of the little company had not been evident. Now in comparison to the spruce military elegance all about the savanna, the hungry one-eyed desperado and his urchin henchmen appeared in their true light. Pineda was amazed, though not ashamed. He looked at Carranza, nodded, and slunk back into the forest.

34

Orellana did not move, nor did any of his men. Juan de Illanes, on Orellana's left hand, stood empty-handed and forlorn, the sharp gambler's glint a faded memento in his weary eyes. He wore his breast plate but had no helmet, and dirty brown hair matted his pale forehead. The huge wound in his cheek was scabrous and repelling. His doublet was ripped down the seams and gouged at the knees, his toes protruded from the rotten hulk of his boots, his shield was filthy.

The Portuguese Hernández had nothing in his hands, little on his body, and blankness in his sad face. Muddy blood covered his right forearm, briar scratches of dirty brown gaped through large rents in what had once been a leather surcoat.

On the proud knight Blas de Medina, all that remained of his rich armor were the pallettes that hung dejectedly from the leather shoulder straps of a rotten hauberk, and muddy silver spurs over ripped chain mail chausses. His fine blond hair was brown with filth, his face a pox of insect bites.

Behind Medina, in ranks of twos, peering from the forest, were the others, conscious of their rags, identifiable as warriors only by their precious weapons: eight with arquebuses, six with crossbows, a few with lances, all with swords and daggers. Only seven had boots and these scarcely worthy of inventory. There was not a whole doublet in the lot.

A guard spurred out of the camp on a gelded chestnut and reared before them.

"Who comes?" he challenged.

"Go with God," Pineda responded. "We are of the company."

The guard looked down from his rich trappings in disbelief.

"Your name, Señor?"

"Captain de Pineda, escort to Captain General Francisco Orellana and twenty-three companions."

The guard's eyebrows shot up until they were out of sight under the steel of his beaver. He had heard of Orellana. He looked quickly about for a one-eyed man, and saw him. Then he looked back at Pineda.

35

"Since you say so, Señor," he said, raising his lance. "You will permit me to accompany you to the general's quarters?"

Pineda smiled. "We know the way," he said quietly, "but as you wish."

The guard bowed stiffly in his saddle. "This way," he said, and wheeled his horse down the avenue.

Orellana clamped his lips and followed. Tactfully, Pineda drew off two paces behind and one to the left of Orellana, as befitted his rank of captain general, with Juan de Illanes on his left. Stooping with fatigue, his limp much more noticeable than formerly, Hernández fell in step behind Pineda, conscious of his lack of sword. In pairs bravely, sucking into their bodies the pride of Pineda, the rest of the company fell in, making what show they could.

Antonio Carranza, an odd gleam in his bold eyes, drew up the rear, marching alone. The company proceeded down the camp street, running the gauntlet of contemptuous eyes, past tent after tent arrayed with banners and flashing with steel, around which men loitered, patching and polishing their harness and gear, cleaning quarters, or loafing in the humidity-choked sunlight. The wheeze of a blacksmith's bellows and the merry tap of hammer on anvil cut through the commotion of scratching spurs and creaking harness, the hubbub of many conversations, and the far-off lowing, barking and grunting of the livestock. A cook looked up from the grill on which he was roasting horsemeat and smiled as the hungry beggars closed their eyes against the savor. An orderly, sweeping a fly-swarmed pile of strong manure, paused over his brush. Three men scoffed briefly at the company, then went on covering with dirt a latrine whose stench hung heavily upon the air.

But no foot soldier rose to his feet to salute as the companions marched in. Orellana walked erectly, looking straight ahead at the rump of the escort horse. They reached a division in the company street, a crossroad punctured by a staked tent with bright awnings and the pennon of St. Iago on a lance pole before an entrance guarded by two foot soldiers. The company passed in silence, though Orellana obviously had been ready to return their respects.

36

At the end of the line, Carranza winced. As he passed the bright tent he broke ranks, seized the pennon of St. Iago with a curt "Por favor, Señores," walked with stretched steps boldly to the front rank, and raised the banner to his shoulder five paces ahead of Orellana.

The company began to march more smartly. Carranza could feel a quicker rhythm in the feet behind him, and ahead he saw soldiers coming to their feet to give this unknown captain the respect that he deserved. Carranza heard his name called quietly. The voice was Orellana's. Without turning his head, he acknowledged the address, and heard Orellana say, "Gracias, Señor."

"Por nada, Capitán," Carranza replied, holding high the colors of St. Iago to acknowledge the salutes that now were directed to his banner from both right and left.

Orellana saw His Excellency Don Gonzalo's headquarters from afar. The burnt orange tent with its shade canvases and ventilator lattices of French blue was three feet taller than any tent surrounding. On its downwind flank were stretched four spears each holding a corner of a ten-foot-square mosquito veil that sheltered the general's two horses. Before the tent were five pennons: the colors of Castile, the crest of Francisco Pizarro with its cluttered field, the simpler elaboration of Gonzalo's own shield set upright on two swords and crossed lances before the door. Whipping higher overhead on the ridgepole were two purer banners: Our Lady of Mercy's on the right, the patron St. Iago's on the left. Breaking the corner angles of the tent were four guardsmen, sweating profusely in surcoats of burnt orange and French blue, capes of blue lined in orange. Leaning on their lances before the door, ranged in pairs facing each other, were eight other guards in the general's colors.

Orellana's company halted. The escort climbed ponderously from his gelding under the weight of all his metal, as the captain of Pizarro's guard challenged the bedraggled array. The challenge was contemptuous, in the voice reserved for prisoners and Portuguese.

Orellana ignored the insult.

"Francisco Orellana," he said quietly, "a captain general of Peru and lieutenant governor at Guayaquil, reporting to His Excellency—"

That was as far as he got in a speech calculated to impress the contemptuous guardsman. What happened next made an impression that the guard never afterward forgot. A surge of steel and color swept him from his feet into the dust, and the mighty warrior-frame of Gonzalo Pizarro bowled past him. Gonzalo took the tattered Orellana in his arms.

"The Blessed Virgin be thanked, Cousin," he erupted in a towering voice, "you are here. Come inside, come inside."

"Your Excellency looks well, and I am proud to join you," Orellana answered, but he did not move.

"Then come inside, man, and rest." Gonzalo bawled over his shoulder, "Pedro, González, Hernán—damn your pigsty souls to hell, where are you—ah! Wine and food." As his minions scurried back into the tent, he slapped Orellana robustly on the back and pulled him toward the door.

"By your leave, Excellency," Orellana said, "my men are exhausted. I would see to their needs as well as my own."

"Of course." Gonzalo caught Captain Pineda's eye. "Captain, I would be obliged to you to do everything these men require."

Pineda came to attention without a word.

"My compliments to Campmaster Ribera and—"

A fawning, round-shouldered man hurried up afoot. "I am here, sir."

Gonzalo beamed. "Good. Good. You will draw on stores for whatever these men need. Pitch them tents. Get Indian servants for the hidalgos. Kill a llama and feast them. God in his mercy will not begrudge these men meat on a Friday in Lent."

"Everything has already been arranged, Excellency."

"And boots, Ribera—"

"Yes, Excellency."

"My compliments to Father Carvajal. A dispensation for breaking the fast. And this evening there will be special vesper prayers to the Blessed Virgin for the safety of our cousin."

"I understand, Excellency."

38

"The gentlemen will require horses—"

The spark returned to Orellana's eye as he observed the general. This attention to minute detail was so characteristic of him, the bawling, the exhibitionism, the opulent fellowship. He watched as Gonzalo gushed orders at the top of his lungs. The brother of the Marquis had not changed since the conquest of Peru.

Gonzalo was as handsome a soldier as Orellana had ever seen, and certainly the most impelling in Peru. He was six feet in height—tall for a Spaniard—built like a willow with a stout trunk and graceful mobility. No wonder, Orellana thought, that he likes display, with such a form on which to hang the trappings of knighthood. The general was dressed to the eyebrows in glitter, debonairly comely in the dark Estremaduran manner, sleek, superbly confident, his open and engaging features revealing that he was a man who could not keep a secret. He had the high spirit of a four-year-old filly which gave him the easy manner of the common soldier, a fearless mischievous eye that denoted him a devil with the women and with the enemy.

Full armor fitted his great frame as though the weight of it was nothing to him. Over his plate and running up to tuck under his gorget was a brilliant sobre vest of orange velvet, fringed with delicate French blue lace. His surcoat was of yellow, with the cross of St. Iago upon the left breast. The cuisse and genouillière covering his legs were silver plated, golden spurs rode his ankles. The lack of cape and helmet were his only surrenders to the stifling atmosphere of the camp, and his only weapon was a poniard in a light Algerian belt of gold-tooled leather with an immense buckle of silver and gold.

Orellana knew that Gonzalo was the best lancer in Peru and one of her best swordsmen, but he had not expected such chivalric splendor in the midst of the jungle. He tried not to be confused by the glitter. Rather, he remembered Gonzalo's small mind that insisted upon attending personally to minute details that should be beneath him, his inability to lead large bodies of men but of his invincibility with a small band of loyal followers, his tendency to strike down ruthlessly any man who displayed greater ability than his own, his quick hot temper so beguilingly concealed beneath an open, easy manner. Watching him now, far removed from the leadership genius of his brother, Orellana was tempted to the quick conclusion that Don Gonzalo was not very smart, for all his glitter, and that behind his pose hid an undisciplined mind whose wild enthusiasms were apt to cause trouble. Orellana made mental note not to underrate the general, and for his own safety and future to render loyal service. Even so, he would need luck and a close mouth.

Gonzalo's respects to the priest reminded Orellana that now he had returned to Castilian customs and must be careful to obey them. He did not know this Father Carvajal, but he knew that he would meet him soon, and he could only hope that the chaplain was not a Dominican. Orellana had good cause to hate Dominicans. With some surprise, he heard Gonzalo's comment that the Lenten season was under observance. Orellana had left Guayaquil before Ash Wednesday, and had no idea what the religious season might be at the moment. He must be careful, he thought, to refurbish his observance of the Mass.

This recalled a characteristic of Don Gonzalo's that he had heard somewhere, that might come in handy: the general was an enslaved devotee of the Beloved Virgin. Well, Orellana thought, he had invoked the intercession of the Virgin often enough before, and for less cause than now. But he must not forget.

Gonzalo was completing his orders.

"Señor Ribera," he was saying, "you will pitch my cousin's tents in the space at your back, across from my own tents. I desire that our new comrade be close to me."

"Yes, Excellency," Ribera answered, ill concealing his envy.

Gonzalo turned and again slapped Orellana on the back.

"And now, Cousin," he said, "come in. We must refresh you and outfit you in metal worthy of your skills."

He led the way, crossing himself at a wooden crucifix that hung over the entrance canopy, and tossed his bemetaled frame upon a couch rich in vicuña skins. The tent was airy and simple, the general's possessions being neatly stowed in three large baules that could in need serve as seats along the west wall. A Florentine dining table and two heavy rosewood chairs commanded the center of the tent, under a swinging brass lantern, and Orellana thought of the effort that must have been expended lugging that furniture across the mountains. An image of the Virgin on a silver chain hung above Gonzalo's couch, just within reach of his hand.

Gonzalo indicated one of the Florentine chairs, and Orellana sat. Indian servants immediately set a fine madeira and a large smoked ham before him.

"And now, Cousin," Orellana heard Gonzalo say as he drained the wine cup and put his dagger to the ham, "I have many troubles to discuss with you before tomorrow's council meeting, which you will attend. But first, tell me about yourself."

6

RAIN began during the night watch with a long roll of muffled thunder like a hundred military drummers saluting the dead. Snug in a warm poncho, Orellana heard the narcotic patter of the rain on his canvas. The knowledge that all his men, likewise dry and fed, must also be listening to the rain from ample shelter, was an unguent to the aches of his body and a sedative to his tired brain. He put all thought from his mind, and gave himself up to the blissful luxury of sleep.

In the morning he was out early, in new boots and armor plate, to select a horse from the expedition's reserves and to inspect his own detachment. His men were recovering rapidly, he observed, seeing Juan de Illanes, his wounded cheek in bandages, already deep in a game of vingt-et-un in which he was acquiring an agreeable wardrobe.

Mass was being said in a small grove near the llama pens. Orellana saw in passing that no one appeared in attendance except two priests and Don Gonzalo. Orellana frowned and went on to breakfast. Then he crossed the company street to a space near Gonzalo's quarters to attend the council that had been summoned.

He was early, and renewed his acquaintance with some fellows of old campaigns in the wars of Peru. Leather-faced, wizened Antonio de Ribera limped to him, honey in his voice and shiftiness in his eye.

"You have everything you need, now?"

"Yes, thank you, Don Antonio," Orellana replied, nodding affably to the campmaster and casting his hand over his new armor. "You have done well."

"Your tents?"

"Excellent."

Ribera bowed. "I am at your service at any time."

Now Orellana bowed. Ribera limped away, then turned casually.

"By the way, Don Francisco, I am tempted to give you one of my best men to help you."

"I have my lieutenant, Illanes," Orellana said. He wanted no cast offs thrown at him.

"True, true," Ribera said, "but you need a man to strike your tents and look after your horse and make you easy. Not exactly a page, mind, but an old and trusted hand, an equerry. I have just the man. I would part with him reluctantly, but Don Gonzalo suggested it, and for you, Don Francisco—"

"What is his name?"

"Don Cristóbal de Segovia, Señor, better known by his mother's name—Maldonado."

"An hidalgo, to wait on me?" Orellana was astonished. There was more here, he thought, than met the eye.

"A soldier, sir. I thought perhaps you knew him. He was in Nicaragua about your time, and also with Benalcázar, a tremendous swordsman and handy with horses. You will need a veteran, Don Francisco, and it will be no dishonor to an hidalgo to serve as bodyguard to one so distinguished as yourself—especially since His Excellency—"

There was nothing Orellana could do. "Thank you," he said. "I shall see him after the council."

The council appeared to be in session now, for the hush of waiting dropped over the gathering. Ribera hurried away, and Orellana's rescuer from the jungle, guide boss Pineda, drew alongside but did not speak. Only a half dozen men were present, Orellana noted, looking about him quickly. So few, in fact, that all of them could stand under the shade of a single tree. The sly campmaster faced the entrance to Don Gonzalo's tent, to be first to attention at the appearance of the general; and, Orellana observed, he stood alone. An old acquaintance from the civil wars, Juan de Acosta, now Gonzalo's ensign, was nearby beside a young man who, from his red hair, fair skin and Visigothic countenance, was obviously an Andalusian.

Leaning toward Pineda, Orellana whispered, "Who is the arquebusier with the red goatee and the brown surcoat?"

"Alonso Robles, only lately come from Spain," Pineda said. "He is lieutenant of the rear guard, and a very fine soldier."

"He looks it," Orellana rejoined, admiring the immaculate grooming of Robles' armor and harness, the cleanliness of his boots, the trim cut to his flaming beard and goatee, and the confident but not boastful set of his wide eyes, deep in sockets as though his face had been cut as an afterthought to shelter them.

Don Gonzalo emerged from his tent, accompanied by the white-robed, black-hooded friar of the Order of Saint Dominic. This, then, was the expedition's chaplain. Orellana looked him over thoroughly as the general and the priest advanced to the trunk of the tree, and Gonzalo paused to strut a little before his staff and to marshal his words.

Father Gaspar de Carvajal, who was destined for a great role in Orellana's later exploits, was no prepossessing man. In fact, he was on the peaked side, Orellana thought. Frail of frame, pale of face, eyes black-rimmed with fever, his holy robe hung hungrily about him from his stooped shoulders to his large, flat feet. At least, Orellana thought, the padre had sense enough to come hard-shod upon a hard journey, for stout shoes rather than sandals poked from beneath the folds of his robe.

With this first impression, Orellana went over the man again. Having only one eye, he sometimes found advantage in looking twice. The observance was rewarded by a glimpse of a very dirty neck, which was surprising to Orellana in view of the spotless robe. The black hood hung loosely from its collar, and the face in it, Orellana thought sadly, was that of a stern man. There came immediately to his mind the recollection of Friar Valverde, urging the Spaniards to slaughter ten thousand Indians with the words, "I absolve you."

44

He looked again at the shorn black head, bald on top, the slovenly beard, the stubborn jaw, the unyielding hooked nose and high cheek bones of this man of God, and he was reflecting upon the unhappiness of blind belief that bigoted men's hearts and froze the blood in their veins, when he caught the priest looking at him. Quickly he bowed across the shaded circle, paying his respects. The priest continued to stare, and Orellana decided that a little impudence might be in order. He stared back, caught full in his face the impact of the priest's sternness, and held the gaze unflinchingly. This priest's eyes, so dark-rimmed and ill, were peculiar. Orellana could not at first discover what their odd quality was, and he had to focus his one eye intently before he discerned that Father Carvajal's pupils were as golden as the Inca throne, an amazing color for a Spaniard.

The priest looked down, and Orellana followed the gesture. Carvajal's hands were clasped before him, holding his missal with long, white fingers. A twitch, perhaps of irritation at Orellana's long survey, flicked back the priest's sleeve and then Orellana was surprised indeed, for the wrist and forearm he saw were those of a fighting man, one who had known good steel in his hand and could be counted on to acquit himself in an extremity. Orellana liked him better, then.

The general was discoursing in a loud voice. Orellana pulled together his attention. The question, the general said, was the proper timing of their future course. Father Carvajal had advised him, Gonzalo informed his captains, to remain in their present camp until the end of Lent, that they might pay fitting tribute to Our Lord, whose Name be praised, until after Easter. However, he said, he was reluctant to spend another three weeks in a camp in which already he had loitered ten days, as inactivity caused dissension and gambling among the men, the stores wasted away without profit, and the Indians suffered great disaffection from the tropical heat.

Orellana knew that in a moment the general would ask for the opinions of his chiefs, and cast about in his mind for something to say that would be worthy of his maiden words in this company of cavaliers, and also impressive to the bold, impetuous spirit of his commander. He

45

could appreciate Pizarro's desire to push on. Don Gonzalo had not made the passage over the mountains without severe losses. In addition to the hundred men, mostly Indians as Orellana had since been advised, who died in the great snowslide on the mountain, eleven had been lost in a skirmish with Indians in the jungle. Only the fact that his Indians were mountain born had saved him from losing all his equipage. The expedition had reached this point, which Orellana estimated to be about one hundred miles from Quito, reasonably intact and reasonably provisioned, although malaria, dysentery and chiggers, the three chief foes of white men in jungle, sapped the strength of the idle men. From Don Gonzalo's point of view as leader, the more haste made now the better, while food and men survived; this should be Orellana's recommendation, though he was reluctant to say so.

His opinion was asked first, which surprised him and all the rest. Particularly Campmaster Ribera belched an uncontrollable gasp when Gonzalo, finishing his discourse, turned at once to Orellana.

"We would profit from your comments, Cousin," he said in the same loud tone he had used to address the assembly. The eyes of everyone, particularly those of the priest and the redhaired Andalusian whom Orellana had not yet met, revolved automatically from the handsome general's face to the gaunt, one-eyed visage of the newcomer.

Orellana did not hesitate. "I agree with you, Your Excellency, that haste is the most important consideration. Nothing is ever gained by idleness."

His Excellency nodded expansively, as though saying to his council that he had made no mistake in seeking first the opinions of the lieutenant governor of Guayaquil.

"On the other hand," Orellana went on, "my own men and I are in no condition to advance through an unknown jungle at this time. We should only slow the progress of all of you until we feel the ground again to be solid under our feet."

Orellana could sense that Pizarro did not approve this line, although nothing in the general's attitude admitted it.

"Furthermore," Orellana said, "in my rather brief inspection of

46

the camp this morning, I saw fully two score men down with the black retch, and from the stink of the latrines, dysentery must be widespread. On the one hand, the presence of disease would recommend urgent removal to some distance." He saw that the general was pleased again and continued. "But the problem arises whether weakened men have sufficient stamina for a long march through selvas."

"Nonsense," said Campmaster Ribera, "the best cure for the trots is to walk them off. The best cure for malaria is sweat. Let the sick walk; it will be good for them."

"That may be true, Señor," the priest intervened, "but in my own condition I should not like to travel far, or it might well be too far for anything but a trip out of this world, may God forgive my sins."

"Enough, gentlemen," Pizarro cut in. "We shall get farther if we speak one at a time. Proceed, Cousin."

Orellana considered the situation. Evidently the priest was close to Gonzalo, and the priest did not want to move. Compromise might be effective, and boldness might be fruitful.

"This savanna runs toward the north and a little east," he said. "Do we know how far?"

"It has not been surveyed," Pineda said.

"Very well. It is probable that it extends for some distance, as there appears to be a ridge here, and the river runs in the same direction."

The general nodded.

"The savanna affords grazing, and we have many animals. The forest offers nothing but peril. I doubt the horses would be of much use in it."

The general's nod again appeared agreeable. Orellana plunged.

"Why do you not yourself lead a party into the interior, Excellency, to see what's there? The cinnamon cannot be too far off. A strong party, afoot and well guided, might in a few days' reconnaissance put us weeks farther along. If you discover El Dorado, the main body is close at hand. While you explore, the camp will graze slowly northward to the end of the savanna. By the time you return the ill will be well, Father Carvajal will have purified our souls through the Passion

47

of our Lord, and our provisions will still be intact. Then we shall go forward with certain knowledge and some purpose."

Orellana could see that the general liked the suggestion. A man who is at his best leading a small party leaps to his specialty. The irksome routine of camp is left behind. Action is assured, and any discoveries belong to the leader alone. The religious mind, loath to violate Easter, is conscience minded. Orellana did not fear the reaction of the other captains. Ribera, as campmaster, would remain in camp and escape the hated jungle. Pineda, the guide boss, would go forward with Gonzalo, a prospect to his liking. Father Carvajal would be pleased that his Holy Days were not ignored. With these three in favor, the others would remain silent.

So it turned out. Gonzalo was vastly pleased. "Then we shall depart tomorrow," he said. "These rains grow worse. We are in for a rainy season."

"Tomorrow, Excellency," said the priest, "is the Sabbath."

"Monday, then," Gonzalo said. "After the Mass at dawn."

Some discussion followed concerning the route, and the general's suggestion was accepted that the exploration should cover a wheel starting southeastward and circling toward the north, with smaller parties working inward along the short axis, and outward along the perimeter. In this way many square miles might be combed with the least passage of the main arm.

When all the details were drawn, Gonzalo called Orellana to him and placed a hand on his shoulder. Every mouth was hushed at the gesture.

"You, Don Francisco," he said, "shall be in charge of the main camp while we are gone. You I appoint my second in command and henceforth you shall be first in council and first in my thoughts after God and the Virgin, and you shall bear the title of lieutenant general."

Orellana knew then that he had made no mistake, and that his forty thousand pesos had been, after all, well spent.

7

GONZALO PIZARRO had scarcely departed, with half the camp leaders and seventy-five men, when Don Cristóbal de Segovia reported to Orellana for duty.

Orellana had not wanted him. He liked no man as close to his person as an equerry, and he felt that Juan de Illanes, or perhaps the mountain man Gutiérrez, might better be trusted with such details of personal service as he might require.

Don Gonzalo himself, however, had settled the matter. Meeting Orellana at Mass on the final morning in camp, he had mentioned Maldonado, within the hearing of his campmaster. "I feel safer leaving you, Cousin," he said gruffly, "knowing that Captain Pineda's own equerry has been detailed to your service. Maldonado is a special favorite of mine, so I know that you will be in good hands."

Under such patronage, the knight moved into Orellana's tent, although instinctively Orellana disliked him from the beginning. Don Cristóbal de Segovia, familiarly called Maldonado to distinguish him from several other men of Segovia among the company, was an experienced conquistador of forty years, native of Torrejón de Velasco, suave, personable and of forceful bearing. A suggestion from him, Orellana discovered quickly, was accepted as a command by the ignorant men of the company, so confident was his utterance and so secure his position of favor under Don Gonzalo. Now, moved to Orellana's service, his prestige was the more enhanced, implying that to whoever commanded the camp, Maldonado was indispensable.

Danger lay in so much oblique power close to himself, Orellana realized, especially in the first critical days during which he must establish his own authority. If Maldonado were merely an equerry, well and good; but Orellana doubted that this was his only function.

Spanish captains do not bestow their best men upon rivals without devious design. Something was in the wind, and Spanish winds are variable. Maldonado's manner even suggested this. He had the interesting quality of implying, without obvious gesture, that his hand was quick to his sword, and that any who disputed him might face a sharp blade in a practiced hand. The implication was effective upon the common soldiery. When Maldonado adopted the same attitude toward Orellana, however, Orellana felt that the man would not dare to strike such a pretension except under the protecting armor of very special favor.

Had Orellana been able to put his finger on any characteristic of the man as visibly repugnant, he might have shaken him off and returned him to the service of the campmaster, despite Gonzalo's benediction. But there was nothing to touch. Neither in looks nor manner, and certainly not in speech and performance, was Maldonado at fault. The impeccability of the man was in itself an irritation. His character was in full armor, visor down, unassailable. His deportment was too perfect to be anything but studied, and studious behavior implies concealed motives. But it was entirely implication, as when a man, waking to fumble for his dagger in the night, conveys from instinct to understanding the presence of an assassin behind the arras.

Maldonado, as he was ever after known to Orellana through all that followed, was big of person, full chested and post-legged. His only armor was a breast plate, and he wore his boots high and doubled under the knee in the Flemish manner. For breeches and jacket he inclined to brown leather, with a leather sobre vest unadorned, and a simple stout belt at his waist to hold his sword. For the march he had a fine French cutlass, but in camp his companion was a delicate, double-edged rapier which he said had been made for him in Florence to the exact balance of his forearm. He never went anywhere without his cape, and here again Orellana drew the implication that Maldonado's rapier, coupled with the defensive cape, would be stern weapons in the way the Italians had perfected of warding off the thrust with the cape, and darting the rapier from behind the ambush of the unfurling cloak. It was a method of personal defense well suited to the agile deceitfulness of the Venetian mind, and by implication was suited in like manner to Maldonado.

But his eyes, brown and pleasant, were unbeguiling, even appealing. The perpetual slight starboard nod of his trim-bearded face was the pose of a man who listened to, and gave, trusted confidence. The stance of his great legs was wide, without being boastful. He did not pose, gape, strut or shout; neither was he menial. He could win or lose at cards with equanimity, but never played for stakes high enough to put him in jealousy or jeopardy. He never misspoke, or lost control. He was a true balance, weighted equally on both sides. Yet Orellana felt that the fulcrum of the scales somewhere was spiked with a fine wire that inclined the measure, but in what direction he could not even guess.

As equerry, Maldonado was perfection. Orellana's armor was faultlessly maintained, his arms were sharp, his boots clean, his saddle oiled but not too much, his horse groomed and healthy. His care of the leather was miraculous, for leather deteriorates in a few days in the jungle. Once having acquainted Maldonado with his habits, they were coddled. Orellana's dagger was always at his right hand when he retired; his mirror was tilted slightly to throw its gleam into the right eye; his comb, brush and buckle hamper were to the right of the basin, never on his blind side. His siesta, which Orellana devoted to planning rather than to sleep, was never interrupted. His distaste for strong llama meat, peccary, and watercress were quickly discovered. His horse was always ready for his dawn ride about the camp, and spurs were never coupled to his boots except when he was going hunting. Had Maldonado been a devoted, hero-worshiping younger brother, he could not have attended to Orellana's person with greater perfection, as Orellana irritably conceded. And there was no evidence, in the first days, that Maldonado communicated to anyone the confidences of Orellana's tent.

Yet on the third morning after Don Gonzalo's departure, Campmaster Ribera heard of Orellana's decision to break camp much sooner

51

than he should have in the routine of camp communications. No evidence fixed the blame on Maldonado, but an awkward incident occurred.

Orellana was compelled to move. His order was given quickly, in an emergency, without convocation of a council. Orellana knew that he might be accused of arrogant assumption of authority, but he took the risk. He had to. A twenty-two hour deluge had mired the ground, eddying refuse into pestholes, drifting the offal of men and animals into tents and storage boxes. To remain even half a day was to invite pestilence.

Within a few minutes of the order Ribera, who could not ride owing to an old hip wound, limped painfully into Orellana's presence in a great rage.

"It is easy to give orders to move," he snapped, "but it is I, the campmaster, who must execute them. How can I uproot a host of men and animals on a moment's notice? Do you deliberately humiliate me before the entire company? I must have more time."

Orellana eyed him coolly.

"There is no time, Captain Ribera," he answered. "Two pigs died during the night, and eight dogs in a fit of vomit. Another day here, and we all risk death."

"A council should be the judge of that," Ribera said significantly.

"There is no time for councils. I have a duty to His Excellency to keep this camp alive during his absence. In matters of life and death, not only will I make decisions, but I shall expect you to execute them."

Further argument would have been insubordination. Outwitted, Ribera bowed. "As you wish, General," he said acidly, and limped away.

For a week Orellana had no time to reflect upon the possible results of this interview. The wisdom of his decision to change camps was evident, and that was sufficient for him. The expedition drifted across the savanna toward the north, at the pace of grazing livestock. The hundred sixty men proceeded as slowly as the cattle, for of them eighteen were too ill to walk.

Before nightfall on the day of departure, the Indians reported cholera among the pigs. Without halting the march, Orellana inspected the drove of sixteen hundred animals, separated more than one hundred that were listless, diarrheic or lacked appetite, and ordered destroyed three that showed a pale purple cast on the abdominal skin. He knew that the best protection against any swine infection was to keep the herd continuously on new ground.

This precaution, however, was not enough. The llamas next were hit. These stout, arrogant beasts of the highland Indian were porters to the entire camp, carrying all the heavy equipment, munitions, salt, tent stakes and sidewalls, the cured meat and maize. They could easily transport a sixty-pound burden ten miles a day. In addition, they were to be slaughtered for meat once their burden had been expended, and the hides cured to repair boots and harness. They were as precious as gold.

No one knew the nature of the malady that struck them. The almost ceaseless rain, the wet forage grass, probably had something to do with it, Orellana reasoned, for the llama is accustomed to dry, cold altitude, not wet, humid jungle. Whatever the cause, the symptoms were everywhere, in bloody feces and the drying up of milk in the females. The sturdy bodies weakened rapidly. Five days after a llama became infected, it died.

Orellana put aside every other problem to concentrate upon the llamas. First he tried a remedy used in Guayaquil to cure chickens of similar symptoms. An herb, which the Spaniards called yerba de gallo, grew in profusion on the fringes of the savanna. Orellana directed the Indians to gather it, and he himself cut the incision in the neck of the infected llamas and applied the herb. The llamas disdained the medication and died on the fifth day of their illness. All food and water was withheld from the herd then, but in the confines of an enclosure the pestilence only spread more rapidly. Campmaster Ribera muttered, accusing Orellana of ineffectiveness, but Orellana ignored him.

"A little sunlight, General," the master of the herd said one morning while reporting to Orellana the deaths of twelve more llamas overnight, "would cure them."

"Wish for your home in Spain, Señor," Orellana snapped, "it is closer." That day eight pigs had died, and Orellana's usually agreeable humor was fast dissipating as though the unknown pestilence was eating at his own bowels.

"Turn them loose in the forest," he directed, "and watch them closely. God plants natural remedies for the ills of his beasts. Perhaps God will lead them to medicine."

Father Carvajal, who had been standing nearby, nodded. During all the days of Orellana's command he was not far away.

"A divine inspiration, General Orellana," he said. "God in his mercy performs many miracles." He trotted off with the herdsmen to witness the event for himself. He was active again now, recovered of his own infirmity, as were all the Spaniards, and Orellana's own detachment had rallied rapidly under the medications of food, companionship, and security. Illanes was up and about, freed of his cheek wound except for a handsome scar, and Gutiérrez worked night and day to save the pigs.

That day Orellana pitched his tent on a slight promontory from which southward the undulations of the savanna rolled moistly away into the mist. The expedition had reached the northern boundary of the open country, only fifteen miles from the old camp. To the north, a distance of a thousand paces, began the underbrush beyond which reared the dense buttresses of the jungle, stretching away into an infinity of blue haze.

Released from confinement, the llamas broke toward the lure of jungle greenery, trailing their palsied and feeble behinds. A few animals, Orellana observed, could not get up. As the herd spread out, Orellana barked orders for horses to be saddled and herdsmen mounted to keep the llamas from straying too far. Father Carvajal trotted on a jennet in the wake of the herd as the galloping horsemen sprang to overtake the sick beasts.

Father Carvajal was the first to return. The miracle was not to his liking.

"Well, padre?" Orellana asked, skeptical of miracles but desperate enough to believe anything.

The priest flipped himself and his robes adroitly from the jennet and patted her on the nose with real affection. "The llamas are devouring the leaves of a small tree," he reported. "They search in the forest until they find this tree, and then strip it of leaves as high as they can reach, but they have not been cured."

"They are eating nothing but the leaf of this one tree?"

"Nothing else, General."

"They must know what they're doing, then, Padre," Orellana said. "When the stomach is upset, even a miracle takes time."

He felt, for the first time in a week, as though he might have been able to smile, but the muscles in his face did not contract. Instinct kept them from tautening in the presence of the white robe and black hood of the Dominican.

Father Carvajal was not amused.

"A miracle," he said testily, wheeling his jennet toward his own tent, "is instant, General Orellana. When it occurs, there is no doubt of God's intention."

It was a miracle, all the same. Next day not a llama was seriously ill of those that had gone into the forest, and the symptoms of their peculiar scourge were disappearing.

Orellana rode out to look at the miracle plant, as the herdsmen had designated it, and saw a bush not unlike the Spanish laurel, but of brighter green. He broke off a few leaves in his hand and found them thick and viscid. On several of the bushes was a fruit. The unripe portions were much like a green apple, the ripe ones bright yellow. A ripe fruit in Orellana's hand scented his glove. He broke it open, found a sweet white meat full of kernels like those of the pomegranate.

"Gather some of these fruits," he told the herdsmen, "and feed them to the Indians who are still sick with dysentery. It may cure

55

them, too. . . . And have the Indians gather a good supply of the boughs and add them to the llama rations for a few days."

Father Carvajal had bounced up on his jennet meanwhile and was inspecting the fruit for himself.

"Do you think it is right," a herdsman asked him, "to feed these berries to the Indians? How do we know they are edible?"

Carvajal turned on him a fiery countenance. "What our Blessed Lord has set before us, we do not spurn," he shouted. "Do as you are bid, and leave off speaking heresy. See, I eat the fruit myself." He bolted large mouthfuls of an unripe ball he held in his hand.

He regretted it, though, next day. The fruit had a violently astringent quality that cured the Indians of dysentery overnight, but bound the padre in such intestinal knots that all his Dominican discipline scarcely enabled him to say the Mass that morning.

Orellana said nothing, but he was amused when the priest thanked God, during the Mass, for the miracle that had been performed, and had promised to call the strange fruit "the apple of Our Lady," in memory of the great service done to the expedition.

The holy father was much impressed. This was his first personal encounter with a miracle. In his missal he entered carefully this proof of God's benign favor, which he knew would greatly move His Excellency Don Gonzalo. He was even tempted to put down that Orellana had invoked the Virgin's aid in curing the llamas, but he was not sure that Orellana had done so, and forebore the impulse.

The camp likewise was impressed, particularly since the pigs also mended. Clean ground, the availability of soft earth and forest roots for forage, slowly cured them. When the scourge was past, Gutiérrez the mountain man came to Orellana with the final toll of death. One hundred sixty-six pigs had died, and twenty-nine llamas.

Always abrupt, always frank, Gutiérrez consoled his chief over such heavy losses to food and portage.

"They are no more than we would have eaten," he said, "had there been no pestilence. And the miracle has helped Your Excellency a great deal."

"What do you mean?"

The mountaineer shrugged. "I would not bear tales, General," he said, "but it is helpful to your friends that God is on your side."

Orellana asked no further questions. He appreciated the fact that Gutiérrez had put him on guard. Such is army *esprit de corps* that none may give intelligence to a general. He must learn everything for himself.

He sharpened his eye, however, to discover what had occurred during the three weeks he had fought the plague, and became aware that Campmaster Ribera would not meet his eye, and that often with him was the equerry Maldonado. He observed also that Carranza and Gutiérrez had moved their tents from the main body of soldiery to the enclosure of his own quarters. During the pestilence he had leaned heavily upon them, Carranza for his undoubted skill in medicine, and Gutiérrez for a deep understanding of pigs that he could only have acquired during his boyhood in Castile. The weight of these duties did not, in itself, justify their personal presence so close to his person, but Orellana could not ask them to explain their purpose. He could only wait until the reason became clear. Like the casual remark of Gutiérrez concerning the miracle, the interpretation must be discovered by Orellana himself.

Camped on the fringe of the savanna, the company settled down to await Don Gonzalo's return, but he did not come. Three months passed without so much as a courier from him. The jungle had swallowed him as a boa might gorge an insignificant agouti without even humping a ridge in his scaly trunk. Father Carvajal intoned his Masses day after day at dawn, marking the passage of Easter, St. Mark's Day and Ascension. Whitsunday, the day of Pentecost, rounded the sweep of time into the month of June, followed by Corpus Christi and the day of John the Baptist.

The rainy season ended, and the jungle summer set in, feverish with humidity, noxious with the pungent reek of lush vegetation. The overflowed river retired to its banks, leaving behind a spawn of rancid pools alive with mosquitoes and malaria. Intermittently during every

57

day rain fell, so that nothing in the camp was ever quite dry; leather deteriorated, prepared food spoiled, and billions of biting ants attacked both men and animals. Fretful, the men turned to sport. They would starve a few dogs until they were ravenous, then take them into the forest to hunt agouti by night. The sport was fierce, for the dogs tore the game apart, but the huntsmen were excited by the brutal chase. Don Gonzalo was now two months overdue. Orellana could do nothing but wait. The haughty governor would not welcome any such expression of anxiety and misconfidence as a rescue mission. Orellana had his orders, and he obeyed them.

During the tedious wait, Carranza acquired two friends. Watching the companionship grow into inseparability, Orellana was surprised, for Carranza did not strike him as the type to cling to friendships. Further, Carranza had not once attended Mass, which in itself was subject to comment and cause for isolation.

As days passed, two older men of the camp came to share Carranza's remoteness. They also were lonely. García de Soria, veteran of the Peruvian wars, was the first. His mind was failing, and already he had only half a wit about him, the simplicity of a child, the affection of a spaniel. He mumbled of vast treasures in gold that he had secreted in Peru, and was heir to every practical joke born among the idle company. The men delighted in teasing him, for his drawn face registered acutely his aversion to buffoonery; they could always count on a laugh at his expense. In Carranza's company there was no cruelty, and there Soria was content. They would go fishing by the river bank, observing the camp's master fisherman, Gabriel de Contreros, from afar off, as lazy cronies will watch another man at work.

One day they were joined by Antonio Hernández, the Portuguese who, since Orellana's arrival in Don Gonzalo's camp, had been in eclipse. Among Castilian knights, there was no place for a Portuguese. He had found work as a hostler among the expedition's extra mounts, work that Ribera considered fitting for a man of Hernández' race. Then suddenly, for no explicable reason, Ribera had dismissed him.

Idle, he gravitated to the other outcasts, the senile and the Jew. Thereafter the three were inseparable.

In the relaxed discipline of a leisurely camp, Orellana thought for a time that the anxiety he had felt over his own security had been wholly imaginary. Naturally Maldonado would seek the company of his old friend Ribera. As naturally, the two men on whom he most relied, Carranza and Gutiérrez, would stay close to him.

He had, in fact, almost forgotten his fears, when he discovered an unusual rupture in the camp life. Twice he observed that the Mercedarian Friar de Vera, Carvajal's assistant, had not attended the evening vespers that were among his duties. In fact, the friar was nowhere in camp. De Vera, he knew, was Don Gonzalo's confessor. Was it possible that the friar might be in contact with the long missing Don Gonzalo? Surely if His Excellency were in the vicinity, he would communicate with Orellana himself. Yet what other purpose might account for the absences of the priest?

June had almost ended when one day, from his promontory, Orellana looked down at the lazy bustle of his camp: the gay Spanish tents pitched in orderly streets, the humidity-listless pennons of saints and knights, the cooks' stinking fires of wood so waterlogged that they were blushed to flame with a bellows, the corrals of horses, the compounds of pigs and llamas, the myriad movement of a thousand dogs, the dejected swift sidle of the muffled Indians, and beyond, the haze of the fetid jungle.

His eye turned southward, hopeful for the approach of a courier from Don Gonzalo, but evident in a quick-rising summer shower was only the faint movement of the camp outrider. Orellana did not actually expect Don Gonzalo from that quarter, but he overlooked nothing. Gonzalo would, if plans were followed, break out of the forest from the north. Here too Orellana saw, more plainly at this short distance, the form of the outrider through the sheet of rain. Off eastward there appeared to be movement, and he watched as a horseman galloped rapidly toward the camp. But hope was short-lived. The horseman was alone, and Gonzalo had taken no horses with him. Probably just a change of guard galloping in out of the wet.

Orellana had decided, after a cast of the eye that enveloped Carranza seated in the folds of his own tent, to follow the guard's example and seek drier quarters, when the horseman wheeled into the commander's street and, still at a gallop, bent straight for the lieutenant general's tent.

The rider was the captain of the rear guard, the immaculate, red-bearded Alonso de Robles. He reined but did not dismount.

"Yes?" Orellana said.

"There are evidences, General," Robles reported, wiping the rivulet from his helmet out of his eyes, "that a party of Spaniards has passed to the east of us, scarcely a league away."

"What kind of evidence?" Orellana asked. Two years had passed since any Spaniard might possibly have been in this vicinity, except Don Gonzalo himself.

"The vines have been cut by a machete, not bent and broken by hand in the native manner. And in the ashes of a campfire there is no firestick. Therefore it must have been set by flint."

"How old is this fire?"

"It was built yesterday, General, or at most the day before."

"Are you sure?"

"I did not see it personally. One of the men, scouting for fruits, ran across the track. In that muck, it is impossible to distinguish footprints, but the man swears the party wore boots, and was heading north."

"It must have been some of our own men," Orellana said calmly. "There are no Spaniards hereabouts unless they be of His Excellency's party, and they would hardly pass us by."

"Very well, sir," Robles said. "You do not wish me to investigate?"

"Many thanks, Señor Robles," Orellana said, "but I would not myself care to go in this rain, and certainly I would not send you. Double the outriders as a precaution—if you are uneasy—until the rain clears. The sun will be blistering us again in an hour."

"Yes, General," the captain said, and made off at a gallop.

Again Orellana was about to seek shelter when he was halted by a curious question. If the tracks were fresh, and were those of Gonzalo, why had His Excellency not returned? Why had he deliberately avoided the camp? Was Friar de Vera, then, in contact with him after all?

The perplexity of his face must have attracted Carranza, for he found the man beside him.

"You sent for me, General?"

Orellana started to dismiss him, then paused. "I have heard you were a necromancer, Carranza," he said, "but I doubt even you can conjure thoughts into a person's head."

Carranza smiled. Even in the rain his curly hair was unprotected. "There are those who say it has been done, General—especially to pretty girls. As for me, I would not know. The general looked perplexed. I came to see if there was anything—"

Orellana glanced about him to see whether Maldonado or the priest was within earshot, but the rain had driven them away.

"Perhaps there is something you can do," he said. "Come inside."

In the shelter of the tent he relayed the information Robles had given him. "I am not concerned, mind," he said, "but rumors spread rapidly. I would like a close-mouthed man to investigate."

"I understand. May I take Soria with me?"

"By all means," Orellana agreed, and as a conceit to prove his alertness, added, "and Antonio Hernández the Portuguese, if you like."

The mark was effective. Carranza's bushy head nodded, concealing his eyes.

"And if I discover, General, that the tracks are new?"

"You will keep the evidence from everyone except myself."

Carranza nodded.

"You may be off at once, then."

Here Carranza hesitated. "If it may please you as well, sir, I would like to postpone my departure until tomorrow. I do not relish being alone in the woods this night."

"Nonsense," Orellana said. "It is only a league away, and this shower is practically over. Take horses, man, and return tonight."

"But—"

His eyes were pleading. Orellana pressed him again to leave at once, and Carranza departed.

Not until he was mounted and gone did the look in Carranza's eyes return to Orellana's recollection, and he pondered it. Finally he dismissed the request as nothing important. Even Carranza, the man apart, must have some relaxation. And since he was reputedly a necromancer, it might well be the sort of venture best covered by the shades of night.

8

THE RAIN ended abruptly near sundown, but the humidity blanket remained dense, and smoke from the campfires meandered upward unimpelled by any breeze. The men, returning from the evening meal, congregated in groups beside the fires, close to the smoke as a ward against flies and mosquitoes.

Father Carvajal, having led his vespers (his assistant, Friar de Vera, was unaccountably absent again), began to make a sociable round of the fires. Alone on his promontory and worried, Orellana decided to do the same. Anything, he thought, to mark the passage of time until Carranza's return.

He walked down among the men, unwelcome as a commander has always been among soldiers. Their aloofness reminded him of the way women avoided him, although for a different reason. No matter where he was, or what he did, he was alone, and tonight loneliness, accentuated by peril, lay heavily upon him.

Before a group of men from Guayaquil he paused; they at least would not mind his company. The knight Blas de Medina was there, and the gambler Illanes, and a few others. Illanes was speaking.

"No, it's not like that," Orellana heard Illanes say. "Now you, Medina, you are a nobleman. Tell us truthfully, does it make any difference to a girl what breeding your blood has, so long as it is hot?"

Medina laughed.

"Depends on what she wants," he answered. "Most women don't want love. They trade what they have for what they want. It has always been so. The more they want, the better use they learn to make of what they have."

"That hasn't been my experience," the gambler said. "They want exactly what you want; some of them just don't know it, that's all.

Once you teach them—joder!—there is no getting away from them."

"That may be among peasant women," Medina said contemptuously. "I am speaking of women of the world, great women, the consorts of great men. They can climb to great heights, with judicious use of what God gave them."

"They're not all so calculating," Illanes said. "I knew a woman once in Seville who was as rich as anyone could want. Her husband —well, no matter about him. Enough that he was as rich as Pizarro. But his wife was poor. She had everything in the world: luxury, position at court, money, six horses to draw her coach; everything in the world, I say, except one thing, and it was that one thing she needed. I told her so. Never mind how I met her. At first she did not believe me. Then one night I offered to prove my argument, and she consented."

He looked around the fire, smiled rakishly at Orellana who leaned against a tree, and shrugged.

"She loved me for it. I tried to get away from her; it was no use. It is because of her that I am in this cursed forest today. Her husband finally tumbled and ran me clear out of Spain."

"That reminds me," someone else began, and Orellana walked away. Every man had known love but himself. He tried to imagine what might happen if he climbed the wall of a gentlewoman's house. What screams for the guard! What revolt against the ugly socket of his eye! Not even as shabby a love as Illanes had described could come to him. And he wanted no shabbiness. No, when he claimed a woman, she must love him for himself, love him knowing his ugliness. If he could find a woman to do that, there would be a love indeed!

He wandered into the smudge of a fire rather larger than the rest, where serious discussion was in progress. Father Carvajal was there, and Maldonado, talking with the immaculately groomed, red-bearded Alonso Robles and several other fair-skinned Andalusians who were, it appeared to the eye of Orellana, the more learned gentlemen of the camp. They listened, hungrily it seemed, to Robles, and Ore-

64

llana recalled that this lieutenant of the rear guard was lately arrived from Spain. Robles was much away from camp, on his duties at the rear of the line of march. This perhaps was the first opportunity men long in Peru had had to question the new arrival concerning affairs in Castile.

His helmet removed, showing a broad, strong forehead under a fine mass of red hair, Robles was even more prepossessing than Orellana had at first considered him. And his Castilian speech was the cultured, careful address of the Andalusian, punctuated with Moorish idiom and gentle accent, for the Andalusian hidalgo was as proud of his traditional culture as of his feats of arms and the richness of his native soil. Robles was intelligent, and well-informed, and the priest Carvajal was cross-examining him intensely. Orellana squatted at the hem of the group, signifying his desire to listen rather than to speak. Impressed by this addition to his audience, Robles expanded visibly.

To men now ten years from home, nourished by scant intelligence from supply ships, without correspondence from friends and relations since scarcely a man of them could read or write more than his own name, news even several years old was fresh, and Robles had been in Spain only three years earlier.

"For the moment, Spain is at peace," Robles was saying, "or was when I departed, although many say there cannot long be peace while Charles holds half of Europe and Francis of France is alive."

"Our last advice," Carvajal pressed, "was that Charles had recaptured Milan."

The sordid history of continental intrigue was confusing to men who had been away from it for so long, and hard to follow. Carvajal alone paid close attention, prying from Robles' recollection the zealous maneuvers of ambitious Francis, jealous Henry VIII in little England, the adagio diplomacy of Macchiavelli in Florence, and the encroachment of the infidel Turk from the east. Charles V, monarch of more than half of Europe, Holy Roman Emperor in Germany, King of the Netherlands, King of Castile and the Iberian peninsula, Ruler of Sicily and Naples, Protector of the Holy See, brother of the King of

Bohemia and Hungary, was big and vulnerable to depredations at every hand.

"How can it be," Carvajal went on, "that Henry of England is on the side of France when our gracious princess of Aragon, daughter of Isabella, God rest her saintly soul, is queen of England?"

Robles looked perplexed. He knew the answer, but he was hard put to explain the restlessness of England and the continent to a Dominican. The Dominicans were charged with the Holy Office, and even to mention in the wrong words the heresies of the new Europe might be construed as heresy within himself. Evidently none of his hearers had any inkling of what had happened.

"Henry has put her away, Father," he said carefully.

"Pope Clement allowed it?" Father Carvajal gasped.

"He had nothing to say about it, Father. The English church does not recognize the authority of the Holy Father."

"Impossible!" Carvajal shouted. "Choose your words with care, young man."

Robles needed no such warning. He was already speaking as carefully as he knew how. Watching from the shadowy fringe of the fire, Orellana could see him laboring his mind.

"I think, Father," Robles said, "that I had better go back a little in history and tell you what I know."

He recited the list of treasons of the past decade. How within the confines of Charles' own Holy Roman Empire had arisen a heretic named Martin Luther who had made his own translation of the Bible, and struck off thousands of copies on a newly invented printing press for all to read. How other men, inspired by Luther's dramatic act of burning publicly the Bull of Excommunication against him, had translated the Bible to suit themselves into other languages, using ancient Greek texts rather than the Church copies. How a religious teacher named Calvin had excited France against the Church; how Sweden and Denmark had turned from the Holy Faith to what they called Protestantism; how heretic protestants had grown to such proportions that under the leadership of princes they could take the field in battle against the Catholic church in Switzerland and the German states. And how, taking advantage of the continental chaos to rid himself of his Spanish queen and marry a court strumpet who had not even withheld herself from him until she was queen, Henry in England had beheaded so many churchmen that his English bishops yielded, and to save their own necks had thrown off all Papal authority and proclaimed their ecclesiastic allegiance to God and Henry alone.

"Impossible!" was all that Father Carvajal could say. He did not dispute the accuracy of Robles' analysis, for the young man obviously was an Andalusian scholar. "I do not understand it," he said, shaking his shorn head.

"It is past understanding," Robles agreed. "You know, of course, that the Vatican was sacked and looted by our own Spanish soldiers, causing the Holy Father, Clement VII, to flee, and that our own emperor held the Pope captive for seven months up in the mountains."

"Charles did that? Miseracordia, that I should live to hear of it."

"The authority of the Pope has not been the same since."

"God with fire and sword will bring His own vengeance on heretic dogs," Carvajal said. "I do not question His reasons for allowing such manifestations, but He will end them in His own good time."

"The example of many clergy may not be to God's liking, Father," Robles said cautiously. "God may be punishing them for their sins."

"That may well be," Carvajal admitted. "It may well be."

"Of course," Robles went on, "the world has also been greatly upset by published attacks upon the Church. A few copies have reached Seville, written in excellent Latin."

"Cannot the Church throttle these presses?"

"Seemingly not, Father."

"What are these books?"

"In England, one Thomas More has argued for reform of the Holy Church to give greater voice to the laity. But he was beheaded."

"Well he should be."

"But he was beheaded, Father, for refusing to allow the Church to be subordinated to the State."

67

"God of our fathers! What heresy else?"

"In Rotterdam," Robles went on, praying silently that Carvajal might not realize that he had actually read any of these forbidden works, "one Erasmus, a great scholar and himself a priest, argues that there are errors in the Church's translations of Scripture and that they should be changed."

"Mother of God!"

Orellana found himself listening intently.

"Well—God will strike him dead in His own time," Carvajal said.

"Great will be the slaughter on that day, Father. There are many of them. Calvin, in France, is organizing a church."

"A church, the upstart dog!"

"Yes, Father. He preaches directly from the Bible and his followers form their own minds on how they shall believe."

Father Carvajal jumped to his feet and crossed himself. "It is a sin even to think on such things," he said, "and a great sin to speak of them. How do you know so much?"

Robles felt the baleful eyes of the priest upon him, and looked hesitantly toward Orellana for protection.

"The clergy in Seville discuss little else, Father," he replied. "I would not speak of these things now, except to acquaint yourself with them. As a vicar in the new world, you should see the devil in all his guises."

"Yes, yes, of course." And seizing this opportunity to ask other questions on a subject his heart told him he should put out of his thoughts, Carvajal said, "This man—what do you call him, who burned the Papal Bull of excommunication—"

"Martin Luther he is called, Father."

"Yes. I cannot understand why he is not crushed."

"He is an Augustinian monk, Father, a professor at Wittenberg. Even after his excommunication he went on preaching and teaching."

"This—this could not happen. What does he preach?"

"I scarcely like to say, Father."

"Go on, son, tell me. I absolve you. It is well that I be enlightened of this devilment."

"Very well then, but what I say is merely what the priests in Seville have told me."

"I understand," Carvajal said. Orellana smiled into the dusk; this Robles was no fool.

"Luther believes that indulgences were not created by Christ, but by the Church, and therefore are not only worthless but sacrilegious."

"In the name of the Holy Trinity, what else?"

"He says the Pope is no more divine then any other prince, and therefore the church has no authority over civil government."

"The rebel should be gutted and his bowels fed to the dogs. And the Church does nothing about it?"

"Too many people have learned to read the works of the new printing presses for the ideas to be quickly crushed out, Father."

"It is a phase," Carvajal said unhappily, "otherwise the Church would not permit it. . . . You have made me ill, son. Excuse me."

He walked quickly to his tent. Orellana saw him fling himself prostrate upon the dirt in penance for the heretical discussion which his weakness had permitted him not only to join, but to encourage.

Orellana took Carvajal's place close to the mosquito smudge.

"What else is going on in the world?" he asked.

Robles shrugged. "A colony called Buenos Aires has been established on the east coast of New Spain, General, did you know?"

"I did not know," Orellana said, with great interest. "Where is it?"

"Two thousand leagues from Cuba, sir, so there must be much land below Peru. I heard about it at Santo Domingo on my way out. And they say a French priest, named Cartier, has found a way to the western ocean by a river far to the north, in the latitude of Denmark."

"That would seem doubtful," Orellana said. "But who knows? If there is this much land to the south, there may well be this much more to the north. If it is like Nicaragua, the French are welcome to it."

The company laughed. Nicaragua had eroded most of them from youth to age, and they were pleased to think of the effete French struggling through the same vicissitudes. The experience might make men of them.

"How long did you say it was since you were in Seville?"

"Three years, more or less, General."

"I sailed from there," Orellana said. "Down the Guadalquivir to San Lucar. It was a long time ago. Seville is still the same?"

"The same, sir," Robles said, "but larger. I watched it grow with my own eyes. By royal decree, it is the only port of entry for goods from the new world, so it has grown big and rich and has attracted the men of many nations, both great and small."

"I will never forget Seville," Orellana said. "The bells were ringing in La Giralda as we sailed down the river, and the last we saw of the town was the shining tower of the new cathedral, the minaret of Giralda, and the Alcázar sprawling on the hilltop. . . . One does not forget his last look at Spain."

"Especially in this cursed selva, eh, General?"

It was Maldonado who spoke. Orellana had, for the first time in many days, forgotten his presence, and did not relish the reminder. He chose to ignore the equerry, and turned back to Robles, whose red hair now was ruddy brown in the quick-gathering twilight. Rain was in the air again.

"You Andalusians are lucky men," Orellana said. "You have everything. Sometimes I wish I had been born an Andalusian—in Cádiz, maybe—so that I had learned to smile, and read and write. I should like very much to learn to smile."

"I have a cousin, General," Robles said with a broad grin, "who could teach any man to smile. When you return to Spain, you must meet her."

"Ah," Orellana said, "you Andalusians too highly endow your women."

"But we smile, Señor, and our women smile. We laugh, and our women laugh. We love—and they love us for it. . . . They know

70

how to live, the Andalusian women. They don't shut themselves up behind brick walls and lace mantas and the frowns of duennas as do your women of Estremadura. The way your women live is what rivets the frown in your faces, if you will forgive the reference. I speak only in generalities."

Orellana was not offended. This talk of women stirred him. Not of women as the gambler Illanes used them; Illanes was not loved, he was merely eased. Alone in a new world man comes to recognize one unassailable truth: that every man must have one woman, to him perfect, who clings to the defensive strength of his right arm, who imposes against his strength her frailty, against his coldness her warmth, against his ambition her approbation, against his conceit her applause, against his hunger her breast, and against his issue her child. Man needs memories of a woman's warm hair smell to ease his lonely bed in far lands, and anticipations of her gratification to speed him home again. Man without a woman is a horse without a bridle, an arm without a sword. But as it must be a particular horse of known strength and eccentricity, or a steel of tested resilience, so it must be one understandable woman.

All his life Orellana had been building his house. Panama, Nicaragua, Puna, Cuzco, Salinas, Guayaquil, these were the scaffold. The framework was stoutly built out of the materials best suited to a man's house: patience learned from long waiting for his chance in Panama; stamina developed in the swamplands of the merciless isthmus; courage to withstand privation on the long trek into Peru; alertness to the perfidies of Spanish friendship once the Inca was dethroned, and finally, tactfulness and charity in the administration of his own domains. With such timbers firming the ridgepole of his house, Orellana was confident of his ability to cope with anything Spaniards might devise against him in the future. Now, a lieutenant general and second in command of a great expedition with the promise of a governorship, he was tiling his roof. But the keystone of a house was a woman; his house had no keystone, and therefore would surely fall.

71

As a youth Orellana naturally had thought of returning rich to Spain, to the lush arms of a Spanish woman. But that was before he had lost his eye. He was ugly. To be illustrious was not enough. Robles, with his dashing goatee, his flaming hair and warming smile; even Don Gonzalo for all his coarse-mouthed distemper had a godlike body: these were the men for whom beautiful women were born on earth, not for the one-eyed likes of Francisco Orellana.

He was piqued, however, by Robles' suggestion that in Seville he might meet a girl who could make him smile.

"No beauty of Seville," he pursued the subject, "would look at an ugly man like me."

Robles was unruffled. "You do not know my cousin, General," he said. "Andalusians are more interested in the soul of a man than in his leather. They have for too many generations had to accept men mutilated by the Moors to favor outward beauty overmuch."

This was a concept to warm Orellana's heart.

"She will be taken before ever I get home," he said.

"I doubt it," Robles went on. "Even beauty must have a dowry, and unless I, through the merciful kindness of God, am able to provide it, there will be none. Besides, she is still very young."

"What is she like?" Orellana asked rather shyly.

Robles was pleased to please his general.

"She was just turning fourteen when I left home, Señor," he said, a wistful coaxing tenderness in his soft Andalusian voice. "She was just ripening into a beautiful pomegranate from the innocent beauty of youth. She is tall and straight as a reed, and her eyes are straight, too, Señor, though at first glance you might think them a little bold. It is not boldness, just curiosity. She has a saucy mind."

"I like spirit in a woman," Orellana said. "I like response when I spur."

Robles smiled. "She is just waiting to be spurred, Señor. I noticed it particularly before I left. One day she had been a child. And then suddenly she was a woman. Mother of God! What a thrill to look on her and think to oneself, 'She is ready.' It made me tingle, I tell you."

It made Orellana tingle, too.

"There she was, when last I saw her, standing by the common well with a jar on her shoulder. Her arms were over her head, Señor, the ripe fruit bulging out of her bodice, her hips and legs as rippling as the wind on a clean sea. 'By God,' I told her, 'I will come back and have you myself.' She knew what I meant, and turned on me the fair face of a madonna—I mean it, Señor, a madonna, no less—her eyes melting and her smiling teeth two chiseled rows of ivory." He paused to nourish his reminiscence.

"What did she say?" Orellana asked. He was tense, and dared not look up from the wet ground.

"Oh, she laughed, and said, 'Not for the lazy bones of a poor relation was I intended.' And she said, 'I am going to marry a hidalgo, maybe even an adelantado, who knows?' And she laughed as though she knew that what she had at that moment would have any adelantado in Spain sliming in the mud before her red petticoat."

Orellana was confirmed at that moment in his ambition to become an adelantado, governor of Quito province. He even fingered in his mind the conceit that his dream of governorship, so long germinating, was perhaps linked with this beautiful Andalusian child whom he had never seen.

"What color is her hair?" he asked.

"The color of rich Jerez Ambrosia, General," Robles said, "long braided and clean. It is a glory to her. She must wear a black mantilla over it at church to keep the communicants from unholy thoughts. But then it is the hair you would expect on a girl whose ancestors were Visigoths, Señor."

"Her eyes are blue, then."

"No, brown. The brown of cocoa, and as easily melted."

"And what is the name of this perfection?"

Robles smiled again. "The name is Ana de Ayala, General," he

73

replied. "You will find her in the house of her stepfather Cosme de Chavez, in a red-tiled house on the Avenida Teresa just under the morning shadow of the Alcázar. You cannot miss it, for there is a knotted olive tree sheltering the gate, and a silver bell to ring."

"Ana de Ayala," Orellana repeated.

"That is right, Señor."

9

Heat broke up the group. Orellana sought his tent, but Carranza had not returned. This was odd, for Orellana thought he had detected, as he sat listening to the story of Ana de Ayala, the countenance of Soria pass by, and Soria had gone with Carranza into the jungle. Carranza's tent, Orellana assured himself, was empty, and Soria was quartered at a distance.

He was about to retire when Maldonado entered the tent to receive his orders for the night. Usually he slept in the foyer, on a litter across the door, so that any intruder would stumble over his sleeping form and arouse the watch that stood outside. In his usual efficient manner he gathered up Orellana's wet harness and placed dry clothes and spotless accoutrements on a chest close to the general's right side. The used apparel would be dried and polished in the morning.

Orellana took from his waist the double-edged dagger encrusted with seed pearls that served him as a fruit knife by day and a protector by night, and stuck it lightly in the wooden head of his couch. Maldonado stood beside the oil lamp, looking down at his recumbent chief.

"Will there be anything else, General?"

"No, that's all. Thank you, Señor."

"Then if Your Excellency has no objection, I wonder if I may be excused from duty tonight. My old companions from Popayán are going agouti hunting with the dogs. Night hunting has become great sport, sir. The dogs have been starved for three days in anticipation, and I have not had an opportunity—"

"Yes, yes, Maldonado, by all means go," Orellana said.

He lay a long time in his tent, his head throbbing with the possible implications of Robles' strange story of the European men who had defied the Church, but in the end he could make little of it. It was all

75

too confusing, and besides, he could not concentrate, for the vision of yellow-haired, cocoa-eyed Ana de Ayala constantly intruded. He could see her by the common well, hands raised to hold the jar to her shoulder, a gesture that tightened the tunic about her young breasts. Then his mind would revert to actuality and he would wonder why Carranza had not yet returned. The man had been gone long enough to travel half a dozen leagues instead of two. He sank into sleep, his dreams occupied for the first time in a dozen years with the exciting inspiration of a woman.

In black darkness he awoke. Weight as of a heavy stone crushed his chest. Immediately a gagging, searing rend tore the flesh from his throat, and the acute rake of a dull cutting blade scarred his right ear.

Assassination! The thought was quick, but reflex had been quicker and his right hand shot out for the familiar clutch of his dagger. It was not at the bed head. Again great weight struck him, this time in the belly, puffing the wind from his lungs even through the tight hold that was on his throat. The arm fumbling for the dagger met a vise that closed on his forearm, a vise of torture with steel spikes in its jaws that bedded deeply and then began to tear. Stifled, choking, unable to cry out an alarum to his guard, his eyes afire with red sparks, his head bulging with bursting pressure, Orellana was hopelessly pinned from hip to head. He kicked. A steel vise found the calf of his left leg. Again the torture of spikes, the rip of flesh.

With his right leg, Orellana found the stout upright beam of his tent and pushed with a lunge born of panic, at the same time twisting his torso away from the wall. He rolled over, his back against the edge of his litter. Another surge and he was on the ground. The weights on his chest and belly rolled with him so that now he was on top, and the monstrous attackers beneath. His head came down hard, burying his eye and cheeks in something soft and malodorous. He could barely breathe. The choking at his throat was tighter. But he needed no sense of smell now to identify his foe.

He was under attack from dogs. One at the throat, one at his chest, one at his right arm, one at his right leg. Noiseless, methodical, ferocious, well-trained, hungry dogs. Peruvian dogs have no bark, and Orellana could not cry out. Now a fifty-pound weight broke onto his back and sought a hold on the back of his neck. The vise on his neck held, but could no longer rip the gullet from his throat, for the weight of his shoulder had pinned the dog into immobility. Yet Orellana's defense was of little use. If they would only growl, or yelp, Orellana thought in the last clear functioning of his mind—but the dogs were as silent as the night.

"Mother of God," Orellana tried to say, "have mercy on me," but he could not speak. He could not move. Hairy weights were all about him, holding down his flanks, probing at his legs, raking his shoulders. He could hear his own breath, a high thin wheeze as though he were sucking air through a hole in his throat. His knees found contact with the hard dirt, and he half rose, dragging the dogs with him, but immediately the jaws at his throat took advantage of the clearer arena to rend again his flesh, and he fell, one elbow deep in the belly hair of a heavy dog. He lay where he fell, listening to the suction of his thin breath, while the pressure mounted to the crown of his head and his eye sockets reflected the inferno of fire within his brain. His hands closed on a dog's open mouth, and he pulled with all his might, feeling the jaws give and break under his fingers.

Dimly he heard a new confusion, but he could not identify it. His brain was past distinctions. The new intrusion seemed to be a noise, but it was a far choir to the anvil chorus within him. The noise throbbed and waned, throbbed and waned again, and now there seemed to be a flame. For a second he regained complete control of his consciousness, smelled the pitchy fire of a torch and knew that he was done for. Whoever had loosed the dogs now was setting fire to his tent. This was the end. With this final effort, Orellana's consciousness surrendered to the attack, and abandoned his body to the enemy.

When consciousness returned, Orellana lay on his back. The weights were gone from his limbs, but not the pain. He opened his eye, ready again to defend himself, but he saw that he needed no defense. Before him, a blazing faggot in his left hand, a two-edged sword in his right,

77

stood Antonio Carranza, tottering uncertainly on his feet. About him lay the stinking carnage of an heroic struggle—six camp dogs.

Orellana attempted to speak, but his throat was swollen shut. His right arm was a dead weight. His left arm fared better, hoisting Orellana's body to his knees. Carranza swayed stupidly, kept from falling by the sword, which propped his hip. Orellana arose and shook himself. His dagger was neither on the bed head, nor on the ground.

Reviving, Carranza staggered to the litter and sat down, the burning faggot still in his hand. Orellana took it from him, lit an oil lamp with it, and went to throw it out the door. His guard was not on duty. The company street was deserted for as far as he could see.

Returning to the tent, Orellana took stock of himself, his mind a fury of revenge against the perpetrators of so vicious an attack upon his life. First the sword arm. It was no longer dead. The tingle of circulation crept down the arm to the fingertips as Orellana tentatively stretched his fingers and finally swung his whole arm. Immediately he felt better, and smiled grimly, congratulating himself and thanking the Holy Virgin.

The pleasure was short-lived.

"God of Abraham," Carranza muttered, "your face is a mass of bloody pulp, Your Grace. Let me go to my tent—I have certain herbs—"

Orellana touched his throat and felt the blood. He leaped to his mirror; the throat was raw and punctured and still bleeding.

"What do you know of all this?" he asked, fighting to keep control of his rising anger.

"Nothing, Your Excellency, before God. I returned to report to you—the rest you can see for yourself. Three of the dogs you had killed before I arrived. I put a torch to the others. I do not see how you could possibly have killed the three, with your bare hands."

They stared at each other a moment, then Orellana relaxed, but he remained grim.

"I will find and hang whoever did this thing if I have to rack every man in the camp," he said tensely.

"I would not advise you to talk too much, General, until the throat—"

"Get the herbs, then," Orellana said, suddenly weak and shaky. He fell back on his cot, his mind sorting out possible assassins.

Carranza returned instantly. He showed now that his reputation as a physician was honestly carried, by the manner in which he put the poniard in the oil lamp while he spread out his herbs and unguents upon a clean cloth. When he approached Orellana, however, the General held up his hand.

"One moment," he said. "I do not often ask questions of any man. But one must know that the skill of his physician is honestly come by."

Suavely Carranza smiled. "But certainly, Excellency," he said. "I studied medicine and astrology along with the sons of princes, under the greatest instructor known among the Moors."

"Among the Moors?"

"It was before the days of Spanish greed in Andalusia, Excellency. Now if you are convinced—"

Orellana exposed his neck, and Carranza set to work upon the torn throat, probing the wounds with gentle fingers.

"You are lucky," Carranza said once. "Your beard has saved your face."

In pain from the probing, Orellana merely grunted. He wanted to close his eye, but could not be revealed susceptible to so mild a torture, even before the physician alone.

From his clean cloth Carranza took up a box of unguent. "An old recipe, General, proven in a hundred wars. Prevents maggots and festers, keeps the skin from drawing into scars."

"Get on with your work," Orellana said.

"There are two holes here," Carranza went on quietly, as impersonally as though he was calling attention to a pair of rips in a surcoat, "and one is quite deep."

He took dry herbs, rubbed them to powder in the palms of his hands, and pushed them into the incisions with a fingertip.

"Don't choke me, man!" Orellana gasped. What he might better have said, he knew, was that the pain was killing him.

79

Carranza nodded. "Unlike most tortures, Excellency, this one is necessary." He went on with his work, talking as he did so.

"This will hurt, Señor."

"Hang the hurt. Finish the work."

Carranza took the poniard, now red hot, and a needle and thread in his hands. The smell of burning blood and flesh, the faint hiss of searing skin, caused Orellana at last to close his eye. The poniard moved swiftly to its work, the needle following.

"That should do," Carranza said, wiping his dagger on his knee leather, and rising.

Orellana reached for the mirror and surveyed the work. He had been neatly patched. Clotted blood still clung to his throat, but the holes were gone, and the unguent was spread over the wounds.

"Hold your head high for a day or two, Señor," said Carranza, "and forebear the breastplate. Then you will be all right."

Orellana was better already.

"And now," he said, "where is my guard?"

"If it please Your Excellency—"

"It does not please me to be called Excellency. In my city of Guayaquil, yes; here I am a lieutenant general only."

"You recover rapidly," Carranza commented drily, "if you can be angry over little things so soon. Lie down awhile. Morning will be time enough for investigations. Gutiérrez is outside. He will guard your tent. Morning cannot be far away."

"Gutiérrez!" Orellana exploded. "What is he doing here?"

"We thought it best, Señor—"

"You thought it best! You and Gutiérrez. You thought it best to conceal from me something I should know, that was like to cost me my life. Now speak, or it will cost you yours."

Orellana was in a mood to cause trouble. The best antidote for spilled blood is someone else's blood. He began to buckle on his harness. "And Gutiérrez—get him in here."

"Yes, Señor."

Gutiérrez came swiftly, but remained standing in the doorway.

80

"What do you know of this?" Orellana asked.

"Nothing, General, I swear it—"

"You just happened to be passing and you heard the dogs," Orellana said sarcastically.

Gutiérrez remained silent.

"And my guard?"

"If I may be so bold," Carranza cut in soothingly, "I am an old soldier of many wars. Incidents of this kind require caution."

"Caution, when I am beset by dogs, like a savage or a slave?"

"The more reason for caution, Señor. The very baseness of the attack would greatly hurt your prestige, if it were known. Find the assassins privately, and hang them for something else—but not for the attempt upon your authority, lest you break down your authority completely. You have need of respect, Señor. . . . What I have discovered—"

"Mother of God, yes," Orellana said, "what did you find out?"

"That a large party of European footmen has very recently passed this way."

"There can be no mistake?"

"None, Señor."

"How large?"

"I could not certainly say. I would hazard fifty or sixty."

"Did Gutiérrez go with you?"

"No, Señor. When I could not return in time, I sent Soria to him with word to guard you. Unfortunately he was too late—"

"What do you mean—'in time'?"

Carranza was caught. Or perhaps, Orellana thought, he had let himself be caught.

"I suspected an attempt upon you, Señor."

"You just suspected it? You were not sure?"

"No, Señor, I was not sure."

Orellana knew he would learn nothing more. "Everyone," he said, "seems to know more about this than I."

"The more reason for caution, then," said Carranza, "until you learn the facts. You might begin by observing something that is out of order in the camp. That is all I can say."

Out of order? The only thing out of order was the absence of Friar de Vera. Surely—

"Where is Friar de Vera?" he asked.

Antonio Carranza relaxed and smiled. "I do not know, Señor," he said, but every muscle of his body called him a liar.

The trudge of feet and the clink of arms sounded outside, accompanied by voices.

"Oye!" The shout was from outside the tent. "Ho! Guard!"

There was no response.

Orellana rushed to the door. The captain of the guard snapped erect.

"Aquí, aquí!" A member of the guard detail, behind the tent, had found something. Face down in the muck lay the guardsman. He was dead. A fine poniard, with seed pearls set in the hilt, stuck jauntily from his left shoulderblade.

The captain bent over the corpse, extricated the dagger, arose, and with horror held out the weapon toward Orellana.

"But, but—" he said aghast, "this poniard is yours, Excellency."

In the faces of the guard detail Orellana read his own guilt. Nombre de Dios, he thought, they don't think me—

The captain of the guard did think so.

"It is irregular, Excellency," he said. "I do not know what to do. But I must report the matter, and this evidence—" he held up the poniard—"to the council."

So the assassins, Orellana thought, had after all a two-edged weapon. To have escaped the dogs—for this.

"Of course, Captain," he said quietly. "I expect you to do your duty. I know no more of the affair than do you. I was busy with other matters—as you will see for yourself if you will be so kind as to step inside my tent."

10

IMMEDIATELY after Mass next morning, Orellana summoned Friar de Vera. The priest came hurriedly, but looked as though he had been roused from sleep.

Orellana looked him over coldly. He had paid no attention to the Mercedarian previously, for Father Carvajal was chaplain of the expedition and de Vera played so minor a role to the dominant padre as to be virtually an acolyte. What Orellana had heard concerning de Vera was not in the man's favor. He was a rogue, a gambler, an opportunist. Just as the New World had attracted the dregs of Castile from every level of society, so it had drawn reprobates from among the clergy; discredited at home, they fled abroad. De Vera was one of these. Even the gambler Juan de Illanes had no use for de Vera, saying the friar cheated at cards. And when an Indian girl was sometimes captured and brought to camp, de Vera was among the first to violate her. These things Orellana knew.

Gonzalo de Vera's appearance belied his character. He stood before Orellana in his priestly garb the picture of saintliness and abnegation. He was of average height, perhaps a Gallician from the patrician benignity of his strong face and the crystal innocence of his blue eyes, a man erect of bearing but of humble dignity. A bishop, confronted by de Vera in the role of parish priest, would have trusted him immediately, so open was his countenance, so broad his brow, so firm and unwrinkled his face. He was strong, too, Orellana noted, and walked with the muscular readiness of a man trained in chivalric display, horsemanship, a quick lance, an accurate blade. He might have been, from his appearance, the younger son of a great duke, who donned the cloth with aspirations to the red hat and grandeur of a cardinal. That this was not so, Orellana knew. Father Carvajal had told him in confidence that de Vera was a foundling. He had been deposited at the gates of a Mercedarian cloister, had been raised by the monks and eventually had embraced their order. Then he had run away, pursuing a charwoman of the town, and had returned to the cloister six months later, begging forgiveness. In atonement and penance he had undertaken a mission for his order among the savages of the New World. Don Gonzalo Pizarro had seen him near the mines of Potosí, had taken him into his household, and had made the friar his confessor. Obviously de Vera was well qualified in such a trust for a man who trusted no one and whose mind was constantly taxed by suspicion, intrigue, and petty fear.

The friar waited to be addressed, and Orellana kept him waiting. He did not like to treat with loathsome beasts.

"As you see from my bandages," he said at last, "I almost lost my life last night."

The friar was most concerned.

"I shall be honored to undertake prayers of thanksgiving for your victory over this evil," de Vera said with all the suavity of a diplomat, his manner implying that there could be no other reason for this peremptory summons into the general's presence.

"Prayer is not what I require of you," Orellana replied, hating the priest. "When the attack upon me was made, you were absent from the camp. I require an explanation."

The friar appeared to be amazed. "You do not suspect—? Your insinuation—no, Excellency. Where I was, I cannot say. The duties of a priest call him everywhere, and his comings and goings are known only to God. Sufficient that I was absent. An absent man can do no hurt."

"Your conscience crowds you, Father," Orellana said. "I did not accuse you. I merely ask where you were last night, and whether your repeated absences from among us menace our common security; that is all."

"Mere man does not call a priest to account, General. Such presumption is reserved for one's ecclesiastical superiors, in the name of God."

"In an army, the commander asks whatever questions he likes, Friar de Vera."

"Then I must remind you, General, that you are not the commander."

Orellana coolly surveyed the upstart.

"You imply that your absence was, then, upon duty for His Excellency Don Gonzalo."

"I had certain instructions from him."

"And you were carrying them out last night?"

"I was."

"Very well, you may go. But God have mercy on your soul if you are lying to me."

De Vera bowed, and retired slowly, his face impassive, his figure for a long time visible from the knoll on which Orellana stood. Orellana watched him go. Had de Vera told him a great deal, or nothing? He was inclined to believe that it was a great deal. Certain items fit into the general pattern. Don Gonzalo had not once sent back a runner for information concerning the welfare of the camp. Therefore he must know from other sources than his lieutenant general what was going on, for Gonzalo was, if nothing else, a suspicious man. Being suspicious, he might have planted spies in the camp. Who better than his own confessor and the equerry Maldonado, perhaps the only men in a company of scoundrels low enough to undertake such work? Easy enough for de Vera to slip from camp at night, meet a trusted runner a few leagues away and convey to him all that Don Gonzalo needed to know. Granting this to be true, de Vera must have an accomplice somewhere who knew the secrets of the council and the true state of conditions. Only one eligible arose in Orellana's mind—Campmaster Ribera, Maldonado's former chief. The only man to clash with Orellana's authority, he would color the incident to enflame a naturally suspicious mind such as Gonzalo's. And if, now, Gonzalo was returning disappointed in the fruits of his scouting tour, he would seek an excuse for failure, someone on whom to lay the blame.

But why assassination? Why not better a clean death sentence at the hands of a pliable council? Something yet was unexplained.

Now he would face the council on another charge—that of murdering his own guard. He did not belittle this peril. Next to gold and God, the Castilian loved the law. He caressed each phrase of it as lovingly as he might the hair of a woman, and he would rather litigate than eat. The law was to the Castilian a guardianship of liberties unparalleled in his age. The Cortes could and did upset the king, and even the Pope; and this championship of the rights of man against power and privilege increased in vehemence as it filtered down the social scale from large minds to small. The smallest minds usually are in an army, and the shabbiest of these are in a colonial corps composed of rascals, renegades, and fortune hunters. The smaller the mind the more dogmatic the law and the less watered by the diluting compassion of mercy.

Of all this Orellana was aware. He had seen men sent to death on trumped up charges clothed in the respectability of the law, all forms observed as faithfully as the ritual of the Mass. And he knew that the most lethal charges, at law, were not those based on fact, but on conspiracy.

His only defense was to gain time—to insist that a matter of such grave weight affecting the camp lieutenant commander must be submitted to Don Gonzalo alone. Any other course would be an assumption of Don Gonzalo's prerogatives. Orellana thought this argument might weightily affect Ribera, who at all costs must not antagonize his chief, and at the same time might confound the lawyers who could not dispute the immobility of prerogative. There at least the law was on his side. Gonzalo was a man of such whims that his attitude toward Orellana might easily change. This was Orellana's only hope.

But how, virtually under arrest, might he maintain his command in camp? To be superseded, while awaiting trial, would be fatal to his authority. Don Gonzalo, returning, could seize the obvious excuse

86

that Orellana was no leader or he would not have lost his leadership. Until the council met, however, Orellana remained in command.

At once Orellana issued many unnecessary orders: for a stouter dog compound, for an inquiry into the method by which the dogs had escaped, for the abolition of starving dogs in future for personal hunting. He asked Father Carvajal to give thanks, at vespers, for his deliverance from the attack. None disputed these tests of his authority. He was still in command.

Orellana's body ached from his night's mauling. Large bruises covered his arm and leg and the back of his neck. His throat was constricted and sore, so that he ate and breathed with difficulty. Carranza made him a gruel of sow's milk and maize and some secret compote from his scarf, which Orellana managed to swallow. He sat on the knoll, keeping an eye on the camp, and let the day's questions come to him from responsible captains. Above all he did not want to be seen by the rank and file of soldiers until his neck was healed, his stiff back straight again, his bruises mended. In his own compound he was at least safe from the eyes of the soldiery.

That the attack upon him had been carried out by Maldonado now was obvious. The equerry admitted to starving the dogs, brazenly stated that several had been left behind in the compound and that they must have escaped by themselves. The method also was clear. Maldonado had slipped into the tent, his presence unchallenged by the guard, taken the dagger, and killed the guard so that the blood smell before the tent would lure the hungry dogs inside. That Campmaster Ribera was involved was apparent; but whether he had ordered the murder himself, or acted for Don Gonzalo, was not yet clear. Conclusively, Don Gonzalo was in the vicinity, yet why had he not come into the camp, after such a long absence? Friar de Vera was the key to that.

Orellana longed for a ten-minute talk with his old friend Diez de Pineda, from whose sharp eye no intrigue escaped and who, properly approached, would sell even the soldier's code of honor for a price. Pineda, however, was with Don Gonzalo.

He turned over his problem for a long time, acutely aware that, since an attempt had been made upon him, he was no longer in Don Gonzalo's esteem, and someone in the camp knew it. What had swerved the fickle governor from the confidence he had displayed toward Orellana before his departure?

Unable to answer this key question, Orellana was tempted to summon Alonzo Robles, the Andalusian who could read and write and who knew how to smile, and learn more of this Erasmus who said worship was in the heart, and of Calvin, whose followers formed their own beliefs, and of Luther, who challenged both church and state. He was deeply moved by Robles' campfire recital of affairs in Europe. Here at last, some of the questions that had pursued Orellana to the New World, were being answered. Along with the answers, there was before him the face and figure of a girl who did not look into a man's face for beauty, but into his heart. Ana de Ayala! The name kept rippling through his mind.

He called Carranza, intent upon summoning Lieutenant Robles, when an idea injected itself into his mind with such forcefulness that he commanded instead the appearance of the Indian most versed in the jungle dialects. At once he might pursue a hobby and, perhaps, extract useful information.

A wizened little man of inscrutable age—Indians never look old and seldom young—came to the knoll and squatted on his haunches in the Indian manner.

"Your name?"

"Francisco González," the Indian said.

Dear God, thought Orellana, the unoriginality of the priests! Every Indian who had ever been converted seemed to have been christened Francisco González. It was as though the Dominicans had perpetrated a grim joke. He made a mental note to chide Father Carvajal one day on this point—if he survived the council meeting—and if possible to discover who the first memorable González was and what he had done to deserve such immortality.

This Indian, González by prudent allegiance to the Holy Trinity, was not a Quechua, as are most of the highland born. He had been taken to Quito, he said, and later to Cuzco, during the leadership of his father, a tribal chief, to be educated in Inca ways. His schooling had ended in misery with the coming of the Spaniards.

Under Orellana's polite probing, González said that he was of the Poamayna people, who inhabited the headwaters of the River Chambira, but of its location he was unprecise. He had been away from home for many moons. In speech, however, he traced himself to the region of the Upper Napo, for he had no difficulty with the language of any of those tribes with whom he had come in contact.

Orellana invited him to speak his native tongue, and the Indian obliged lyrically, as though his tongue, freed from long bondage, would run far away. Orellana listened. Occasionally he challenged a word and received its Castilian or Quechua equivalent. In the main, however, he merely nodded. The language pattern was not new. It was the guttural base of many savages, overcast with Quechua words which Orellana doubted were indigenous to the Poamayna. After an hour, Orellana was able to ask simple questions in the native's vernacular, and the Indian rewarded him with a description of the country, its people, its customs, its game and fish.

They were concentrating each upon the accent of the other when Carranza approached with a bowl of gruel. Orellana looked up. The burning sun was directly overhead.

"You cannot shake off old habits, I see," Carranza said, "or is it a gift that lets you talk to these savages?"

"I find it useful," Orellana replied, asking that food be brought to the Indian. "A knowledge of the Indian tongues is helpful in an Indian country."

"I remember," Carranza said, "how you talked Quechua to the Indians in Guayaquil. I don't see how you tell one grunt from another."

"I like to speak directly to every man," Orellana said. "Interpreters are sticks that muddy the water."

"It is perhaps a gift, then," Carranza said. "Now if you ask me about the stars, the signs and portents, those I can read as well as any man, but—"

"I have no eye or ear for the stars," Orellana cut in. "This broth is vile. Bring corn to the Indian."

Carranza departed. Maldonado approached. He had not been far away for some time.

"Shall I flog this heathen to his own mess, Excellency?" he asked. "You seem—"

"When I need your help, I shall call," Orellana dismissed him. Maldonado lingered within earshot, however, Orellana noticed, long enough to discover the cause of this long parley between the lieutenant general and the chief interpreter, before he walked away, probably, Orellana thought, to report this new development to the camp-master.

Now Orellana casually changed the tenor of the conversation from Indian lore to affairs of the camp. Often the sharp eye of Indian guides sees evidence civilized men overlook. They talked of the condition of the beasts, the welfare of the Indians, the possibility of attack. This last was the goal of the circuitous conversation.

"I wonder," Orellana said, "whether possibly any Indians have slipped by our outriders and infiltrated into the camp."

"My eyes have seen no such signs," the guide said.

"Yesterday morning, I thought I saw an unusual track coming out of the east, off to the left of the road our huntsmen take."

"It was not an Indian track, General," the guide said. "I saw it. It was white man's track. Good boots."

"So?" Orellana was unconcerned.

"One pair were followed by another, treading carefully. The lead man must have been a priest for his footsteps were swept about him by a skirt or brush of some sort; the following man was no priest, but a good hunter, who favors his left leg in walking."

"Your eyes are sharp," Orellana said.

"They have seen the same marks before."

"Often?"

"Several times. At first only the priest's. Then one night that of the spy. Ever since then—the spy, too."

"How far do the tracks go into the forest?"

"To the owl grove two leagues away, where there is a clearing and a puma trap and good water. They are lost then in the general pattern, many tracks."

"Yes. And the spy? You are sure he was not a priest?"

The Indian was greatly surprised.

"You do not know who he is, General?"

"I did not say that. I asked you."

The Indian nodded gravely.

"It is not my business to inquire, General," he said, "when the tracks come from your own compound."

"That is right," Orellana replied.

From his own compound! Not Maldonado, certainly; he would know without spying. That left Carranza and Gutiérrez, and it might be either, since they knew so much. Yet neither of them was sore in the left leg.

Then suddenly he had it. The Portuguese—Antonio Hernández, Carranza's friend. Hernández had a permanent limp. The Portuguese could disappear and no one would notice.

He dismissed the Indian and summoned Hernández, who came slowly and in fright. Orellana noticed with satisfaction that it was his left leg that he favored. Coming up from Guayaquil he had not attended this detail. He took careful stock of the Portuguese, as one will of a man who has been a vague silhouette in a crowd and suddenly is standing alone.

"You have done me a great service, Hernández," he began, "and I wish to thank you."

The Portuguese was surprised, indeed. Arrogant Spaniards did not humble themselves before his race. He sat, curling his spindle legs under him so that gnarled knots of knees pushed through the rags of his hose.

"You need not thank me, sir," he said. "I have lived long enough among Spaniards to recognize a rare one—and to preserve him if I can."

"I am curious to know what prompted you to follow the priest."

Hernández' upper lip curled back so sharply that the fringes of his straggly mustache vibrated like a plucked string.

"I meant to kill him," he said.

"So."

"I made the mistake one day of confessing to him. It was my first confession in years. I swore to make it if God saved me from the mountains. The friar used the confession against me. I was in Ribera's household, with plenty to eat and even a bottle of wine now and again from His Excellency's supplies. Now I am alone, and Ribera refuses me a place because once I was a thief, and de Vera is the cause. He violated my confession."

"So you tracked him into the forest."

"I did. A knife in a lonely grove would rid the world of a very evil man. It would be a service to heaven. But while I tracked him he made contact with another man, one I knew was with Don Gonzalo. Out of curiosity, I did not strike."

"It is a good thing you did not."

"Yes."

"It was a great service to me."

"So gentle a man should live, not die."

"How would you like to join my staff, Hernández? I can use you." He replied quickly, "No."

Orellana understood. "Not as a spy, Hernández. I do not hire spies. Or assassins."

"I hoped you did not."

"You may help Carranza who is now my cook. There is a great deal to do. It will be honest work."

"Well—yes, then."

"Fine," Orellana said.

Late in the afternoon, alone on the knoll, Orellana decided his course of action. There were still facts that eluded him, but not many. Only Pineda could enlighten him, his friend Pineda who was with Don Gonzalo and whose ears absorbed everything. Pineda, at least, would talk, if the price was high enough. Whether he could save himself he did not know. At least he would act. At least he would be safe for a time, and his plan was too simple to appear a subterfuge.

He called Maldonado to him with a show of anxiety.

"Last night," he said, "while you were hunting, did you cross the track of a large body of men, working northward?"

"No, Señor. It was dark and—"

"Of course. I forgot that you were in the dark." Orellana allowed the irony to penetrate before he resumed. "Yesterday Lieutenant Robles reported an outrider had seen the fresh track of white men only two leagues away."

Maldonado started visibly.

"I do not wish to alarm the camp," Orellana continued, "but I should like someone to inquire of Señor Robles the exact location of the track, and investigate. If the track is new, much must be done."

"By heaven, yes," Maldonado said. "I will go at once."

"Please do so. Take whom you wish, and hurry."

"You may count on me," Maldonado said, hastening away.

Orellana almost smiled. Maldonado played his part well. But if Orellana suspected aright, Maldonado would throw the scent away from Gonzalo. By vespers his discoveries would be camp gossip, and by mosquito time the camp would be in alarum, with outriders quadrupled and camp streets echoing to the anticipatory clank of steel preparatory to meeting an unknown enemy not far away. Then he would act.

Maldonado was explicit upon his return. He trailed a hundred men after him as he galloped to the knoll, and lieutenants leaped from their horses behind him, alert for orders. Evidently Maldonado was as good a town crier as he was an equerry, Orellana thought drily, and naturally he had good proof that the tracks could not be those of Don Gonzalo.

The evidence, said Maldonado, was new—not over a week old. The party—at least two hundred men. Footprints—undoubtedly European, accompanied by Indians. No horse. Could it be, he gushed, that the German bankers, those Welsers, were back again? In Popayán they had found Nicholas Federmann—

Orellana said he was not interested in speculation, only in facts. Any party of Europeans could be assumed to be an enemy, since Don Gonzalo was nowhere about. What fact more?

Very little. The trail had approached from the east. He had back-tracked on it for more than two leagues, found it a scythe-swath wide and economical. In a clearing it had spread out into a camp, then turned abruptly northward. Perhaps scouts had seen the Spanish camp—

Orellana again asked him to spare speculation. Questions and conjectures now were as thick as insects in the camp, and he thought best that Maldonado be given liberty to nourish them.

"Very well," he said. "That is all I require."

Maldonado sped away, surrounded by lieutenants. Orellana sat back in the gathering twilight to draft his orders for the morrow. Carranza appeared with the evening meal.

"These insects do you no good, General," he said. "I beg you to have your supper indoors."

"Put the bowl beside the tree," Orellana replied. "I have some work to do, first."

"You work very well," Carranza said, with a shade of his old impudence. "Neatly contrived and neatly executed."

An hour later Orellana concluded from observation of the camp that the time for action had arrived. So far as he could see, no risk whatever was involved, and much might be gained. The camp was alight with glowing fires, not mere smudges now, but broad bands of flame by the light of which men burnished leather, sharpened steel and prepared for action. The camp was mobilizing for a fight. Had the prospect been for action against Indians, even El Dorado himself, the activity would mainly have been among the dogs, lashing them to fighting fury, and among the arquebusiers. This threat, however, was from Christians, probably even Spaniards, and every man sharpened his mettle as well as his sword.

Orellana began to issue orders. Pages raced down the company street: to the tents of Don Antonio de Ribera, master of the camp; Juan de Acosta, ensign; Lieutenant Alonso de Robles, chief of the rear guard and cousin of the fair Ana de Ayala. To every member of the council went an urgent summons, not to meet but to disperse, with appropriate manpower, and scout the exact position of this enemy that was upon them. Father Carvajal was asked to pray them on their way.

If Orellana's conclusions were correct, contact with Don Gonzalo would be welcome. And if the party could not find him, the search would occupy the council for a long time. He doubted, however, that Gonzalo would be found—Campmaster Ribera would see to that.

The energy thus generated did not spend itself for ten days. Alarms and rumors of alarms kept the camp at war peak. Their common security menaced, none of the principals of the expedition suggested a council on the matter of Orellana's guardsman. Ribera kept among his belongings the dainty poniard with the seed-pearl handle, and that was all.

On the tenth day, along toward llama-feeding time in midafternoon, an outrider galloped heavily in from the north.

"Captain de Pineda approaches," he reported. "He brings His Excellency's orders to break camp and follow quickly. His Excellency awaits you seventy leagues away."

Orellana at that moment felt that he might easily have smiled, even unaccustomed as he was to such gestures.

"Very good," he said. "My compliments to Campmaster Ribera and will he prepare to leave immediately after Mass tomorrow. I shall see Captain Pineda immediately when he arrives."

Pineda indeed! What luck that Gonzalo should send in the one man who could answer the question that to Orellana meant life or death, and who, furthermore, might be persuaded to sell his knowledge.

Orellana went to his tent and prepared a welcome for his old comrade with especially thoughtful care.

II

ONLY grave personal danger could have moved Francisco Orellana to invite Gonzalo Diez de Pineda to share his tent that night.

Pineda carried about him constantly the pungent sweat smell of a man who has no use for water. This night, however, Orellana put up with the stench of Pineda's boots and body, even in the humid confines of his tent, because this was necessary to him. For all his odors, his filthiness of person and tongue, Pineda was a man of quick mind, and when the information about to be extracted from him concerned as high a personage as Don Gonzalo Pizarro, subtlety was the only approach to him, for subtlety he could not understand.

Pineda would scratch fleas from his hair and snap off their heads between the nails of his thumb and ring finger while engaged in conversation, but he missed no word of what was said. Being a guide boss, in constant association with Indians, he had his share of fleas. It was even said of him that, when no Spaniards were present, he would join the Indians in a familiar occupation, that of picking fleas from each other. The Indians would sit in a circle front to back, each searching the hair of the one in front for fleas, grubbing among the hair stalks like so many monkeys. The Spanish joke did not go so far as to insinuate that Pineda disposed of the fleas thus found in the Indian manner—by eating them—for Pineda's sword and his temper were sharp enough to welcome disputes and brawling and, to carry the Spanish joke as far as it went, the scales of dirt on his flesh gave him the protection of chain mail.

Pineda had never been known to bathe. The one memorable occasion when he was immersed in water was still talked about among the conquerors. Crossing Lake Titicaca in search of an island temple

96

decorated with sheets of gold, Pineda had been dumped from a boat by a caprice of wind. In heavy armor, he had sunk to the bottom of the lake, and his companions had left him there until he was unconscious to give him, as they said, a good soaking. Upon reviving, Pineda was reproachful, rather than angry.

"I have spent years, señores," he lamented, "arming my body so that no insect will come within a foot of me, and you have undone me in one minute. It is not considerate of you, señores, that you expose me to death by mosquitoes and chiggers."

In the campaign years since, he had restored his protection. He brought his personal fleas with him into Orellana's tent, and Orellana gave him a drink from the great gold cup of Atahualpa. Drink was Pineda's weakness.

This was the first appearance of the cup since Quito, and Orellana made sure that Maldonado was far away. He set the cup before his guest and filled it half full—all of a quart—with Spanish brandy from the stores of Don Gonzalo. Pineda drank deeply, holding the cup by its massive condor-head handles, soaking up the spirits. He did not even notice the brilliant workmanship that told the story of the cup's origin, nor the tenseness with which Orellana filled the cup.

"God, how I've needed that, Sisco," he said. "After what I've been through—"

"I assumed as much," Orellana said.

Pineda held out the cup for replenishment, and glanced quickly about the tent. "Are you sure we are alone?"

"Quite sure," Orellana said. "I have sent everyone away. Since my last guard was killed, guardsmen are reluctant to come within ten paces of my tent."

"Your guard was killed?" Pineda asked quickly. Murder in Spanish camps always had implications.

"Of that later," Orellana replied. "First of yourself, and Gonzalo."

Pineda's story was lachrymose. The quart of brandy, hurrying to his head, unloosed his tears, as he told what he had been through.

Orellana ignored them. He had been long enough a soldier to know that, after the shock, soldiers all weep. Pineda's story was well-scored for an obbligato of tears.

The expedition had found no trace of El Dorado, the man of gold. For more than two months the eighty men and eighty Indians had hacked their way through jungles so thick that the sun never appeared in them. Under heavy exertion, their food supplies had been exhausted quickly, and they were at the mercy of the jungle. Rain was almost constant. Twice they were attacked by Indians. Eight Spaniards died. Then the Indian porters had begun to die. For no apparent reason, Pineda said; they just died, as though the heart had gone from them.

Orellana, who was having the same difficulty in his own camp, nodded sympathetically.

Carrying their own luggage, wielding the machete and the broadsword, the Spaniards had come finally to a mountainous terrain far to the east and a little north. There, on the slopes of mountains, they had found the cinnamon.

"Aha!" Orellana exclaimed, his mind leaping to fix the route over which the precious spice might be tracked out of the jungle to his city of Guayaquil for shipment to Spain. Now, he thought, Guayaquil will amount to something. Ships in the river, throngs of Spanish traders ashore, money, affluence!

"The cinnamon," sobbed Pineda, "is no good. After Christ's own trials in that wilderness, the cinnamon is no good." He put his head on his arms and sobbed. Orellana waited until he had recovered.

The cinnamon, Pineda explained at last, was of fair quality, what there was of it, but the trees were located in thin, scattered groves on the side of rocky mountains in an almost impregnable wilderness, and so meager as to be worthless commercially. Convinced of the futility of further exploration, Don Gonzalo had turned back, searching for El Dorado with renewed purpose; but he had not found the man of gold, either. Pineda's disappointment, buoyed by the strong drink, surged again into his eyes.

"I can go on from there for a little while," Orellana said quietly.

Pineda was not yet drunk enough for questions. "You returned almost to camp, then turned north."

"Your outriders are good men," Pineda said. "Don Gonzalo could not return, then. His disappointment over the cinnamon, his futility in searching for gold, would have wrecked the expedition. Not a man would have followed him another step."

"I appreciate that," Orellana said. "So you advanced about ten leagues, built a bridge across a river and destroyed the bridge after you. Why did you destroy the bridge?" He wanted Pineda to become accustomed to simple questions now.

"The Indians!" Pineda said, begging another cup of brandy and taking a long drink. "The savages have dogged us constantly since——"

He paused. "I am not a soft man, Sisco. I do my duty like any other Spaniard. But I have seen these past days something even the Marquis Pizarro would shrink from, and I cannot get it from my mind. You are my friend, or I would not mention it, but I must tell someone. It haunts me like a sacrilege against the Holy Mother."

Discreetly Orellana set aside the bottle as Pineda, with a shudder, drained the giant gold cup, for he knew he must listen to a long story. It was regrettable, but necessary.

"What haunts me," Pineda said, "was the uselessness of what happened. I think His Excellency was salving his disappointment over the cinnamon. There can be no other explanation.

"We were five days from the cinnamon mountains en route home when it happened. Every step we cut from the forest with machetes until all of us were like to die. Going in, there had been some purpose to give strength to our arms. Coming out the machetes were as heavy as pole axes. We made slow progress, and the general raged. I have never seen him so angry. He cursed us most of the day. Cursed us with a whip in his hand, threatening to turn the dogs on us. The dogs were hungry, too.

"At noon we did not stop for rest, since the general said we had not earned it. Had we not so badly needed his leadership in that pesthole jungle, we should have killed him and left his body to the biting

99

ants, of which there were more than enough. In the afternoon we came to a miserable native village where there was food for the taking. We took it. We were starved. But we got no rest. The general ordered every savage rounded up, and by nightfall we had them trussed in their own house."

Orellana nodded again.

"These Indians," said Pineda, "were a miserable lot. Sores all over them. Weak. Our men wouldn't touch the women, so you know— They all lived together, the whole two score of them, in one big house and went naked mainly, painting their bodies. The general put them all inside the house and brought the men out one by one in the darkness. He asked them about El Dorado.

"But they didn't know! I, who have lived among Indians so long, knew they didn't know. The general said they were hiding the information from him, and that he would have the knowledge or hang them.

"I was translating. I told the general finally that he would learn nothing. He called me names my father, God rest his sinful soul, never even called me. Then an old man, with a headdress over his eyes and wearing a skirt, with ornaments of grass, and bones hanging from his knees and arms, was brought out. He was the witch doctor. I told the general who he was—leader, venerable old man, whatever you want to call him.

"The general said, 'Fine, now we will get somewhere,' and had the old man spread-eagled on a spit before the lodge, where the Indians cook at a common fire. I repeated to the native the questions I had asked the others, while Don Gonzalo stood by, watching the flesh roast on the old man's back. The witch doctor said nothing.

" 'Turn him over,' Gonzalo said, and we turned him over. It was merciful, for the fumes from the fire killed him. The general screamed when he died, and whistled for the dogs. They made short work of the carcass, but they were still hungry, and the general smiled. He smiled, Sisco, by my mother's honor I swear it! When the next Indian was brought out, he asked only one question, and when there was no reply, he set on the dogs. They tore the man apart, there before the entrance to the hut, with the women and children inside watching with big eyes but without a word or a cry.

"Their silence angered the general even more. He had wanted them to scream. He had wanted them to run out in fear, and confess what they knew of El Dorado, but they stayed inside, silent, big-eyed with horror."

He shuddered, and Orellana gave him a small refill in the gold cup. Pineda was grateful, and revived.

"There is a dignity about the savage, my friend Francisco," he said, "that a man remembers. Once you have seen it, you cannot forget. Not even brandy can wash it away." He sighed.

"Well—the dogs ate the savages one by one. Ate them alive, Sisco, tore them apart. They didn't say a word. The general stood by, goading the dogs. I shall never forget his fury. When the men were all dead, the general turned to me and said, 'Fire the lodge.' I could not believe it. Inside were a score of women and children; outside, growling, the blood-mad dogs. I just looked at the general in horror. I should not have done so. He turned all his anger on me. He commanded me to take the faggot, light it at the fire, and torch the lodge. . . . What could I do?

"The women and children died, Sisco. Not one came out to face the dogs. . . . And not one of them cried."

He put his head in his hands, and rocked back and forth. "Their blood is on me," he moaned, "their blood is on me. Mother of God! The agony, the stench. The flames went a hundred feet into the air. The fire even drove off the dogs. But not a cry from within the lodge. Not even the little children cried, Sisco! Just silence—silence more awful than the crackle of the flames. The innocence of them, condemned to fire without even a chance to save their pagan souls. . . . Now the cries they did not utter are inside me—" he smote his chest— "and they won't come out, either. I am damned, Sisco, damned."

He rolled sideways onto a litter of llama skins and sobbed. Orellana set aside an empty brandy bottle and, carefully wiping the gold cup, put it in his luggage. Then he sat beside Pineda. The time had come.

"Old friend," he said softly, "old friend, listen to me."

Pineda roused. "Another drink, Sisco, I beg you. This night I must drown myself so that I may sleep."

Orellana slipped an arm around him and lifted his head.

"A whole bottle of brandy, Diez, if you will just answer me a question."

"Give me the bottle."

"First the question. I shall not forget you later, I promise." He held an uncorked bottle before Pineda's eyes.

"Then ask it, amigo, and get it over, for the love of God."

"How close were you to Gonzalo?"

"I was with him night and day, and what has it done to me? Made me a murderer of Indians. My soul will never rest."

Again Orellana held out the bottle. "Tell me, old friend—did Gonzalo order the attack upon me that night when he was so close to us?"

Drunkenly Pineda sat up. "Anything else," he whispered, "but don't ask me that."

"I must know."

"He would kill me. With my heavy sins, I am not ready to die."

"He will never know. My life depends on it. You would not want me to die?"

Pineda reached for the bottle, drank heavily, and gasped as the hot liquid burned his throat.

"You are as good as dead, Sisco. You did not hear it from me, of course, but the attack was on His Excellency's orders."

"Hah!" Orellana said, holding off the bottle again. "Why does he hate me so?"

"Why should he not? Did you not advise him to go out into the jungle while you stayed behind, knowing he would find nothing, and that he would die? Then you would be in command here, and governor in Quito besides."

"What put such an idea in his head?"

102

"When a man is disappointed, he will believe anything. You talk to the Indians in their own tongue. They have told you where El Dorado is. And when Gonzalo is dead, you will lead the expedition there. Then the triumph, the gold, and the glory, will be yours alone. That's what Gonzalo has been told."

"Then why does he not just hang me? Why this foul attack by dogs?"

"He dare not hang you. You have been of too much service to his brother the Marquis, who plans to make you governor of Quito when Don Gonzalo retires. But a man may die in many ways. So it was planned that if the dogs failed, you could be hanged for murder. You are doomed, Sisco. Now the bottle, in God's name."

Orellana handed him the brandy, but Pineda did not drink. As Orellana's hold on him relaxed, Pineda slumped drunk to the floor. Solemnly Orellana capped the bottle and lay down upon his own couch.

12

THE CAMP moved slowly northward in the wake of Don Gonzalo Pizarro, through lands the Indians called Capua, to the banks of a large river where Gonzalo's earlier trail ended at a deep gorge. Progress was slow, for the heavily laden porters, burned out by jungle fevers, were dying rapidly.

At first Orellana tried to help them, but at last he saw that their deaths were as inevitable as had been those of his lowland bearers in the mountains, and he pushed forward with all haste to the junction with Don Gonzalo's party.

With the river on his right hand, Orellana proceeded downstream for some days, in the general direction of north northeast, the river growing ever wider. And though Diez de Pineda, to whom the most insignificant observation was sometimes profitable, watched Orellana closely, he saw no manifestation that his chief was worried.

With nothing to do except to wait, Orellana found himself often riding in the rear of the line of march, alongside the red-bearded Andalusian. To Alonso Robles he could speak his mind. They talked again of Martin Luther, of Erasmus and Calvin, and of Thomas More, the Englishman who had written in Latin a book called *Utopia* in which he had dreamed of a community where, within the framework of the best tenets of civilized knowledge, men might live happily together.

"What would such men write," he burst out one day, "if they could see what I have seen! What dreams would they conjure for society? Civilized man is a beast."

Robles looked startled, and Orellana rushed on quickly.

"You do not realize it when you set out to conquer a lot of miserable Indians. Then your mind is on the gold, and everything you do is excusable, if the gold is found. I have marched with de Soto and Pizarro, and I know. There is much death, but there is also great wealth."

He paused, a look of pain upon his face.

"And then," he resumed tensely, "one day you are surrounded by gold, but you cannot live with yourself. At first you do not know what is eating away your heart, but there is a worm within you, eating and hurting.

"And suddenly—out of nothing but the blue sky—you know. You look back upon the murder you have done, the miserable savages you have cheated and raped and burned, the lies you have told, and you are ashamed. Not just ashamed of yourself, my friend Alonso—you are ashamed for the whole race of men which is capable of these things. . . . And then you hear, as I heard the other night, a story so miserable in its treatment of the Indians, that you cannot get it from your mind, and you look to heaven and cry out, 'How long, O Christ, how long will you permit such things!' . . . But there is no answer, for in your own time, you have done these things yourself, and you realize that it is not Our Beloved Saviour to whom you must appeal, but to your own heart."

He bowed his head. Robles was silent. They rode a long time through the heavy footing, their horses staggering each step through the rotted jungle muck along the feeble swath that had been hacked out of the wilderness by those ahead. Constantly they swung with their swords to sever lacerating briars, or bent low in their saddles to avoid the matted vines overhead.

Then Orellana spoke again.

"I am glad to know," he said, "that in Europe, too, men's eyes are opening. I thought it could happen only to men haunted by what they had done. You are like this Luther, my friend Alonso—you feel without having seen."

"I have seen enough," Robles replied.

"If you have seen enough to know how I feel—"

"I think I have."

"Good," Orellana said. "Then there are two of us, and before God I swear, if ever I am able, I shall atone for some of the miserable crimes we Spaniards have committed in this New World."

Lieutenant Robles was not too pleased with the implications of this conversation. He realized the personal danger in those words, "Then there are two of us." To be in favor with Orellana was not at the moment healthy. To be intimately associated with a man who soon was to feel the murderous impact of a Pizarro's anger might lead to death. Suspicions among the Pizarros, he had heard, were more dangerous than certainties. And though he had not been long in the New World, he had seen enough to convince him that Peru was no more benevolent than the world he had left behind in Spain.

At the same time, he was proudly excited by the mark of Orellana's favor, as young men always have been who suddenly find themselves approached by a general; and despite the danger, he responded to Orellana's attentions. The aloof, unsmiling commander, who from his promontory had conducted the affairs of an idle camp through months of tedium, was a model a young soldier must admire, for he had broken pestilence among the livestock, prevented disaffections among both men and Indians by a firm but benign leadership that involved neither floggings nor hangings. And so far at least he had survived a personal attack upon himself in which the most powerful influences had worked against him.

Orellana's administration of the camp, his tolerant understanding of the needs of both men and animals, his quiet manner so sharply in contrast to the bawling exhibitionism of Don Gonzalo, was an example of military leadership of which junior officers dreamed but seldom encountered. The younger officers, Robles knew, and the rank and file of the men, were more than loyal to Orellana—they also admired him and, cautiously when gathered together, cursed their own inability to help him against the powerful conspirators. They had even discussed presenting an ultimatum to Don Gonzalo that if Orellana were hanged, they would quit the expedition; but this had been abandoned since Orellana showed no perturbation over his forthcoming meeting with the general. If Orellana was not worried, the revolt of his officers could only embarrass him.

Robles, however, was not so sure that Orellana was unworried. His outward easiness might well be one of the disciplines of leadership. Now, taking advantage of this unusually intimate discussion at the rear of the line, Robles put to Orellana a direct question.

"May I be of any help to you, General," he said, "in your meeting with Don Gonzalo?"

There was no doubt that Orellana was pleased. "Thank you, Lieutenant," he answered, "but it would not be wise for you to become involved in my affairs. I want your neck on your shoulders when the time comes to introduce me to your cousin."

"You are not worried about your own neck, then?"

Orellana's eye twinkled momentarily.

"Who knows?" he said. "I don't. But I do not believe in worry, which has never yet won a battle or saved a life. Plan, yes; then when there is something to do, act. Worry is a landslide across one's road, preventing passage, and man's road is rough enough without such an obstacle. I propose to wait and see what happens, keeping my mind clear meanwhile so that when the time for action arrives, I will think clearly. That is all I can do."

"Then you have no plan to counteract the charge of murdering your guard?"

"His Excellency is too elusive for anything so inflexible as a plan. I have an idea, nothing more."

Robles did not approve of such vagueness.

"I am afraid, Señor," he said, "that the situation requires more than an idea. Only a miracle can save you."

The unhappiness was so apparent in his face that, despite himself, Orellana smiled.

"Maybe," he said, "that's my idea." And he spurred his horse toward the head of the line, ending the conversation.

A few hours later the river broke out across a wide flatland, and the advance guard, freed at last from the labor of hacking a trail through wilderness, set up a shout. Ahead lay a rich savanna, and the supply train, the llamas, the pigs, the dogs and the Spaniards, spread out gratefully on the grassy plain.

Watching the deployment, Orellana knew that now Don Gonzalo must be nearby. The long delayed ordeal was at last at hand.

He sent for Father Carvajal. By the time the priest arrived, riding his jennet, Orellana could see in the distance a clearing a half-league wide, liberally dotted with fruit trees and hard by a small village.

"Father Carvajal," he greeted the priest, "how are the Indian pack bearers?"

"They die in great numbers, Your Excellency. I am busy from morning to night with absolution."

"They will soon be able to lay down their burden," Orellana said. "Yonder lies the camp of Don Gonzalo."

"I saw it, Excellency."

"You wish to ride in ahead of us?"

"I would greatly appreciate it. From what I hear, His Excellency is suffering great mental anguish, and at such times a priest is a consolation."

"Exactly," Orellana said. "It might cheer His Excellency to know that in his absence his Beloved Virgin watched over his camp, even performing a miracle to save his food supplies."

Father Carvajal bowed. He was still deeply under the spell of the miracle that he had witnessed with his own eyes, and had documented so carefully in the fly leaf of his missal.

"I know," he said, "that the General, holy man that he is, will be awed, as are we all, by what has happened."

"Then go with God," Orellana said. "News of spiritual import he should hear first from his own chaplain."

"I am grateful to you, Excellency," the priest answered. "You are generous and thoughtful."

He trotted away thumpingly on his little jennet, and Orellana, watching him, was in no hurry to follow. He keyed his own pace to the leisurely walk of the grazing llamas. Behind him he could see

Campmaster Ribera and Friar de Vera, chaffing to put spurs to their horses, but not daring to outdistance their commander. They remained behind, complaining noisily, while Orellana, ignoring them, rode deliberately at a walk across the savanna.

Finally, however, the encounter could no longer be postponed. He could see the general now, pacing heavily before a rustic shelter of matted leaves on a hillock overlooking the river. Father Carvajal was not with him.

Spurring forward, Orellana approached, leaped from his horse and stood before the governor. His hand was tightly on the rein of his mount.

"What kept you?" Gonzalo roared. "Did you wish us all to starve?"

Orellana relaxed. For the moment he was safe. He was shocked by Gonzalo's appearance. The elegant trappings of knighthood were no longer on him. He stood sword-girt in a dirty linen shirt and leather breeches, his eyes deep-set and hungry, his flesh withered. His great bones probed through stingy flesh. He was years older.

Orellana made traditional excuses for his slowness, feeling such to be the safest course. He emphasized the malady of the Indians, that had cut in half the once proud train of two thousand luggage carriers. Gonzalo could not well complain—he had lost all eighty of his own.

"You did not abandon our supplies?"

"No, Excellency. They are all here, even your great table and chairs." He could not interpret Gonzalo's mood, and his mood was the difference between life and death.

At the mention of his own effects the governor brightened, ordered his great tent brought and set up, and turned his back on his lieutenant general. Orellana slipped away.

His respite was short, for within an hour a page asked him to attend the general. Gonzalo remained seated, and Orellana saw the poniard adorned with seed pearls on the great table before him. The conspirators had already been at work.

So, too, had a good dinner upon the gaunt frame of the general. A stubble of pork bones lay before him, and a half-consumed bottle of brandy. He was once again in all his splendor, from shining helmet to white leather boots, his beard and hair were clean and oiled, and a cape of burnt orange and French blue lay on the litter beside him.

He did not immediately attack. Rather, in tedious detail he told what had happened to him, except that he did not mention burning the Indian village.

"I picked up a native chief," he said finally, "a man named Delicola, who tells me there is a rich land farther down the river. Now that we are united, I shall proceed downstream."

"Yes, Excellency."

"If he is lying to me, I'll rip his belly open and let him watch my dogs eat his guts. I don't trust these heathen; I brought Delicola along as a hostage."

"Yes, Excellency."

"And now—" The general's eyes were impudently amused, "we shall hear a report of yourself." He took up the poniard by its point.

Cautiously Orellana began with the camp census, enumerating the details of supply on hand, ignoring the dagger, sparring for some opening that would lead him to Gonzalo's frame of mind.

"Yes, yes," the general interrupted testily, "I know all that."

"The hog population is growing again daily, Excellency. I ordered all the sows bred immediately the sickness passed. The llamas, too, although it is too early yet—"

"How does it feel," Gonzalo shifted the conversation suddenly, "to be attacked by dogs?"

Momentarily Orellana was thrown off balance by the swiftness of the attack, but Don Gonzalo did not notice it, and covered Orellana's confusion for him by speaking again.

"I am advised that my favorite bitch, Eschenita, died at your hand —and my guard likewise."

"The bitch, yes, Your Excellency. The guard is another matter of which I am as ignorant as yourself."

"What makes you think me so ignorant?" Gonzalo goaded him

brazenly, enjoying his power, giving it added effect by swinging the seed-pearl handled dagger in his hand.

Orellana did not reply; there was no reply.

"By God," Pizarro went on, "I have hated you. What I suffered in the jungle! Does it disappoint you that I am still alive?"

"I should gain nothing by your death," Orellana said quickly, remembering Pineda's remark that Gonzalo feared the wrath of the Marquis, "except the enmity of your brother—and that is not a thing a man deliberately invites."

"Indeed not, by God's mercy!" Gonzalo said. "We Pizarros are good haters."

"In your absence, I undertook only to command the camp as you yourself might have done, and return your command to you reasonably intact, as I have done."

"Over a few obstacles," said Don Gonzalo.

"Over a few obstacles," Orellana conceded.

Don Gonzalo laid aside the dagger, and picked up his silver figurine of the Madonna. He looked at her softly.

"But you had help, cousin," he said to Orellana. He kissed the image, crossed himself, returned the figure to its post of honor at the head of his bed, and remained gazing at it.

"How I have risked Her displeasure!" he exclaimed. "No wonder these evil days have fallen on me. Father Carvajal told me this afternoon what She did for you. Of course I would never have believed evil against you had I known. My campmaster is not only a blunderer, he is a fool. And de Vera, the scoundrel! Why did he not tell me?"

Orellana clamped his jaws in silence. This was Don Gonzalo's scene, and Orellana knew better than to steal it.

Don Gonzalo turned away from the Madonna after a long silence, refilled his brandy glass and then, filling another, extended it to Orellana. The gesture cleared Orellana's mind of all its fears.

"If our beloved Mother works miracles for you, cousin, who am I, sinful mortal that I am, to show you any less confidence? . . . To Her precious mercy."

"To Her precious mercy," Orellana agreed, drinking the toast with greater fervor than Don Gonzalo could realize.

"Besides," the governor went on, "I liked the way you handled the situation. You came into my camp still in command, no small feat under the circumstances."

"Thank you, Your Excellency," Orellana murmured. "And now that your doubts are eased, may I ease one of my own?"

Don Gonzalo was eager to pay penance. "Anything you like, Cousin."

"On the day of the miracle, I was likewise marked for death, but something happened, and the attack was not carried out. Did you know of it, too?"

Gonzalo arose, his eyes flaming. "I did not," he roared.

"I am grateful," Orellana said. "Your anger in the wilderness I can understand and appreciate. But if there was an earlier displeasure, I should like to know, so that I may best serve you by not making that same mistake again."

"I know nothing of it. By the Holy Mother, I swear it."

His eyes narrowed. Again he picked up Orellana's dagger.

"I like competition among my captains," he said. "Soldiers who must be vigilant for their own lives keep their brains keen and do their job better. And if a man dies, it is because he is weak, and is better eliminated."

He held out the dagger to Orellana.

"Do not let me find it in Campmaster Ribera's ribs," he said. "Such evidence is awkward. Take time, Cousin, always to remove your dagger from a wound. . . . But let no harm come to Maldonado—he is useful to me."

"I understand, Excellency," Orellana said. He took the dagger and departed.

13

FOR TWO weeks the camp rested by the river, and during that time the last Indian brought from Quito by Don Gonzalo died. The fiery jungle summer, with its heat, its dysentery, and its chiggers, had been even more cruel to the highland Indians than were their Spanish masters.

The camp life had been organized around their menial services. Without them, it soon broke into disorder. Most of the food foraged from the jungle had been gathered by them; now Campmaster Ribera depended upon the pigs and llamas for meat. This was inevitable, anyway, since without Indians to herd the animals, the Spaniards could not long have kept them alive. Also, without Indians the Spaniards were afraid to eat jungle growth; previously they had let the Indians sample new plants and if the experiments failed a few Indians were buried by the Spaniards who lived.

The roster of Don Gonzalo's expedition on the Day of Transfiguration was discouraging. Of the two hundred fifty-four Spaniards, counting Orellana's detachment, nineteen were dead. Of the two hundred horses, there were now one hundred seventy-two. Of the twenty black slaves, only two were living, attached directly to the service of the general. Of the four thousand Indians, none. Of the sixteen Indian guides, one only, christened González, and native to the jungle. In forays on savage villages, sixty Indians had been impressed to attend the camp, but of these thirty were women and so occupied with providing the soldiers a service peculiar to their sex that they had no time or strength for other work, and of the men ten were chiefs or hostages who did nothing to earn the food that they consumed.

Obviously, with the Indians gone, there was no need to keep two thousand dogs. A few hundred were enough to attack the insignificant jungle natives who were encountered. Thus logically, with the pigs and llamas marked for extinction, the mainstay fare of the expedition's table became dog meat. Even Don Blas de Medina, who had sworn on his conscience that he would starve first, ate it hungrily. Dogs, however, are poor meat, and many had to be slaughtered to provide three meals a day for two hundred men. They did not last long.

At last Don Gonzalo gave the command to break camp and move downstream. For Orellana, the order created a problem in transport. Which, he asked the general, of the camp's great trappings might be left behind?

"Your massive table and chairs, Excellency, will be difficult to move," he said cautiously. "Your trunks require porters. Your tent alone bends the backs of eight men. Every captain, every hidalgo, has the burden of at least two Indians in his tent. What is your pleasure?"

Don Gonzalo wasted no effort in thought.

"Send out a party to round up all the able-bodied in the native village south of us," he said. "With the women we already have, there will be porters enough to carry my equipment. Let every other man take with him only what he can carry on his own horse."

"Your table and chairs go, too, Excellency?"

"They go," Gonzalo said.

In five days the expedition reached a junction with the River Coca, where there was a large native camp. Arriving there, the porters put down their loads and fled.

Much to Orellana's surprise, Don Gonzalo exercised unusual caution against alarming the villagers. He sent Diez de Pineda forward to treat with them, holding back his main force. The Indians had fled in their dugout canoes, and were coursing the river in boats, examining from the safety of the water the strange armada of bemetaled men and horses. Patiently Don Gonzalo launched onto the stream large planks laden with bells and trinkets which the Indians picked up out of the water. The gifts, however, did not entice them ashore.

Finally Don Gonzalo summoned Orellana.

"I am advised," he said testily, "that for some purpose of your own you have been making diligent study of these native tongues."

"For the better service of Your Excellency, I have studied them."

"I have heard otherwise, but for the moment I choose to ignore it. Put your knowledge to some use. Speak to these stubborn fools and tell them I come in peace."

Orellana took his Indian guide González and walked to the river bank. The Coca was deep and beautiful. On the far bank were rank marshes. The wind off the river was clean, the first clean smell that had purified Orellana's nostrils in nearly six months. It calmed his spirit, and softened his voice.

He stood quietly, while the swift canoes, artfully propelled by native oarsmen, thronged the river just out of spear range. Some of the canoes reckoned as many as a dozen men, Orellana noted. Spears poked above the snub-nosed prows. Don Gonzalo sat at a distance on his horse, awaiting summons that Orellana had successfully coaxed the Indians ashore.

Orellana was in no hurry. The natives watched him, cruising curiously back and forth in the river. Orellana ordered a large log to be brought to the river sand. Deliberately, with wide overhead strokes, he began to hew the log with an ax. The exciting ring of steel echoed across the river. Large chips of wood flew from the log. Warily the Indians drew closer. Orellana paid them no attention.

The log cleaved. A hubbah of surprise came from the water. This man, they exclaimed, must be a magician, to cut the log with such speed! Orellana heard, but did not look up. Selecting a convenient section, he began to sever the log anew.

Now the Indians in one canoe drew close to the shore for a better look.

"Get back," Orellana shouted in what he hoped would be a vernacular understandable to them. They looked surprised, palavered among themselves, and remained. Orellana continued his work. The canoe idled into an eddy and coasted to the shore, the oarsmen alert to stroke if they were attacked. Orellana went on cutting, with broad sure strokes, flipping his chips into the water.

An oarsman picked up a large chip, handed it to his leader. The leader marveled and his boat swung about so that he, in the stern, might see. Without stopping, Orellana looked up at the peak of his stroke, and smiled. González, standing beside him, waved a friendly hand. The canoe touched the bank. The leader stepped out. Orellana finished his work and withdrew a few paces, ax in hand. The leader was fascinated by the ax. Orellana handed it to him with a few words. "Iron. Cuts wood. Try it."

The Indian took the ax clumsily. Orellana showed him the use of it. The Indian brought it down, deep into the wood. Orellana showed him the side stroke that dislodged the chink. The Indian stroked. A chink flew out. He dropped the ax, picked up the chink and fitted it back into the log, calling his companions to see. At that moment Gonzalo charged down to the beach on his big stallion. The Indians leaped to their canoe. But Orellana was as quick as they. As the canoe swept away, he extended the ax to the native leader, saying, "Take it." The Indian took it and fled.

The contact, however, had been made. By midday another Indian had claimed an ax, and returned to the river also with an adze and instruction in its use. Orellana had no difficulty with the dialect—he was understood.

The next day a chief appeared, and Don Gonzalo met him with great ceremony, giving him trinkets and salt. The condiment pleased the chief greatly, and he expressed a desire to reciprocate. Don Gonzalo then began to trade, careful to take nothing from the savages without payment in ironware, bells, tinsel, and salt. For salt the chief gave liberally. The Indians brought maize, yucca, sweet potatoes, teeming canoeloads of fish. More important, they stopped guarding the river, so that men of the expedition were able to course about in search of the ducks and turkeys that were profuse in the marshes. Gabriel de Contreros was first of the companions to fish at the river-bank, learning quickly the Indian tricks. Usually Carranza and Soria were with him, and the Portuguese Hernández who, now attached to Orellana's personal service, had little to do.

The expedition fattened and rested for many days. Orellana had occasional talks with the native chief, learning that he was of the Omagua nation, a peaceful people that lived on the river and drew abundant food from it. For necessities they required and could not supply, they traded with other tribes of their nation farther downstream. They were a small population, composed of a few huts, with weak affiliations in nearby villages. The Omaguas knew nothing of any El Dorado. The few golden ornaments they possessed were symbols of authority, worn only by chiefs and their wives, and had been acquired in trade from men who many years before had come over the high mountains from the west. They had no gold of their own.

Orellana passed his time with the Omagua chief because he had little else to do. In camp, Don Gonzalo supervised everything, down to the smallest detail. And in the last days Orellana had felt that he was not well regarded. Someone had again filled Don Gonzalo with doubts.

Then one day a soldier, denying strictest orders, took from a native woman two ear hoops of gold and hid the metal under his breastplate. The Omagua chief appeared before Gonzalo immediately, demanding redress. Gonzalo, that day in one of his whims of temper, curtly refused to search for the guilty soldier, and ordered the chief from the camp.

Within an hour the river filled with warlike canoes. Slingstones peppered Gabriel de Contreros and other fishermen. Three crossbowmen, sitting in the swamp awaiting the evening flight of ducks, were killed.

After fruitless prayers to his figurine of the Madonna, Don Gonzalo told his council they must move in search of food. But where to move? They could not carry their equipment back through the jungle without porters, and they did not know in what direction they might find the elusive El Dorado. They might follow the river except for the war canoes that stood them off as effectively as any navy.

"We must build a navy of our own," Gonzalo said. "A brigantine might easily be built at the water's edge."

There certainly was plenty of wood for timber. Such a bark, the general explained, could serve three purposes: first, to drive the canoes from the river, thus allowing the Spaniards to fish and hunt; second, to carry the supply of munitions, iron, and weapons in the absence of porters; and third, to transport the sick, of whom there was a growing number.

Everyone fell in with the plan except Orellana. He opposed it and the general was displeased.

"We are now five hundred miles from Quito," Orellana argued, "and we grow weaker each day. It would appear far better to retrace our steps through the jungle before our track is overgrown, encamp at some settled place and send back to Quito for supplies. In the end, we might make more haste by cautious delay."

"Lieutenant General Orellana," replied Gonzalo, "does not say all he means. Perhaps the Indians with whom he has been in such deep conversation these past days have told him where El Dorado is, and he wishes us to turn back before we find what we seek."

Orellana denied the charge. All that the chiefs had told him, he said, he had communicated to his general.

"Then you will build the brigantine, Cousin," Don Gonzalo said. "Perhaps the work will take your mind off these native languages."

"Very good, sir," said Orellana. He set to work at once, sending out detachments to fell trees, searching personally through the camp for iron with which to make nails. He was well embarked on his work when Carranza appeared.

"This is not the time of the moon to be cutting timbers for a ship," he said. "Timbers cut other than in the first quarter will soon rot and your boat will sink."

Orellana ignored him. The work went on, sped by acute hunger, and by the end of October was completed. The brigantine was a two-masted, square-rigged little vessel with a four-foot draught and a clumsy tiller astern. Its square mainsail was a patchwork of blankets from Don Gonzalo's own stores. The ship had flush decks and a square uncovered hold around the centerboard. She accommodated twenty-five men, with some crowding. As in the galleys, she was fitted with two oars. In the hold, with expert stowing, she could carry the expedition's most precious stores of axes, adzes, iron and leather, ammunition and cavalry tack.

Gonzalo was well pleased with the brigantine, though still cool to Orellana. On the morning when the vessel, completely stowed, floated by an ivy vine hawser close inshore, Don Gonzalo, accompanied by Father Carvajal, Friar de Vera, and the principal captains, formed a procession to the river bank. Carvajal, in spotless vestments, led the way, the Host held high above his head. Friar de Vera was second, chanting from the missal. Then came a page, with the general's silver medallion of the Virgin on a pillow. He was followed by Gonzalo in his finest mail and his best cloak and gloves, with Orellana a pace behind, as befitted the second in command and engineer who had built the ship. Behind them strung the captains and after them the entire company.

Father Carvajal paused by the water and cleaved the air with an aspergill. Every man of the company except Carranza crossed himself. A solemn Mass followed, and the little brigantine was formally inducted with the name *San Pedro*.

Father Carvajal, with hunger gnawing at his belly, ascended a stump for a rousing but brief sermon on the meaning of the ship's name. Let it be henceforth, he said, a constant reminder to all of them, that no task of great worth is attained without commensurate suffering. He likened the tribulations of the present camp to the hungers, the shipwrecks, the martyrdom of the great Saint Peter, first Bishop of Rome and founder of the Church, depreciating the present trials in comparison with those sustained by the saint whose life and work they commemorated and who, henceforth, in the living name of the brigantine, they would emulate.

For a man suffering acute stomach agonies, sapped by his old weakness of dysentery, and the debilitating effects of the jungle heat, his face puffed with insect bites, he appeared to Orellana at that moment a remarkable man. Oblivious of the burning sun and the cruel reflection from the water, sweat pouring from his shorn head and flowing down his flushed face, Father Carvajal read his Mass and delivered his sermon and still had strength enough to go aboard the brigantine, bless it with holy water, and commend it to the service of his Lord, his Majesty, and His Excellency.

The expedition set out downstream immediately after the Mass. There was no tarrying for breakfast, since none was available. The companions also had fifteen Indian canoes which Don Gonzalo had confiscated, and these were loaded with arquebusiers and fishermen. Having horses, the hidalgos fared the worst—they had to walk, leading their mounts and hacking their way along the bank.

Dogged by hunger, constantly under the menace of surprise attack from the artful native canoemen who picked off stragglers, but once again provided with fish and a few fowl, nourished also by an occasional horse, the expedition cut its way downstream. The oars and sail were useless in the shallow water, and the ship was propelled by poles. Each day the mouth of some tributary creek, too deep to ford and too swift to swim, impeded progress. Occasionally an Indian village yielded a scant ration of manioc, and some guava was found along the bank; these were carefully hoarded against the lean days that were as inevitable as dawn.

Halting only on the Sabbath, the party continued downstream while October turned to December, and Father Carvajal, so weak that he now was transported on the brigantine, began to give thought to the celebration of Christmas.

Not overly worried for his soul, Orellana was anxious over the reality that Christmas again would usher in a rainy season. The river in summer was a narrow, rapid-flowing channel, but he did not like to imagine what it would be under the impetus of seasonal deluges, sudden freshets, cascades from tributaries, and the rubble and snags of rising water.

The brigantine moved efficiently along, under the command of one Juan de Alcantara, a stout-hearted gallant from the maestrozgo of Santiago in the hills of Estremadura, a man of resourcefulness if little skill at sailing. The Indians he kept at bay, and Gabriel Contreros, from a pitch aft, directed the fishermen in reasonable security.

At last they paused for Christmas about two hundred miles from El Barco, as they had called the village where the ship was built, too weak to go farther. To add to their discouragement, the hostage Chief Delicola now said that beyond them lay a vast, uninhabited region containing nothing but grievances. Even savages could find no food in such pestilential swamps.

On Christmas Day, Orellana communicated this news to the general. Delicola had told him, he said, that the closest food lay five or six days' journey by Indian canoe down the river to the junction of two large streams, then one day's sail back up the other river to an abundant village. At the present rate of progress, the expedition could not reach the spot for at least six weeks, and in that time not a man would be alive.

For once Don Gonzalo's bluster left him. "If the guides are correct, Cousin," he said, "I don't know what we can do. We cannot go back."

"Let me take the brigantine and go forward, then," Orellana proposed. "Let me find the food and return with it. In the ship we can move rapidly, and we should be back in ten to twelve days' time."

Don Gonzalo's eyes narrowed. "Is this the time you have awaited before leaving us?" he asked. "By heaven, I didn't expect you to conspire for the brigantine, too."

"Then send someone else, Excellency," Orellana replied. "I do not propose to go if Your Excellency has lost confidence in me. I volunteered only because I know these languages and perhaps might have the best chance to get through. You will recall that I alone of all your council opposed building the boat."

Don Gonzalo nodded. "Then why did you build it so zealously, my Cousin?"

"For love of you, Your Excellency, and because you ordered it of me. Having been ordered, I could not conscientiously give it other than my best, even though I opposed it."

Pizarro said nothing.

"Loyalty," Orellana continued, "does not consist of words behind a man's back, sir, but of deeds. I should have knifed Ribera when I had the invitation."

Don Gonzalo laughed. "It is often a mistake to waver in such matters. You waver overmuch, Cousin."

"I regret it myself, but it is my nature, when I am in command. It is a weakness I have yet to overcome."

He thought it prudent to ply his request again.

"Do not send me if someone else will go, but for the love of God, Señor, send someone. We are starving to death here."

"I grant that," Don Gonzalo said, grimacing under a stomach cramp that lent force to his words.

"There is much restlessness among the men, too. They want to turn back, but the privations we have suffered make folly of failure."

"You thought otherwise three months ago."

"That was eighty leagues hence, Excellency," Orellana said. "Only a handful of us could fight our way back, now. Let me go in search of food. What have I to gain by running away? I staked my whole fortune on this enterprise. Without your success, I lose everything, including my life. Give me the boat and the canoes—pick the company yourself if you wish. Meanwhile you can work on downstream to meet us. With luck and the help of God, we should be back before it is too late."

Orellana's positiveness, where no other positive existed, swayed Don Gonzalo.

"What proof have I that you would come back?"

"My love for you, Excellency, that brought me from Guayaquil under such hardship that I arrived naked in your camp. My duty to His Majesty, and my desire to serve him. Give me your figurine, sir, and let me prove my devotion on the image of the Beloved Virgin. By Her let me swear, She who has performed a miracle for me. And if I swear falsely, let me lose all hope of Her intercession for me in heaven."

Don Gonzalo was won. He reached lovingly inside his sobre vest and took from it the silver image of the Virgin. Orellana kissed it.

"How many men will you need?"

"About sixty, Excellency, in the ship and the canoes."

"You will positively return in twelve days' time?"

"I shall."

Don Gonzalo thought a moment. "The guides," he said, "speak of a wide river that flows into the Coca four days downstream. At that point leave us five of the canoes, so we may cross, and we shall come that far to meet you."

"Yes, Excellency."

"Very well, then. I want Friar de Vera to go with you. He needs disciplining. Pick the rest of the men yourself, and go with God."

Orellana turned to leave. He felt on his face the first spatter of rain and looked anxiously overhead. The first storm clouds of the season were forming.

"Cousin—" Don Gonzalo called after him.

"Señor?"

"You will take Maldonado with you, too. And see that he does not die."

14

To his great disappointment, Orellana discovered that half the men who would accompany him down river had been chosen for him by fate.

They were not even strong men. Rather they were the weakest of all—men who, too ill for duty, lay feverish in the hold of the little brigantine. To put them ashore was to burden Don Gonzalo with such a liability that he would be unable to march down the river bank. Therefore they remained aboard, totaling twenty-five, including Father Carvajal. Nine of the men actually were dying of hunger, a sorry crew indeed with which to begin a journey of such hazards as none could imagine, upon an uncharted river through the lands of hostile savages.

In compensation, Don Gonzalo granted Orellana leave to select any other members of the expedition whom he might require. He chose with agonizing care.

Alonso Robles, the immaculate, red-bearded Andalusian, was Orellana's first choice. Robles, for several reasons, he selected as lieutenant and second in command in preference to the loyalty-tested mountaineer Gutiérrez. First, because Robles was an hidalgo, and the men would respect him. Then, because he was immaculate of person, the sure test of a good soldier, and because he was an arquebusier, which might become important. Also, because he was no veteran of the Peruvian wars, and thus he had no past loyalty to any clique; he was, therefore, of all the company the most reliable. To a leader, frustrating minorities are always more deadly than outright foes, for an enemy may be shot, but a disloyal ally must be reconciled.

Orellana also favored Robles for another reason, not sharply defined in his mind but important to him personally. This Robles, who sang the hymns of Luther, who sympathized with the desires of men for freedom from the sordid impositions of civilization, was a man who touched Orellana's heart. Orellana wanted to reach out to this young man who could read and write and sing and smile, and learn from him all he knew, in this way clarifying his own resolution sworn before God. Furthermore, had not Robles promised to lead him to the woman who could make him smile, the sauterne-haired, cocoa-eyed Ana de Ayala who these days was so much companion to his thoughts?

He feared that if he left Alonso Robles behind, he would leave also the vision of Ana, and that, he knew, he could not do. Orellana treasured Robles' description of her as though it were a cameo that he might take from his breast pocket. She had become, in his eyes, the woman for whose sake the sufferings of the jungle were undertaken, for whose vanity he must become a governor, for love of whom his life now had purpose. He knew this as surely as though he carried her favor with him on the journey, a ribbon from her petticoat, perhaps, or a rose from her hair. Robles, her cousin, was evidence of her existence—indeed, the only evidence Orellana had that she was anything other than a dream. No, he could not leave Robles behind. Robles was Ana's cousin, a man to trust, whose mere presence was the symbol of the attainable dream. He put Robles with himself in the lead canoe.

Three others he selected for sentimental, as well as practical reasons. Gutiérrez, the loyal mountaineer, Hernández the Portuguese, Carranza the physician. All had attributes which made their choice logical: Gutiérrez as chief of his personal staff, Carranza as minister to the cluttered sick bay, Hernández as aide. He took them primarily because he was fond of them, and because he could trust them to carry out an order without supervision. Having them about him made him feel at home. He could relax with them.

The remainder of the crew were handpicked according to talent: the fisherman Gabriel de Contreros, a handy man upon an expedition that would start with little food; the man who had built and now commanded the brigantine, stout, stubborn Juan de Alcantara; the lieutenant from Guayaquil, gambler Juan de Illanes, admirable in command of scouting parties; the scrivener, Francisco de Isasaga, in case there was need of a notary; the woodcraftsman and stone mason Diego Mexía, best of all among the companions with the crossbow. Alcantara requested the inclusion of his helmsman, Pedro Domínguez Miradero, since he could measure nautical miles, tend the tiller and in emergency take command of the *San Pedro*. Carranza asked to take Soria, but here Orellana drew the line.

"No, friend," he said, "the old man is in his dotage. He would be a liability to us. We are already overburdened with the sick; let us leave behind the feeble-minded." Carranza, however, at the last moment gave Soria a dose of some herb that put him on the sick list, and therefore aboard the ship. Two Negro slaves, offered by Don Gonzalo, Orellana accepted. Two men must be constantly either poling the vessel or at the oars, and one of the blacks, named Nogal, had been a stroke oar in the galleys and therefore had great value.

Christmas fell on Sunday, and Orellana told the crew to be ready the following morning. Carranza protested.

"Monday is an evil day to begin a journey," he said. "You will surely fail. Start Tuesday, which is auspicious for new adventures."

"You said the wood in the brigantine would rot, and it has not done so," Orellana said. "Apply yourself to medicine, Carranza, and leave off these superstitions."

Carranza shook his head. "A journey begun on Monday will not reach its destination," he replied. "It is an old saying, but a true one. We shall end in some manner we cannot foresee, in some place we did not intend. Stay until Tuesday."

But on Monday, the second day of the Feast-tide of the Nativity, Orellana embarked immediately after the Mass, with sixty companions and two Negro slaves, but without native guides, charts or compass, little food and little protection. For weapons there were three arquebuses and four or five crossbows; for stores, a case full of charms and trinkets, trading stuff for savages; a little iron and other material for

126

ship repairs, the clothing each man could carry on his back, all the expedition's blankets for the twenty-five who were ill of chills, fevers and exhaustion, and food enough for two days. The brilliant trappings of Don Gonzalo's knighthood, including his massive table and chairs, his bright tent and his six suits of armor, were dumped on the beach, along with most of the possessions of Orellana's comrades, for the brigantine must be empty in order to bring back the anticipated food supplies from down river.

Orellana took his emeralds with him, in the bag about his neck. The golden cup he carried in his food sack. All else he left behind.

Before embarking, Carranza found a large earthenware Indian pot, and into it drew blood from a dozen horses until the pot was full. The horses were weakened but not harmed by the letting. Into the pot also went herbs and grasses from the river bank, and the whole was boiled over a fire while everyone else attended Mass. The pottage Carranza put aboard the brigantine as medicine for the sick.

Orellana then assigned places in the strange armada that was to suffer such hardships as Spaniards to that day had never before known, even in the New World. With sick and crew, the brigantine was filled. The remaining men manned the canoes.

And so, commending their souls to God, Orellana saluted Don Gonzalo and set out in the lead canoe, followed by his company, the clumsy brigantine in the middle of the fleet with its commander Alcantara in the bow and its helmsman Miradero in the stern, the two Negroes bending over the poles that propelled the boat in the narrow channel, and Father Carvajal, flat on his back in the hold, crying out in delirious fever to God to bless the enterprise.

A hard rain that had lasted all night followed them down the river.

From his talks with the hostage Delicola and other native chiefs, Francisco Orellana was confident that the settlement he sought was not more than a hard day's drive downstream. He had made a longer estimate to Don Gonzalo as protection against such unforeseen delays as might arise: skirmishes with the Indians, negotiations with the villagers for their food supply, and a generous allowance for the return trip upstream.

This latter detail worried Orellana the most. He anticipated no difficulty locating the food, for his information was explicit on this point. He had only to go downstream five or six Indian canoe marches to the junction of the Coca and another river, then back upstream on the larger river for one day's travel. As the Indians coursed the river, the distance could not be too great, at most a hundred miles, for these savages were a carefree people, and the perimeter of their experience was exceedingly confined. When they moved, as they did perhaps once in each generation, the trek consisted only of a few leagues, and they took several days to it. The natives of Orellana's experience, even on what they considered a "long" journey, were distracted by every fish that jumped, every bird that flew, for food was the primary object of their voyages and they might pause for half a day to bring down a wild turkey or trap a tapir. If, Orellana calculated, the savages then actually covered three Spanish leagues a day—ten and one-fourth miles—on their voyages, they were doing well. Five or six days, therefore, should add up to from fifty to sixty miles.

The Spaniards, however, driven frantic by the fear of death from starvation, impelled by the horizon of food, propelled down a swift-running little river whose current already was making up to three knots an hour owing to the rising freshet of the first winter rains, should be able to cover this same distance in a day's time. Hence Orellana's assurance that two days' food supply would be sufficient for the downstream trip.

The voyage back upstream, Orellana feared, would be the great challenge. Many of the men already were too weak to walk, a few having crawled into their canoes. Twenty-five were flat on their backs in the brigantine. Even the brave Juan de Alcantara, commander of the little *San Pedro*, leaned on a staff as he stood in the prow of his ship. Proud Alonso Robles, Orellana's lieutenant, had been too weak to shove the lead canoe off the sandbar at the start of the voyage.

What chance, Orellana asked himself, had these men to fight the current and the dangerous rapids back upstream? They would be required to pole every inch of the way. If they found sufficient food that their bellies were well-filled, they might be able to cover fifteen miles a day, providing the current did not increase. Now the rain, falling doggedly as it had done since Saturday vespers, already was washing into the current masses of logs, stumps and debris, a sure sign of rising water. These would foul the channel and must be cut away. An increase in the current to five knots an hour and they were done for. Their only hope then was to cut their way up the river bank, their shoulders laden with provision, leaving their weaklings behind. That might take many days.

Orellana had entrusted no one with these misgivings. Not even Antonio Carranza, who plied the oar in the rear of Orellana's canoe and on whose shrewdness and humanity Orellana had come to rely as an antidote to his burning distrust of Maldonado, was in on these meditations. Or Robles, who, more than any other, was his friend. The departure had been too hastily organized for confidences, anyway, and Orellana felt safe with his burden heavily in his own heart. To share a confidence merely adds weight to the burden, for you carry another's anxiety then as well as your own. And he could not, even had he desired, talk to Carranza or Robles now, for Maldonado was in the canoe with them.

Don Gonzalo had put Maldonado in Orellana's boat. Orellana had planned differently. His intention had been to make Maldonado commander of the rear guard, the last canoe in the armada, well out of earshot of Orellana in the van. Gonzalo, without coming out into the open on the role Maldonado played in Orellana's retinue, had publicly given his ward great prominence, and great significance. As the canoes put out, he had called loudly: "Oye, Maldonado, get in the lead boat, if you please. I want my representative close to the captain." Everyone had heard it. No one had missed the implication. Campmaster Ribera, standing beside His Excellency, had thrown a triumphant smile into Orellana's face.

Orellana dug the lead oar viciously into the muddy waters of the Rio Coca. He must return with food, his brigantine and canoes piled high with manioc. His reputation, his future, his investment of forty thousand pesos and his life in this miserable expedition, his governorship and the love of Ana de Ayala, depended on the correctness of his information from Chief Delicola that abundant food lay downstream. No one knew better than Orellana that the chief trick of the native, to rid himself of the cursed Spaniard, was to place a bright lure far beyond the horizon. But to return with food was to return with honor, re-established in pre-eminence as vice commander to Don Gonzalo, restored to sufficient power that he could deal with Ribera conclusively, and leave the campmaster's whitening bones to the snakes that were his fit companions. Then on, to El Dorado, the governorship, and a wife.

His mind relaxed, though his arm bent steadily to the oar in time with the sweep of Carranza's stroke at his back. He must return with food. Everything depended on it, particularly the growing clarity of his future. He was beginning to understand why he had really left Guayaquil, and why he would never return there. He was beginning to understand, but he needed a great deal of ripening.

In Guayaquil, as a lieutenant governor, he had carried out the orders of his superior, the Marquis Pizarro. Even had he been governor in his own right, he admitted, he would not have done what he would do now. He was beginning to see what a colony in this fresh new world should be. The concepts were not laid out in orderly rows, like the streets of a newly founded city, ready for men to build upon them, but they were forming in his mind. Forming as conclusively as that other concept, that what he needed to fulfill himself was a woman to share his life. Again his thoughts went back to the words of Lieutenant Robles, and to the vision of Ana de Ayala, the maid of Seville with the wine-colored hair and the eyes as melting as cocoa.

"We are getting far ahead, Excellency," said Maldonado. "Your Worship shoots these rapids with a better eye than those behind."

Orellana rested on his oar, and looked back. Only two canoes were visible this side of a sharp bend in the river. The fleet had been hugging the shore around the bend, taking advantage of the swift current that cut into the bank, and had not yet swung out with Orellana into the straightening channel. Orellana backed his paddle, and waited until all fifteen canoes and the slow-moving brigantine were again visible. As he watched, Gabriel de Contreros on the brigantine set up a shout and pulled a twenty-pound fish aboard from one of his troll lines that employed lures Contreros had copied from the savages. At least tonight they would eat fish, Orellana thought, even though they starved tomorrow.

"How are your patients?" Orellana asked Carranza, taking advantage of the waiting.

"Nine of them are very bad, Señor," Carranza said. "The horse blood seems to be reviving the rest. But the nine, Señor—I have my doubts."

Nine dying men to go in search of food, perhaps to fight Indians, surely to fight the river current on the upstream journey. Orellana shook his head.

"How is the padre?"

"Oh, he will recover," Carranza replied. "It takes more than a little dysentery to kill a Dominican."

Orellana called out to his pilot as the brigantine came alongside. "What do you estimate our speed to be?"

Alcantara pried himself to his feet and swept the current, then conferred for a moment with the helmsman. "We make it ten knots, more or less, in open water," he said, "but in the shoals we barely move."

The day passed, and the junction they sought was not met, nor on the next day, either. The rain was raw now, the men soaked. Hands had been put to bailing the hold of the brigantine, for, as Carranza had prophesied, she leaked a little, and cupped in great pools the descending rain. The priest had noted in charcoal on a fly leaf of his missal the beginning of the day as they began anew the journey downstream, Orellana again in the van scanning the way ahead for the junction which, Chief Delicola had said, could not be missed. In his mind the chief's words echoed and re-echoed: "To an abrupt turn the Coca flows, and you will feel the current slacken for a half league before you see it. Into another river the Coca runs, and the new river is much wider, and very swift, coming in at your right hand."

Orellana kept watch on his right hand. The men, who had eaten nothing during the day, rested often at their poles. The oars and sail were still useless, but the pace was increasing in the ever-swelling stream.

A wide bend appeared, and as usual Orellana swung hard over toward the outer bank with the channel. The fleet was close together, for Orellana had directed the brigantine and canoes to stay within sound of his hail in expectation of the junction. It was not Orellana, however, who hailed. It was Alcantara, from the ship. He had struck a boulder and stove a rotting plank. By the time Orellana reached the vessel she was heavily head down, sinking fast, and cries of fright and prayer rolled up from the twenty-five helpless men in her hold.

Quickly the canoes clustered about her and prodded her nose toward the shore. She had, however, made up her mind to sink. Gutiérrez paddled swiftly to the port side, reached into the jagged hole and hung on. The *San Pedro's* bow came up a little.

"Bravo, Gutiérrez," Orellana shouted. "Hang on, man!"

Gutiérrez hung on. His face turned black from the exertion. His arm and shoulder were out of sight under the water. His jaws were set in pain.

Witnessing the agony, Hernández sprang catlike from the deck of the brigantine to Gutiérrez' canoe and hurled his own forearm into the hole. Men who an hour before had been too weak to lift a paddle, now jumped into the stream and swam, easing the ten-ton weight of the *San Pedro.*

They began to gain, when suddenly the brigantine swung her stern heavily downstream and fought to free herself and sweep around the bend where she would surely be wrecked.

Father Carvajal, who had been in collapse since the morning Mass, flung off his cassock and dived naked from the deck, a coil of ivy rope in his hand, and swam ashore to lock the line to a stout sapling. The brigantine waddled, tugged, and came about. The men cheered.

Waist deep in water, shivering from the shock of cold water on his fevered body, Father Carvajal raised his eyes to heaven.

"Thank you, Almighty God," he shouted through chattering teeth in a voice that brought every man to pause, "for Thy goodness and mercy which we so little deserve. Surely You preserve us for some great purpose if You have saved us now. It is a sign to us to carry on."

"Courage!" the men shouted. "It is a sign!" They crossed themselves and leaped to the task of repairing the vessel, summoning the strength of horses to haul the brigantine from the water, mend her with a new plank, and launch her again upon the water. They set out once more, but Maldonado, weary of rowing a canoe, pleaded illness and stayed aboard the brigantine.

"The planks are rotting badly," Carranza said to Orellana as they stroked into the current in their canoe.

"God will preserve us," Orellana said, his eye and mind again upon the right bank. "We have had a sign from heaven."

Carranza was amused.

"You, too, Captain?" he asked, his voice taking on the irony that had been familiar even in the frigid mountain pass.

Without altering his stroke, Orellana turned and looked back at Carranza, his eye angry.

"Yes, I too," he shouted.

"Yes, Excellency," Carranza said, immediately subdued by Orellana's baleful eye.

Orellana rowed a moment in silence, then said quietly, "If it is not a sign, it is as good as one, for it restored the spirits of us all. See how fast we are moving, where two hours ago we counted ourselves dead men."

Carranza's continued silence irked Orellana.

"I myself do not believe in signs and portents," Orellana went on, able to speak freely now that Maldonado was not there to hear his heretical words. "I believe that man receives exactly as he gives, from God and man, and from his labor. I believe that a man who prays, when action is required, is a fool, and God knows him for a fool. I believe God answers prayers of men who do their own work and then thank God for having given them the strength. God does not do for men work they should do for themselves. Father Carvajal was right in thanking God for giving weak men the strength to save themselves. In that respect we had a definite sign from heaven. Had Father Carvajal prayed from the ship, instead of carrying a line ashore, he would have been drowned, and we with him. Does it not move you, Carranza, that it was the priest among us who was given this superhuman strength to save us all?"

"No, Captain," Carranza said. "I have often seen superhuman strength in men who were heretics, or Moslems—or, to bring your thinking closer to the point, to wretched Peruvian Indians in a death struggle with so-called Christians. I can't think of an example just offhand, but—"

"I can think of one," said Robles, from his position at the steering oar. "It was told me by Maldonado, who was there, and I cannot forget it."

"So?" said Orellana.

"It concerns Sacresaxigua, Your Excellency, king of the Chibcha people in Colombia, a mighty man in his own dominion, and one rich in gold."

"Until the Spaniards came," Carranza added hollowly.

"Yes, until the Spaniards came. The Spaniard Quesada captured him under promises of peace, and lodged him in double fetters until he should turn Christian and produce his gold. For five months the chief withstood the rack, his mouth speechless, his heart unturned. Even the priests tortured him. Five months he bore it, often smiling at the crudeness of the torture, knowing that in the end the joke would be his, for if they killed him, his golden secret died with him. And in the end, that's what happened. The lash was applied too hard one day, and the chief died. To the end he was faithful to his people, to his kingship, and to his own god."

"And Christians call such noble character savage," Carranza said. "I ask you, which was the savage, and which the civilized man?"

"The savage was the more civilized," Robles answered. "Of that there can be not the least doubt. But Quesada returned to Spain a very rich man, nonetheless. I saw him there with my own eyes, scattering doubloons about like so many dried beans."

"How did Quesada become so rich?" Orellana asked. "I understood, from ships that touched at Guayaquil, that he was only the lieutenant of Governor Don Pedro Fernández de Lugo."

"True, Excellency," said Robles, "even as you are the lieutenant of Governor Gonzalo Pizarro. But the law can always find ways to legalize lawlessness. When the eight hundred men who left Santa Marta under Quesada had been reduced by death to two hundred, and the mountains were not yet scaled, though hope was high, Quesada resigned his command, stating that he did not feel up to the task of leading them farther, and from now on they were relieved of their loyalty to the governor and could go on or turn back as they chose. What could the men do? They organized anew, as brigands free of the governor's authority, and elected to command them the one man who might have any chance to lead them safely up the mountain—Quesada himself."

"Was this legal?" Orellana asked.

"Indeed. It was drawn up in very good ink, by a scrivener, and duly witnessed, that Quesada had done all he could in the name of the governor and now must do what he might to save his own life and those of his companions."

"I see," Orellana said, bending to his oar.

"There is a precedent for it, Captain," Carranza said. "In Mexico, when Cortez burned his ships behind him to prevent his men returning to Cuba, and rallied his men on the beach for the conquest of Mexico, he was careful to relinquish the command given him by the Cuban governor, and to be elected anew by the expedition. No one knows better than yourself that Castilians have the right of free election, no matter where they may be. It is written in the constitution of Castile, acknowledged by the king, and defended by the legislature."

"In Castile, yes," Orellana said. "I am not so sure it would be legal in New Castile."

"You have the same monarch, sir," Carranza replied, "here as in Castile."

Orellana would have discussed this point further, for the Spaniard likes few things better than a dissection of the law, but he was diverted by a break in the right bank. Unquestionably a wide, swift river emptied into the Coca less than a mile away.

He gave the signal the little navy had awaited for two days, and the brigantine and canoes closed file. But the familiar refrain of Chief Delicola's description of the junction soon struck a discord. This was no spacious river. It was another torrent like the Coca, only perhaps twice as large, turbulent with driftwood and a rising flood, immense eddies, cataracts and freshets, stinking with the filthy rot of the jungle.

And in despair Orellana recalled his instruction from Don Gonzalo to leave five canoes at the mouth of a river which could not be forded. This must be the stream. Two days gone, and they were still many leagues from food. There could be no mistake. The error was Orellana's own, in estimating the Indian's daily journey at three leagues.

He drew the expedition up on the near bank, and sent men ashore to cache five canoes under blazed trees, as he had been ordered. The sixteen men thus displaced were distributed in the other canoes, welcome additions to the weakening relays of oarsmen.

Then quickly, before the men might have time to transpose their disappointment into weakness, he gave the order once more to shove off. They must go on and find food quickly, lest they perish. So they sailed on. They were now on the River Canela, afterward called the Napo, but they did not know it. They had no idea where they were.

15

FOR THREE more days the men bent to their poles and paddles from dawn to dusk without any sign of a merger of their river with one even greater. Rain fell intermittently, following the dogged routine of tropical winter. One moment the air was almost too dank to breathe, the humidity nauseating, the weight of the heat like that of iron; the next moment a chilling, soaking drench from the low hanging clouds sent pillars of rain cascading upon men and boats. The rain was not accompanied by thunder, or lightning, or even a wisp of wind. It just fell. Silently. It fell like a curse, submerging the body and drowning the spirit. Then it stopped, not with a clean wind at its back, or a warming azure break in the dull sky, or any other of the promises of fair weather that usually attend the break in a storm. It just stopped. Sullenly. Then the heat weight pounded down again with its stifling burden which the men carried on their shoulders until suddenly they realized that the weight was gone, and the rain had returned. Nature worked in relentless relays to torture the Spaniard.

The men crouched over their oars in dull-witted delirium. On. On. On. On. Each stroke pushing one notch farther over the water, around the bend, in to the shore, out to the channel, away from living and on toward death. No Rosary needed now. Five strokes of the oar for an Ave Maria, twenty strokes for a Pater Noster, seventy-five strokes for the Credo. *Ave Maria, gratia plena: Dominus tecum: benedicta tu in mulieribus, alleluja.* Five strokes farther along the road to death. On. On. On. On.

And as dawn uncertainly displaced the darkness of night on the seventh day, Father Carvajal, whose strength somehow mounted as every other man's flagged, said a special Mass. In fine rich tones he spoke, Friar de Vera on his knees as acolyte because he could not stand erect, commending to Our Lord their persons and their lives, beseeching Him to deliver the company from the miseries of eternal damnation.

Orellana, who had requested the Mass, stood on the deck of the brigantine, his eye wandering over his crew. Thirty-three men could not stand up to their devotions. Eight others who had never been down before were kneeling now. Those whom courage rather than physique still carried upright could be counted on two hands: himself, Carvajal, the lieutenant Robles, the Portuguese Hernández, the Jew Carranza, the mountaineer Gutiérrez, the gambler Illanes, the fisherman Contreros, the crossbowman Mexía. And nine, flat in the hold under a burden of blankets, were so far gone in delirium that, except during the Mass, one or the other priest constantly attended them.

Carranza now had shifted from the lead canoe to the brigantine, better to utilize his physician's skill among the stricken. His place in Orellana's canoe was taken by the Portuguese. Orellana told himself that he had selected Hernández because he was strong, but he knew this was not true. The swarthy, wiry little fellow with the red hair ribbon could not compare as an oarsman with Gutiérrez. Then why the Portuguese?

Orellana could not admit the reason, even to himself. The admission would have been a confession that he had jettisoned hope of survival. If there is any alternate, no man will face death alone; he fears God too much. He must cling to a companion in the extremity of his life. Orellana clung to Hernández. He had not spoken a hundred words to the man, except to give him orders. Yet Hernández was there, watching over him. When Orellana needed reinforcement for his own convictions, he had only to look at Hernández and to read in the little man's face the encouragement he needed. Hernández believed in him. Orellana needed such faith now even more than he needed food.

He selected Hernández and put him in the canoe. And there began a peculiar tacit friendship on the river that day, the sixth of the Feast

138

tide of the Nativity in Father Carvajal's missal, New Year's Eve on the calendar, which was never broken afterward except by death.

The New Year's Eve camp was made in silence. About five o'clock in the afternoon a long sandbar struck out from an island in the river. As by common consent, each boat made landfall there, hauling up easily in the mush at the water's edge. At least here on an island there was no danger of a surprise attack that would have liquidated them without a fight.

Six men who were able, crawled ashore under the leadership of Maldonado and on hands and knees ranged the beach and the woods for roots, bugs, beetles, berries, anything that might give an ounce of nourishment.

Orellana looked over his crew, and knew that if the men survived until dawn, an appeal to their spirit must be made this night. Five days now they had been without food, while sapping their strength with heavy bodily labor. In the eyes of everyone Orellana read the same message: death. Robles, no longer immaculate, bit constantly at the ragged fringes of his beard, and mumbled to himself. Carranza stared vacantly, mechanically rather than intelligently administering to the sick. Hernández, so thin now as to be a living skeleton, stumbled crying about the brigantine deck, his mouth a clabber of foam. And Gutiérrez, the strongest of them all, went about his duties with his jaws locked, as though to open his mouth might expel his last breath.

Orellana knew how they felt. His own eye bulged from its socket from the pressure in his head. Thoughts fumbled about within him as though they were attempting to speak to him in a foreign language, without knowing any verbs. His chest ached with weight, as though heavy lead plates were fixed to his lungs, dragging them down into his stomach. His knees functioned only by the exertion of all his will upon them. His hands shook uncontrollably, and there was no sense of feeling whatever in his toes.

The time had come for a final gesture. Instinct rather than reason guided him as he heaped up a tremendous mosquito smudge on the beach close to the ship, and personally collected from the huntsmen the feeble store of edibles with which they crawled back to camp. The forage was meager, virtually nothing with which to assuage the hungers of sixty-one white men and two Negroes.

He called Carranza, showed him the edibles, and asked what might be done with them. Hysterically, Carranza's old wit flamed up.

"Why," he said, sobbing, "if I had a well-sweated doublet and hose now, a couple of well-worn shoes from chigger-bitten feet with plenty of blood on them, and a little sputum, I might make you such a witch's brew as would send us all to purgatory."

Gravely Orellana nodded. In the jest of the dying man there was a nutrient of reason.

"We are in purgatory already, friend Carranza," he said. "I shall get you the leather, and you will make the witches' brew."

Instinct, the first preserver of mankind, served him better than he knew. Even in old leather there is rich nourishment, particularly in saddle leathers long tallowed and rubbed with olive oil, and harness soaked in the salt of human sweat. He made the rounds of the camp, taking from the men everything of leather they had except their sword belts. A setting sun broke through the storm clouds as the provender went into the cauldron, which began to fill with grain chests, hampers, saddle bows, a shoe, a sweat-soaked belly cinch.

These swelled the pot, to the accompaniment of such hysteria-born ceremony that even the sickest man lifted on his elbows and sniffed the clove-tinted air. In a fever, Lieutenant Robles added three hairs from his red goatee, for Andalusia's sake.

The broth boiled a long time, Carranza stirring it with a stick, as intent upon his work as only a sick-minded man may be. In sobbing frenzy he invoked Lilit, disheveled spirit of the wind, to add a still-born foetus to the pot, cried out to Mare for a singed tongue, and even on Holle-Hulda for a love potion. Anything, he cried, would do; and carefully he counted as he stirred the pot, rotating three times three to the right, three times three to the left, careful not to interrupt the stirring upon an even number. Into the pot he threw a bit of coral, the last amulet in his box, and he begged his mates for an amethyst to sweeten the brew with courage, but found none.

His crony Soria, leaning heavily on a staff, came to give aid, and affected great cheer at the odors, and awe at the pagan inprecations.

"I have itchy feet, my fine necromancer," he said. "Could it mean that I am going on a journey?"

Counting his rotations of the stew, Carranza sobered for a moment. "It means you have chiggers, my friend," he replied, "and you will be dead if you don't pick them out. Get them quickly, and we'll add them to the pot."

Orellana inspected the work, then went to a knoll where all ashore and aboard the brigantine might hear him.

"Gentlemen," he said, "this is New Year's Eve. We have prepared a celebration. Let every man who can, bring his helmet to the ladle. Those who cannot will be served aboard the ship. Join in, comrades, with a good will, to salute the New Year—the day of hope."

Spaniards always rally to a joke. They knew what was in the pot, and they doubted the dawn of any day, least of all one of hope. Hernández seized Orellana's helmet and beat on it with a stirring stick, as had the chef in calling soldiers to the abundant mess of the famous old Italian campaigns, and shouting, as the great Captain Gonsalvo de Córdoba's messmen had shouted in their time: "Oye! Oye! Now is the time to put food in your gut and strength in your right arm, for the greater glory of God and Ferdinand."

The men rocked with uncontrollable whoops of laughter that cackled out across the river and returned in funereal echoes. They approached the pot, some crawling on paralyzed limbs, pushing their helmets ahead of them across the sand, others limping their cadaverous bones down the gangway from the brigantine. Then, having insufficient strength for the return, they squatted or lay beside the campfire with a steaming helmet of brew beside them.

García de Soria, plunging his helmet deep into the broth and coming up with a brass buckle dangling from the end of a boiled strap that until an hour ago had eased the weight of shot and powder on Blas de Medina's shoulder, held high the buckle for all to see.

"As God is my witness, this night there is no dog meat in the pot. For once, gentlemen, we eat in style. The buckle of a nobleman, no less."

Those who could, set up a cheer. Alonso Robles, bending to his duty as lieutenant, entered into the spirit of the gayety and waved his full helmet.

"By my beard," he exclaimed, "what have we here? A full pot! And cooked with herbs! Señor Carranza, you are the prince of magicians."

He gathered his rags about him, flicking a briar from his shoulder with a delicate flip of thumb and forefinger, and then with a sweeping gesture as though gathering a regal cape about his shoulders, he bent his right knee in a low court bow.

Carranza reached up to his dirty grey curls and took off an imaginary plumed hat——a very gay hat of purple velvet adorned with a foot-long ostrich plume, he said——and swept it to the ground in a handsome bow of his own. The entire company applauded.

Miradero, the helmsman, on hands and knees, agony drooping from the foamy corners of his beard, crawled to the fire and received his steaming portion. From the ladle fell a long strip of snakeskin.

"The choicest portion for the helmsman!" he said. "The white meat. Always before it has been my lot to get the gizzard and the wing bone. Now at last, the white meat. Gentlemen——" he nodded gallantly to Orellana although he could not rise off his hips——"it is an auspicious augury for the New Year."

He held up the helmet of broth in both hands.

"A toast, gentlemen," he said. "A New Year's toast. To God, and His Majesty, the Emperor Charles."

He quaffed, burning his tongue and spilling the broth down his neck. But he laughed.

Juan de Illanes approached, and in his portion discovered the tail of a little hedgehog. He held it between two fingers for Miradero to see.

"Now here, Pero," he said, "is something to match your gizzard and wing bone. I shall cast you the dice for it—my tail against your white meat. One throw only."

Miradero shook his head.

"Tonight your dice are no lure to me, Comrade Juan," he said. "This is my great moment—white meat. Do you think I would gamble it for what you offer?"

Orellana watched the pot, as the portions were doled. There was plenty, at least, for all. After the last sick man was nourished, and Father Carvajal and Orellana himself were alone unserved, Orellana filled a bowl for the priest, and a helmet for himself, and gratefully turned to Carranza.

"You have done well, Señor," he said. "Even better than you know. Come aboard the ship and be comfortable."

The men lingered over their meal. García de Soria made much of his brass buckle and strip of leather.

"The difficulty is," he said finally, "that I do not know the etiquette for eating it. I have never been to court before. . . . Do you remove the buckle with a fine steel knife at court, friend Medina, or eat it whole, like a pomegranate, with your fingers?"

"Not with the fingers, by my conscience," Blas de Medina bantered, "or the chamberlain will see that you are not invited again. Cut the meat into fine strips with your sword, and leave the buckle on the plate. It is only a garnish. Here, let me show you."

He started to cut the leather strap, but Soria stopped him with a tornado of fury.

"Break off, there, Señor," he said, reaching for his sword. "Is that the etiquette of court, to take the food from a man's mouth? Eat your own portion, and leave mine." Then relaxing, he added, "I swear, these courtiers are no better than us common thieves, after all."

Soria gnawed at the leather as comfortably as a dog, until he had chewed and swallowed it all.

143

They continued their simulated gayety, watching the unaccustomed sun go down, hesitant to consume the last morsels of their food and be reminded by their stomachs that they were still hungry, when suddenly Maldonado, putting his hands to his belt, doubled up with a moan, and fell to the sand. Carranza was by his side in a moment, a finger down his throat. Maldonado responded to the treatment, spewing his late meal over his shoes. Every man saw that from his mouth came bright green stuff that had not been part of the common mess. He who had gone foraging in the woods had partaken of food by himself.

The greens had made him ill. Carranza rubbed a bit of the greenery between his fingers, and gasped. "Bejuco," he said. The other foragers now became alarmed, and it was apparent that they too had nibbled in secret of the succulent fresh tips of marsh grass.

"All who have eaten this stuff bend over and heave," Orellana said sternly. "Heave or you are dead men."

The threat of death was greater than the disgrace of exposure. The men followed orders. Soon all six were writhing in acute agony, their stomachs puffed like a round ball, their faces purple, their extremities paralyzed. For a time Orellana, and Carranza who worked with the ill men, thought they would die, so great were their cramps, so wracking their spasms of retching. Contreros the fisherman had a little hoard of sugar extract with which he mixed his baits. Carranza took it from him and fed it to the stricken. The upheaval of their diaphragms calmed then, but they were still near death. Carranza put them in the hold, under a pile of blankets.

"What is this bejuco?" someone asked.

"It is a marsh grass," Orellana said. "The Indians along the rivers make a poison of it, with which they tip their arrows."

"Madre de Dios," said Father Carvajal. "Poisoned arrows."

"It is an interesting poison," said Carranza. "I saw some in an Indian camp at El Barco. They bruise the leaves to free the juices, cut them into strips, and boil. Then they pour off the liquid, add some coagulating herb, and they have a very fine poison. It works by shutting off blood to the heart, so that the blood vessels burst."

"Will the arrow poison kill a man?" Miradero asked.

"They do not use it on human beings, only on small animals. The chiefs told me that it is only used on humans a long way downriver."

"Down the river! Maybe we have gone far enough, then."

"It is a subject," Orellana injected quickly, "that I think we all should speak of, now. We have reached an extremity and what we do should be determined by us all. I should not like to make the decision on my own responsibility, although I myself am convinced of what we should do."

The men listened. Too well they knew that in another few days they would all be dead, and the banter of the New Year's fiesta was a very thin lacquer to cover each man's mortal fear.

Having their attention, Orellana walked to the high prow of the vessel where all could see him, and spoke.

"That none of us have died of our hardships so far, when to begin we were half of us dying of hunger, can only be taken as a token from heaven that we are preserved on this river for God's own purpose."

"Gloria in excelsis, Deo," injected Father Carvajal.

"We should be fools indeed," Orellana went on, "to lie down here on this insect-ridden sand and die after what we have already survived. Curiosity alone should drive us on, so that we may discover God's intention toward us."

"Amen," echoed Father Carvajal.

"Before we discuss the future," Orellana continued, "let us look first at the present. It is not a pleasant outlook for the beginning of a new year—but we are men of Castile, and we have faced critical times before."

He paused, letting each man dwell on his own greatest hardship. Some he knew were there who had suffered the long winter with Francisco Pizarro on the Island of Puna and nearly died of it; some had wandered for four years in the northern wastes with Benalcázar; one or two had battled across the causeway out of Mexico with

Cortez, where every step was a choice between death by drowning and death by sacrifice; some had been becalmed for a month upon a tiny caravel in the Sargasso sea; some had mucked through Nicaragua with De Soto; and all had crossed the Andes in midwinter to reach their present crisis. Hardship was the essence of Castilian life in the New World. Orellana did not pause long, however, lest the men begin to realize that in all their experience they had never faced such hopelessness as now confronted them.

He called attention to the fact that nine of their number lay in the hold below, too ill to join them, some too ill to eat. Likewise he mentioned the six recently stricken, and pointed out that because of their greediness they had not only lost the nourishment of the evening repast but had been immeasurably weakened in addition, and now were in God's hands, awaiting Divine judgment for their sin of withholding forage from their companions. He dwelt for a brief moment on the folly of such action, pointing out that the jungle contained more noxious than edible plants, and that common security demanded common action in all matters.

That there would be no more food even for the dying, Orellana said he mentioned only in passing, since the situation was obvious. He admitted frankly that he did not know where on the river the expedition. was, or with any certainty how far away food might be. He doubted, he said, that in their weakened condition they could go on up the other river a day's distance for food, even if they reached the junction. However, he pointed out, the same difficulty faced them if they tried to return at this time to Don Gonzalo, and they knew that in Gonzalo's camp likewise there was nothing to eat.

"Therefore, companions," he said, "we have three choices: to go back upstream, to go on downstream, or to lie down here and die. What is your pleasure?"

The men said nothing. All three forks in the road appeared only to lead to Father Carvajal's extreme unction. At last the ship's commander, Alcantara, spoke.

"It is useless to go back upstream," he said. "The brigantine might

146

make three leagues a day, but it is doubtful. We must pole every inch of the way. The water has risen constantly since we set out, and the current is now more than five knots. We have already come five hundred miles, by my reckoning. At least six weeks would be required for our return, and Gonzalo will not stay there that long a time. I say go forward."

Orellana looked about for other comment, caught the eye of his lieutenant. "Señor Robles?" he said.

Robles stirred painfully. The leather he had eaten sat heavily upon his stomach. He spoke through tense lips.

"When we set out, we expected to encounter a village in two days' time. We are now seven days downstream. Surely we must meet savages soon. And if we see food, we shall find the strength to fight, if necessary, to get it. I say go forward."

"There comes a time," Father Carvajal injected, "when duty to God, to preserve one's own life, is greater than the duty to temporal authority, in this case our obligation to Don Gonzalo. The sin upon our heads of dying by our own hand, doing nothing or attempting folly, would damn us all eternally. Hope, at least, lies forward. I say go on."

None disputed the priest.

"Very well, then, gentlemen," Orellana concluded, "we shall go on. Take heart. What we seek may be just around the next bend in the river. Then, with food in our bodies and on the ship, the road back will not appear so steep. Sleep now in peace, and tomorrow, forward."

"Pray this night, my comrades," said Father Carvajal, "and know that God is merciful."

Next day, the first of the new year, the prayers appeared for a moment to have been answered, for some of the men distinctly heard jungle drums. Hope coursed through the expedition like fresh blood, but the sound was only a delirium, for neither that day nor the next did they encounter any inhabited country.

The eyes of all were bloodshot, now. Scarcely a man could stand.

Orellana, to hide his own weakness, did not leave his canoe, sleeping in it the second night.

Every man was too discouraged to fight on, and again Orellana rallied them.

"Come, gentlemen," he called from the canoe after Father Carvajal's brief vespers, "it is not this bad. Look you—not a man of us has died. Not a man, even though all of us have liked to die a thousand times. Does this mean nothing to you? Can you ignore the fact that we are living, we who by all the laws should have died? For what purpose are we preserved? For something, surely. Take courage, sleep—and tomorrow, forward."

The men marveled at Orellana's faith, and once again took heart. During the night no man died.

Next night the camp was made at a spot where the forest encroached upon the water. Soft bamboo shoots were plentiful along the bank. At this manna from heaven, four men revived sufficiently to gather great arm loads, and to climb a tree to cut down a large palm cabbage, and once again the men ate. But they scarcely had strength enough now to swallow. As usual, Contreros fished from the brigantine, but so swollen was the rising tide of the water from rain that the fish would not bite.

They were eating the bamboo when Orellana looked up starkly, and placed his hand rigidly upon the knee of Hernández the Portuguese who was close beside him in the canoe.

"Do you hear what I hear, or am I, too, gone mad?" he whispered.

Hernández cocked his dark head, and listened. His eyes widened.

"Drums!" he exclaimed.

"Quiet, in God's name," Orellana said. "Do not arouse false hopes again."

The hopes, however, were this time not false. The steady tum-tum-tum, tum, tum-tum, tum, came back to them again and again. There was no mistake.

148

"Gutiérrez," Orellana whispered toward the stern of his canoe, where the mountain man lay either asleep or unconscious. Gutiérrez roused.

"Gutiérrez! What do you hear?"

The mountaineer was immediately alert, and he too echoed back the hopeful word.

"Drums," he muttered, and then more loudly, "drums! The Heavenly Host be thanked. It is—it must be—drums."

"Robles—what do you hear?"

The Andalusian sighed. "Leave me alone. I have heard the drums before. It is only Gabriel, calling to me."

Orellana listened a long time in stunned, unbelieving silence, praying that cruel hope was not again being roused in him in vain. Then he was sure. He stood up, marveling that he was able to do so.

"Oye! Comrades. Drums!"

The camp came to life as though he had mentioned an asado of beef. Now everyone heard the drums. Tum-tum-tum. Tum. Tum-tum. Tum. War drums, nicely tuned in three pitches: treble, bass, and tenor. Hardy, vigorous, strongly manipulated drums, pounded by men well-fed and robust.

Orellana was immediately awake to the jeopardy in which they were placed by a camp so close to the forest, out of which an ambush might leap at any moment. "Lieutenant Robles!" he called, shaking his friend to consciousness. "Fling out guards. Four-hour watches to all who can walk. Stand fast tonight. Tomorrow we dine on corn."

Robles discovered that he could stand erect. So, too, did others. Orellana staggered ashore and personally secured the guards. The drum beats continued, echoing briskly over the water. Once Orellana, listening to them, thought that in any other extremity those drums would carry an ominous overtone, for they were the percussions of determined, fighting men. But he did not want to think of fighting. He wanted to believe the savages would flee, and from this thought he determined his strategy for the morrow, and was satisfied with it. If they must fight, they must. If they must die, death would not be unwelcome. But first they would try a ruse. With God's help, it might work.

16

THE RUSE was simple, as it must be for exhausted men.
The canoes were strapped to the side of the brigantine,
or towed astern. Men too weak to fight were laid flat upon
the deck—even the dying men—their heads projecting over the side
to give the appearance of strong forces. All available helmets were
mounted on stakes and secured where they would show to advantage,
atop coils of sail cable, behind the mast, among the extra ships' plank
that lay on deck. Everything of metal large enough to vibrate a
resonance was assembled, one piece and a stout stave beside each
prostrate man.

Orellana chose his landing party carefully. The crossbowmen were
in the van, under Diego Mexía. Crouched behind them on the brigantine were the arquebusiers Pedro de Acaray, Gutiérrez and García de
Soria, with Gutiérrez in command. Robles led the infantry, Hernández the spearsmen. Only the hardiest men were selected for this enterprise, men who could conceal their frailties behind a strong shield of
courage.

When he was satisfied that all was in order and the men clearly
versed in their duties, Orellana gave the order to cast off. Father
Carvajal cleaved the air with a gesture of Divine supplication, then
calmly rolled up the sleeve that concealed his right arm, and whipped
a borrowed sword to accustom his muscles to the transition from the
merciful gesture of exhibiting the Host to the brutal one of killing.

Dawn and rain came simultaneously as the brigantine shoved off
quietly into the current, the two Negroes at the oars, as they had been
constantly for nine days, the most uncomplaining men of the crew.
Orellana made a last hurried inspection, concentrating upon the

readiness of the shot and powder for the arquebuses, for on them success depended.

Two leagues they coursed in silence, every man as alert as the raindrops that hustled busily about the beards of the men and burrowed like inquisitive fleas under their clothing.

Two leagues they advanced, with no impediment stronger than a chill wind and the driving rain, when from a brake of high reeds on the right bank four dugout canoes darted toward them, three sets of broad savage shoulders propelling each. Following instructions, Miradero stood nonchalantly at his helm, spitting into the water to hide his nervousness, and Alcantara held rigid eyes to the water at the ship's bow, alert for snags and shoals. Orellana stood before the empty mast, sword drooping casually in his hand.

The Indians cut across the ship's bow at the distance of two crossbow shots, then bent away downstream into the chest of the wind.

"After them," Orellana barked, "full speed."

The brigantine jumped under the impact the Negroes put to the oars.

"Stay well off shore," Orellana told the helmsman, pointing to a curve in the river.

They rounded the bend. The Indian canoes were landing, although no village could be seen on the shore.

Up from the low-lying hills on the right bank came the reverberation of alarmed drums, in tempo faster than the previous evening; summoning, urgent, frantic drums.

"They call for help," said Orellana. "Faster."

To the right now showed a promontory a good twenty feet above the river with a sandy beach below. From their experience they knew that on this hill, concealed in the ribald jungle growth, a half dozen large huts threw up their thicketed peaks in competition with the forest trees, and before them sixty or more savages were drawn up bravely.

Orellana jumped to the bow.

"Yonder lies food or death," he said. "Everything depends on order. Each man must look after himself, and all must look out for all, or we are every man dead. Do not exceed your orders. You are all good soldiers. Do what you have to do, and nothing more, in God's name."

"Saint Iago and at them," roared Father Carvajal, as the ship's prow scudded into the soft sand, accompanied by the splash of men leaping into the water.

Three shots rang out from the arquebuses as the crossbowmen and infantry crashed ashore. In the echo of the ordnance a mighty clatter arose from the brigantine as the dying men, organized and now led by Miradero as a maestro conducts a choir, banged with staves upon their resonant metal to the shouts of those who still had breath enough in them. Alcantara leaped like a frenzied man about the deck, exhorting to deeds of chivalry the empty helmets that stood on staves amid the rigging.

The arquebuses fired again, this time from the shore, and with a rush the landing party, Orellana ahead, booted headlong, contemptuous of danger, into the concealed village.

The Indians stood a moment staring, listening to the hubbub, stepping back before the magic roar of the guns. Then they recoiled and the jungle gulped them. The landing party overran the deserted village and cheered.

For a moment disorder threatened, as the men rushed like maniacs into the huts, to emerge fumbling yucca in their hands. At the sight of food, the men forgot the savages at their backs, forgot their orders, forgot even that they were men, and filled their mouths to bloating with the rich meal.

Orellana roared, his devilish eye flashing.

"Enough! Enough!" With his foot he kicked upright a large earthenware pot that lay upon the ground. "Put the food here. Search the village. Find what there is to eat and bring it. Hurry. The Indians may return at any moment."

The men did as they were bidden, restored to sanity by the threat of attack. The kettle was fully filled and another likewise, along with a pot of manioc liquor that had been found.

Orellana staked guards about the camp, close to the shore, loaded yucca and the liquor aboard the brigantine for the dying men, and then turned to his comrades.

"Eat now, gentlemen," he said. "You have earned it. But remember, there is not much here—scarcely enough for two days—and we have a ship and ten canoes to fill."

The men ate. Father Carvajal, writing again on a fly leaf of his missal, marked that the village was captured on Tuesday, the ninth day since they had left Don Gonzalo Pizarro. Three more days and Gonzalo expected them to return. But they were hundreds of miles downstream, and to return was impossible.

Heavy rations of the savage liquor were dispensed to the sick, for Indian drink usually is fermented from good grain and tender forest shoots rich in nourishment, in addition having medicinal power to open the bowels, break dysentery, and stimulate the flow of saliva. Or at least so said Carranza as he went about the sick bay with a native cup in hand, encouraging the sick to drink generously of the stinking brew.

Yucca was not all that was found. Dried smoked fish hung in the huts, and it could be eaten without cooking. Large stores of red pepper also were at hand, and the hot delicacy cleansed the mouth and the breath and stilled the gnawing constrictions of emaciated stomachs.

Within an hour half the company were on their feet again and able to drink from a nearby spring. Acaray brought down a bird while standing guard with his arquebus, and Diego Mexía, not to be outshone by powder and shot, had equal luck with his crossbow. A new search of the village turned up hidden caches of corn. The men rallied.

An hour after noon the jubilation ended suddenly with the appearance above deck of Friar de Vera, his crucifix in hand. A hush dropped over the camp so quickly that the sounds of the forest rushed in to take command: the swish of a rainy wind, the drip of water from giant vines, the shrill call of a heron and an answering squawk from a marshy clump of reeds.

Father Carvajal, who had been ashore helping Carranza and Soria clean the newly killed fowl, hurried aboard the ship.

"Who?" was all he said.

"Sebastian de Fuenterrabia," the friar said, and then, as Orellana came up, he added, "He is one of those who has been ill the entire voyage. He is still living, but I have given him unction."

Orellana nodded. He did not know this man, nor did any of the others, who he was, or whence he had come. He had been aboard the brigantine at the outset, too ill to be moved. Wonder it was that he had survived this long.

"He beat too hard upon a horseshoe during the rush ashore," de Vera said. "It was a pony shoe and made very little noise, and he expended himself. Then when he tried to eat, he withered suddenly, like a flower caught in a fire. He will not last the night."

"God forgive his sins," Orellana said.

The Indians returned about two hours after midday. They came, however, not to attack but to mill about in their canoes offshore like simpletons with no purpose. Orellana watched them for a time, then called across the water in the Omagua tongue.

"Come over. We mean no harm. We wish to speak to you."

A chief came at once, distinguished by a proud necklace of jaguar claws. His torso was adorned with a leopard skin. His entire body was dyed red with achotte, his face further illuminated by four horizontal lines across cheeks and nose in blue-black huito dye and four large, overlapping crosses on his chin. His teeth glistened ebony black from paint. On his head was a crown of plaited palm leaves from which, at the back, rose a brilliant tiara of basetail feathers of the toucan. Orellana, noting the feathers, complimented the chief on his marksmanship, pointing out that he knew the difficulty of shooting so wary a bird, and that the chief's headdress must represent the killing of more than a score of toucans.

The chief responded to this praise of his hunting skill by leaping to the deck of the brigantine, where Orellana embraced him after the manner of clan relatives. He fingered Orellana's leather surcoat and marveled greatly at the construction of the brigantine. Orellana stripped the surcoat from himself and handed it to the chief.

The old man was delighted, turning to his companions who now filled the river in fifty canoes. In response to questions, he told Orellana his name was Aparia the Lesser, to distinguish him from a more important man named Aparia the Great, that he was of the Irimara people, of whom there were some score of well-populated clans in the vicinity, particularly the Ant clan a day's journey downstream.

On finding that Orellana's men desired food, the chief departed quickly with promises to give the Spaniards all they might desire. Within an hour, pirogues began to return. All afternoon a parade of laden native dugouts continued, until the deck of the ship was heaped with maize, yucca, fish, monkey meat, and even two fat wild ducks.

Such opulence swung upward the pendulum of Spanish enthusiasm to such a degree that by the next morning all but nine of the company were on their feet. Fuenterrabia, though dying, was not yet lifeless. So gay was the mien of the companions and so light their spirit that Father Carvajal, in his journal that day, made entry that the men "went about so happy that they were not conscious of any of the hardships that they had endured."

Orellana, however, did not let the men forget that they must return upriver. All but the most perishable foods he ordered stored in the brigantine. To make room for the food he directed that all the ship's stores, including bedding, extra plank and iron, blankets, sailcloth, even the remaining personal effects, be set upon the beach. The sick men likewise were carried ashore and placed in the shade of a giant jacaranda tree bright with blue flowers, and the men set about the task of loading.

But there was grumbling among them. None now except Orellana wished to attempt the impossible upstream current for a rendezvous with Don Gonzalo. They remonstrated with Orellana, but he refused to listen. Finally Maldonado, whose stomach was as weak for the return journey as it was for nourishment, consulted with Lieutenant Robles and Friar Carvajal and then dictated to the scrivener, Isasaga, a petition which he hoped every man of the crew would sign.

Carranza brought this news to Orellana, with the usual cynical interpretation of his own.

"I think, Captain," he said, "that you will soon be the leader of an independent expedition—even as was Quesada in Colombia."

Orellana frowned heavily. He was, with ship's master Alcantara, at that moment stowing food, and he was not generous toward the interruption. He did not reply, but Carranza knew he was listening.

"A petition is being circulated, sir," he said, "asking you not to attempt the trip upstream."

"Nombre de Dios," Orellana exclaimed. "And why do they think we starved to death coming down, if not to go back up?"

"They consider it impossible, sir."

"Get them together and let them tell me that!" Orellana exploded, continuing his work.

The men assembled quickly. Those who had not heard of the petition now scanned it with interest and many a name went down beneath it. Those who could not write had Isasaga inscribe their names.

Orellana continued his labors until all the men were ranged either aboard the ship or on the beach below. He turned toward them with such a baleful eye that Maldonado retreated a step and hid the petition behind his back.

"You stand and watch, gentlemen, when there is so much work for all to do?" Orellana asked.

The leader until that moment, Maldonado was now dethroned by a single sentence. He stood mute and unmoving. A few men looked quickly to Father Carvajal as the one man who might dare the wrath in Orellana's eye, but the priest was too prudent to intervene, lest he precipitate a schism among the company that would endanger his chaplainship. Robles, likewise, was silent. He knew that he acted in Orellana's best interest, but now was not the time to say so.

Meanwhile Orellana awaited an answer, standing defiantly upon the deck, right hand closed about the scabbard of the jewel-encrusted dagger at his waist, the other resting suggestively on the hilt of his sword. In all the company of Spaniards, no one spoke.

It remained for the outcast, the detested Portuguese, to break the silence.

"The men, Your Worship," Hernández said quietly out of the midst of a huddle on the beach, "are of a single mind to present you a petition of their own devise."

"A petition?" Orellana asked scornfully, as though he had heard nothing of it. "Have we time now for petitions, with dangerous savages all about us and our bellies gnawing with recent hunger?"

"It is because of these dangers and privations that the petition has been drawn, sir," Hernández went on in the same modulated tones. His accent, softening into honey the harsh Castilian sibilants, was beguiling. He was as wary as in a rapier duel, knowing well his opponent, understanding even better than Orellana that his leader's great weakness was a congenital inability to take arbitrary action when the men he led opposed it. He insinuated his soft, lazy syllables into Orellana's mind, knowing that in the end the fire would die from that eye. "We have come far, and suffered much, as comrades. As comrades, united in purpose and sure of our deed, we would go on, even if the way leads, as seems probable, only to death."

He noticed that Orellana's eye blinked. That was a good sign.

"We are united in belief," he rushed on, "in the courage and wisdom of your leadership. We have all marveled at Your Worship's faith that has saved us thus far. That is why we have drawn this petition, knowing that in the greatness of your heart you will hear it, and consider it."

He was tactful in the extreme, he thought, using the verb "to hear" rather than the verb "to read." Had he asked Orellana, who could not read, to scan a petition with his own eye, the cause might have been lost.

Hearing no protest from Orellana, Father Carvajal stepped forward quickly from behind Maldonado, taking the petition as he did so. He held up the document as though to read, but Orellana stopped him.

"This is no time for petitions," he said, but his voice lacked mettle. "Am I to understand, Father Carvajal," he asked, "that the men refuse to follow me farther?"

"No, Excellency," said the priest. "They wish merely to be consulted upon the next move, since it involves such terrible hardships for us all."

"Our hardship," Orellana replied, "is nothing compared to that of Don Gonzalo and the seven score men with him who are starving and will die unless we return."

Father Carvajal bowed his head. "We are not heedless of the plight of our commander, Your Excellency," he said, "merely mindful of our own weakness. The flesh has only the strength of the spirit, and our spirit has been too sorely tried."

Orellana stared studiously at the deck and scraped with his rotten boot a little pitch that had oozed up from the seams. He looked out over the expanse of turbulent water that gushed steadily downstream under a five-knot drive, laden with perilous tree trunks, any one of which might shatter the little brigantine. He scanned the rainy sky. Long and speculatively he gazed up the bank of the Napo, where the forest encroached upon the river with so incredibly dense a mat of undergrowth that an oily muck, alive with insects and venomous snakes, covered the ground to a thickness of three feet. To return by water was improbable; to return by land, impossible.

"Very well," he said sadly, "I will hear you. Speak out."

"It is all in the petition," Carvajal said.

"Then read it, if you insist."

Hesitantly Father Carvajal held up the paper so neatly drawn by Isasaga, coughed nervously, and then read as rapidly as he would chant the Mass during a rain storm. He skipped a bit here and there, raising his voice to emphasize only the most important phrases. At this type of recitation he was a master. He knew exactly what to mumble, what to articulate. And from long practice he knew, too, how to gauge the patience of his listener. Orellana, he observed, would stand no long speeches.

After a flamboyant opening that described the journey thus far, Carvajal read more carefully.

"We have come to know from experience and seen with our own eyes, mumble, mumble. We have felt the fear of all losing our lives, mumble, mumble. How much more danger of death there would be for us if we were to go with Your Worship back up the river! Therefore we beseech Your Worship, mumble, not to take us with him back up the river, mumble, mumble. And let not Your Worship take the position of ordering us to do so, for that will be furnishing an occasion for disobeying Your Worship." He paused significantly. "We hereby exonerate ourselves from the charge of being traitors, mumble, mumble; and we are ready to follow Your Worship by any other route by which we may save our lives."

He looked up. Orellana now was staring at him again.

"How many signed?"

"All of us, sir. We are one voice and one request," he emphasized, quoting a portion of the petition that he had mumbled earlier. "Even Fuenterrabia found strength to sign."

"Mother of God!" Orellana said. "Fuenterrabia, too? Well—let me ponder on it."

"Yes, Excellency," Carvajal replied, and quickly framed a gesture that scattered the men to their work like culprits fleeing the cudgel.

17

WHEN the camp awoke at dawn the next day, the companions saw that their leader, Francisco Orellana, had not slept during the night. He stood on a beachhead below the camp, looking off over the jungle-steaming horizon toward a faint pink streak that came toward him, scattering rain clouds before it. If he was wrestling with the problem of the petition, this was not evident to the sleep-drugged men. All they saw was a one-eyed man slapping mosquitoes and scratching fleas.

Even so acute a problem as salvation must give way in the jungle before the onslaught of insects. They are everywhere. They attack with the fury and tenacity of the Saracen, the sting of sharp arrows, the torment of the pox itself. There is no defense against them. A body in full armor is no protection; indeed, it is worse than nakedness, for the primeval man at least may scratch, and there is no scratching through an eighth-inch of iron. They creep between the knitted webbing of the finest velvet, the coarsest cotton, and up the seams of leather to a weakness in the stitching. They insinuate themselves between the sole and the vamp of the boot, suck moisture from the anus, burrow into the roots of the hair, clot the corners of the eyes, and house in the antra of the nose. No part of the body is privy from them. And he who escapes by diving into the water emerges awash with bloodsuckers and water vermin as obnoxious as those on land. The names of the jungle insects are as legion as their numbers, but by far the most tormenting, most insidious and most dangerous of them is the chigger. This morning, to anguish the turmoil of his spirit, Francisco Orellana was frantic from chiggers.

He had felt them shortly after dark. The soles of his feet burned. From long experience he knew that the insidious isangue were nesting in his pores. Because of them he could not bring his mind to concentrate long on his danger. The challenge of the company's petition to his leadership was great, and to relieve the fiery itching and allow himself to think, Orellana walked. Up and down the beach he strode, constantly checking the outposts, scrutinizing the safety of the camp, encouraging the guards, all the while hearing again and again in his mind one sentence, and one only, in Father Carvajal's ringing words: "And let not Your Worship take the position of ordering us to do so, for that would be furnishing an occasion for disobeying."

Mutiny. Flat, unequivocal mutiny. And mutiny was the Castilian's inherent right, if the majority so willed. Castilians may be led, but never coerced.

The most vivid memory of his youth, the memory which had made him hate Dominicans, washed back into his consciousness. The Marquis of Priego had sent criers through the province, summoning the able-bodied from their goats and vineyards on the bleak plains and hills of Estremadura, once more to fight a holy war against the Moslems, this time a foreign war in Africa. The men of Truxillo, and more particularly the men of La Zarza, the little suburb four miles from Truxillo that had spawned the Marquis Pizarro and his brothers, did not want to go. The hogs were about to farrow, and swine were the principal livelihood of La Zarza. From experience the men knew that their droves would be gone on their return. What the women did not neglect, the bandits would steal, taking along the women, too.

Orellana, then eight years old, had watched the men gather before the door of the parish church to hear the notice of conscription signed by His Majesty, Ferdinand. Attesting the holiness of the enterprise, the priest also had read a parish letter signed by Cardinal Xímenes himself, primate of Spain, Archbishop of Seville, and leader of the Spanish Inquisition. The Cardinal, so exhorted the parish priest, was financing this war against the Moslems from his own purse. Sacred, as well as temporal duty, demanded that the men enroll.

The men of La Zarza, however, did not want to go. Even when they were told that the Cardinal personally would lead the expedition, that the Great Captain, Gonsalvo de Córdoba, would emerge from retirement to command the van and the equally great engineer, Count Pedro Navarro, would lead the sappers, the men of La Zarza held back. The veterans of Italy likewise protested, and the levy against Truxillo could not be filled.

The priest urged, the king threatened, but Truxillo held fast. The city's charter expressly provided the independence of its people forever, as a reward for having in the Tenth Century dedicated the city as a Christian outpost against the infidel. In this crisis, which the city fathers saw most clearly as a challenge by the church and crown to their ancient liberties, the men of Truxillo and La Zarza were as fanatic as the Cardinal, the original purpose of their reluctance lost in the greater jeopardy of their city privileges. The aging king, goaded by Xímenes, exerted unusual pressures. Crown officers appeared to scrutinize the taxes of honest men, and the white-robed Dominican preceptors of the Holy Office, with their deathly black hoods, descended like wasps upon the town to examine men's hearts. Some who had hesitated to risk war disappeared into jail, others were swept away into the even more fatal dungeons of the Inquisition. Francisco Orellana's father had been one of the latter. And Francisco, at the age of eight, lighted a beacon of hatred against the Dominican Order and the Inquisition that still burned, thirty years after.

The town held firm. The men of La Zarza did not go to the holy war. They remained on the barren hills with their droves and herds until the siren of riches lured them to a new continent. Orellana had learned, in his father's death and his city's fight against Cardinal and King, that even a swineherd has rights that neither man nor church may contravene.

All his life Orellana had been cursed by the vividness of this lesson. At the founding of his city of Guayaquil, he had listened when his men argued for establishment of the city on the low bank of the Guayas, rather than on a hillside a few leagues upstream. His own judgment had been better, as events had proved, and he knew that Guayaquil would never become the city fate intended until it moved to higher ground. En route to join Pizarro he had listened when the weary men sank exhausted that first night in the jungle, only to be ambushed at dawn. In camp he had listened to Carranza, and had not killed the detestable campmaster, Ribera, and for it he might yet pay with his reputation and his life.

Now sound judgment urged him back upstream, to the rescue of his commander. Again his judgment was challenged by men of Castile. If he refused to concede the petition, he was no better than Ferdinand and Xímenes, seeking to impose his will upon the majority. He would be in the position of defeating the cause for which his own father had died. This he could not bring himself to do. He cursed his weakness, and admitted it.

Yet if he yielded, he must resign his command. His duty was to his general, Don Gonzalo Pizarro. He could not fail in this duty, and continue in leadership. Of course there was a way out—there was always a way out so long as there was a scrivener, a lawyer, and a precedent. There was precedent: Cortez in Mexico, Benalcázar in Popayán, Quesada in Colombia. Orellana, however, would not be classed with rebels such as these. To escape their stigma, he must not resign, for he knew that the moment he relinquished his lieutenancy, he would be elected captain of the hungry band of men who now at once defied and followed him.

The problem was almost enough to drive away even the burning itch of chiggers. There was a further complication that now appeared insignificant but might in time assume dangerous status. Once more Maldonado plagued him. Orellana needed no two eyes to see Maldonado's motive in creating this petition. Maldonado was the henchman of Ribera. Nothing would please Ribera more than a mutiny of the company so strong that in it Orellana died. And Maldonado, who was insidious but not very cogent, had taken advantage of a situation to plant a rebellion his own eloquence could not have aroused, ignoring in true Castilian fashion the fatal risk attending his own life. Maldonado, the favorite of Pizarro, who had taken his place in the lead canoe at the general's public insistence, was a powerful force among exhausted men.

"Is he not," they would argue in their extremity, "as much our leader as Orellana himself?" Particularly they would reason in this vein to assuage their consciences against revolt. And if, by some miracle, the company made later contact with Pizarro, Maldonado as father of the petition would be the savior, Orellana the villain.

Therefore, if for no other reason than Maldonado's future influence upon the company, Orellana could not resign his command.

What to do? Orellana walked the sand, while the smell of food drifted across his nostrils from the camp fire that now had roused the last man from sleep. If there had been support for his task among his leaders, he might yet carry out his mission, but there was none. If Father Carvajal had been with him, he might yet succeed. But the friar was against him. Even Robles, Carranza, and Hernández, whom he would have sworn would be as faithful to him as nuns to their cloister, had signed the petition.

The bitterest canker, that now most troubled Orellana and upset his decisiveness, was the vision of soft-tongued Antonio Hernández, the Portuguese, driving the first wedge. Orellana had befriended Hernández when the Portuguese had neither job nor friend. He liked the crude, homespun fellow who had about him none of the arrogant prejudices of the Spaniard, none of the traditional hatreds, cruelties and superstitions, except an understandable hatred of Spain itself. He remembered how the silent strength of the Portuguese had bolstered him all down the river, reinforcing his own faith. Now Hernández had taken advantage of him, had stood before the crowd, secure in friendship, to present the petition and give Carvajal the opening that the priest would never have taken by himself. Orellana was discouraged as well as perplexed. He had been betrayed by a friend.

As though his thoughts summoned his betrayer, Hernández now approached, a stew pot in his hand, Carranza by his side. They walked hesitantly, as though they had discussed between them the wisdom of coming at all. Orellana watched them, welcoming any diversion from the problem that he could not solve. The terror on their faces even amused him. He wanted to be angry, and to appear angry, but he could not. They were too close to his heart.

"So!" he cried out, and they knew he was jesting, "the company of distinguished Castilians sends a Portuguese and a Jew to take my answer."

Hernández handed him the broth in silence, but Carranza was equal to the occasion.

"I guess we are safe," he said to Hernández. "A barking dog never bites."

The smell of the warm food, in which Orellana discerned the unmistakable odors of palm cabbage, cayenne pepper, and rancid capinuri shoots, reacted genially on him. He held out his hand for the broth, but immediately stiffened as he looked into the cup. Floating on the broth were strips of luscious white meat.

"Son of a dog!" he spat at Carranza. "I told you to save the fowl. Name of God, won't even you follow orders?"

"It is not fowl, Captain," Carranza said. "Every fowl, to the last forest chicken, at this moment is being smoked and preserved. Control your anger, Excellency, it is not becoming to you."

"Then what is this stuff?" Orellana picked up a strand of the white delicacy in his fingers.

"Carachupa, sir," said Carranza, "a sort of a turtle, and tasty. A little strong, perhaps, but this broth needs strength to cover some of its stenches. We—we thought you might like something special. Contreros caught it in a sand bank."

There was reproach in his tone. Orellana tasted the turtle daintily, then greedily.

"Very good, Carranza," he said, "and forgive me. The chiggers are driving me frantic. And when there is conspiracy in the camp, one suspects everyone, and one's friends the most—if they be Spaniards."

Carranza bowed. "As Your Excellency has reminded us just now, we are no Spaniards."

Orellana handed the empty bowl to Hernández, but his eyes were still on Carranza. "Then why did you sign the petition? And you," turning suddenly, "friend Hernández?"

The outcasts looked at the sand. Finally Hernández spoke.

"For the love we bear you, Captain," he said quietly. "Your resolution is brave, but impossible. In the petition there is strength, for in it is unity. United men often find a way to do the impossible, but unorganized men never. We signed the petition because your leadership now means more to us than your favor. Do not think, sir, that we did not ponder it first. Outcasts do not act on impulse, if they wish to live."

"And in what way," Orellana went on, finding a stump and stretching his burning feet, "does salvation lie, except upstream?"

The two men knelt, each one wresting a boot from Orellana's feet. The footsoles Carranza inspected with physician's skill, then pulled a long thorn from his pocket for himself, another for Hernández. The two men set to work, picking out painstakingly, one by one, the fiery chiggers. Occasionally Orellana winced, but more often his expression was that of relief.

"Which way does salvation lie?" Hernández asked, repeating the question as he worked. "It lies in the direction of men united in spirit, and what compass point that is means little."

"But our compass is Don Gonzalo," Orellana insisted, "and the direction is north northwest."

"Have you considered," Carranza intervened, "that the longest way round is often the shortest way home?"

"You mean down river to the sea, and back across the mountains? Yes, Carranza, I have considered that. Suppose this river comes out in the Northern Sea. That would be above Cubagua, likely. Then by ship to Guayaquil, and another five weeks over the mountains with help. At least two months. And where will Don Gonzalo be by that time?"

"Alcantara and Miradero, our boatmen, say we would be lucky to get upstream in three months," Carranza replied. "Remember that the water is swift as a mill race and there are several hundred leagues of it."

"You think we should find another way out, then?"

"I do, sir," Carranza said. "Every man would follow you then, with all his strength. We will need all our strength, whichever way we go."

"That is true," Orellana admitted. He felt better, now that the chiggers no longer burned.

"We could not stomach a rebellion against you," the little Portuguese said. "At first nothing was planned except rebellion. Only the most skillful efforts of Señor Robles convinced the men that a petition, in true Castilian fashion, was preferable to murder."

"And had there been murder," Carranza added quietly, helping Orellana don his boots, "at least five men should have died. Perhaps—" the old twinkle was once more in his eyes, "perhaps Señor Robles, Gutiérrez, Hernández, and I are too curious to see the end of all this, to lose our necks awhile."

To see the end to all this. . . . No, Orellana thought, this was not the end. Sixty men had not been led under God's protection to rot in the land of Aparia. There must be more. The faith that, upriver, had moved him to exhort his men again steadied him. And he was surprised. He had never believed in faith until lately. Faith was a blindness that hoodwinked men's best instincts. Faith was for the Father Carvajals of this world, not for him. Yet here, on this turbulent river, faith and four friends were all he had. He was no longer in doubt. God preserved them for some purpose. He wondered, his mind shooting quickly to Ana de Ayala, if this purpose was perhaps concerned with his return again, one day, to this river. Perhaps here might be established the land of which he dreamed. Else why had he been given, at this time, the friendship of a swineherd, a Portuguese, the hidalgo cousin of a lovely woman, and a Jew? There was more here than coincidence and he must see it to the end.

"Summon the men, then," he said, "and call the scrivener to take down what I have to say."

Fondly Orellana watched the men depart. They were good, and they were wise, and they were right: unity was the salvation. To return upstream clearly was impossible. He would lead the men out by another route, provided they agreed to remain here a month or two in the hope that somehow Don Gonzalo might join them. The men must be kept busy, or there would be further insurrections, and trouble with the Indians.

What could he do to prevent idleness and at the same time challenge their resourcefulness, and engender new hope?

Yes, of course. They might build another brigantine.

18

THE EXPEDITION settled down at the camp, which they called Aparia after its chief, to wait for Don Gonzalo. Orellana knew that he would not come. The distance was too great, the flood too strong. He could only hope that, with the passage of time, his men might find courage once more to undertake the up-stream journey.

His first concern was to keep the men busy, but even before he could organize their work he collided head-on with Maldonado. The former equerry had begun to strut as soon as his chief had abandoned the project for a return upstream. He issued orders as though he, rather than Orellana, was the commander, and the men, conscious that his petition had saved them all from destruction and that Orellana had yielded before him, obeyed him without question. Without Orellana's knowledge the brigantine was beached for repairs and the dying men in her hold were moved to the shore, unsheltered from sun and weather.

"By whose order?" Orellana asked. He had been away visiting the village of Chief Aparia.

"By Maldonado's, General," the workmen said.

"It is countermanded," Orellana said curtly. "Put the ship at once in the river and move the sick men to shelter."

Now he summoned Maldonado, careful to have Carranza on hand as a witness to all that might be said.

Maldonado swaggered to the meeting, sure of his ascendancy. Many men were watching, though none dared to come within earshot. To this gallery Maldonado played.

"Do you want me for something, General?" he said easily.

Orellana did not raise his voice or otherwise reveal his anger.

"There seems to be some misunderstanding, sir," he replied calmly. "It is I, not you, who gives orders."

Maldonado smiled.

"But my orders are obeyed, General. Can you say the same? How many men would follow you back up the river?"

"You provoke me," Orellana said. "I should regret having to kill you."

"And I should regret your trying, General. You dare not draw your blade against me. If you kill me, you are finished with Don Gonzalo, and the men will depose you. If I kill you, you are just—finished. In either case, you lose, whereas I have an even chance. At even odds, I can afford the risk."

"You are a scoundrel," Orellana said.

"One must live," Maldonado said serenely, "and in this stinking land one lives as best he can."

"Even to murdering a man with dogs," Orellana said.

"Your pardon, Excellency," Maldonado said imperturbably. "The job was bungled—otherwise it would have caused you no anxiety."

"I appreciate your candor."

"Where no love is lost, candor is sometimes better than deceit. I know you hate me, therefore I have nothing to lose by speaking the truth."

"The words of a true Italian," Carranza intervened. "Are you sure you were not born in Florence, Maldonado?"

"No, Jew," Maldonado said, "Torrejón de Velasco was my home."

"And you are no kin to Macchiavelli?"

"Who might he be?"

Carranza laughed. "Your brother, sir."

"The old world does not concern me," Maldonado said. "I fled Castille, even as many another."

"It is a useful thing to know," Orellana said.

"I am safe in telling you, Excellency," Maldonado answered. "You are not the kind of a man who turns in his enemies to the Holy Office."

"Right you are, Maldonado. I leave such villainy to men like your-self. When I am ready to kill you, I shall give you time to sharpen your blade."

"Thank you, Excellency, but that will not be necessary. I keep my blade sharp at all times."

Orellana realized that nothing was to be gained from prolonging the interview. Maldonado must be humbled before all the men. Until such an occasion arrived, he was powerless to silence the upstart, and he knew it.

"At least we know where we stand," he said. "That will be all."

Smiling broadly, Maldonado bowed and pranced away.

"The dog," Carranza growled. "I shall find a poison in these woods and rid us of him."

"No," Orellana replied. "That is not the way. He must rid us of himself."

An hour later Fuenterrabia, who two days earlier had been given extreme unction, surrendered at last to death. Oddly, on his person was found a small sack of seed pearls that had been brought along by the expedition, along with many other trinkets, to trade for food.

At once Orellana thought of a way to humble Maldonado. For some time he had suspected that some little silver bells which likewise had disappeared, were in the possession of the equerry.

Discovery of the seed pearls made a stir in the camp, for Orellana had been scrupulous, in doling out the precious cargo of trinkets, to see that the valuables actually reached the Indians and did not dis-appear into Castilian pockets. That Fuenterrabia, the entire voyage flat on his back in the brigantine's hold, had found strength enough to pilfer the storage boxes, caused a half-day's talk among the soldiery.

During the noon meal, with Fuenterrabia's perfidy the common talk, a crier arose among the men and read to them a written order, drawn up by Isasaga and signed by Orellana, directing every man to turn in at once all property in his possession that belonged to the ex-pedition. Forty-eight hours only were allowed for such surrender, and the peril of evasion was death by hanging. The order was well received.

With food their only hope of life, looting of the barter goods was the basest possible offense against them all.

Orellana watched Maldonado as the crier spoke, and Maldonado rewarded him with a quick, direct glance when the penalty was proclaimed. Orellana left no doubt, by his contemptuous mien, that the order was directed at Maldonado.

The next day had almost ended, however, before Maldonado surrendered the silver bells. Orellana was careful, after the proclamation, never to be alone for a moment, and mainly kept old Soria near him, for it was necessary to his purpose that witnesses see, and gossip, when Maldonado surrendered his valuables. Maldonado came forward finally, a thin hour before the deadline and, blocking with his body the vision of those who stood with the commander, held out in his helmet the silver bells.

Orellana responded in a loud voice that drew the eyes of everyone. "What have we here, Maldonado? I thought we gave these bells to Chief Aparia in return for his generous gifts of food."

"So it was ordered, General," Maldonado replied, caught before a dozen pairs of eyes, "but I could not resist holding them against some occasion when they might be even more valuable than now."

The men gasped. The bells were of undoubted value, and Chief Aparia the sole source of food.

"Swine!" old Soria spat at Maldonado. "You steal from all of us." The statement appeared to find general favor.

Orellana turned his back. "Put them in the ship's stores, thief," he said over his shoulder. "I am the judge here of what each occasion requires."

By nightfall Orellana knew that Maldonado indeed had lost caste among the men. His treachery to Orellana they could understand, some even encourage; but his treachery to the expedition bit more deeply. Among men, the greatest crime is a violation of *esprit de corps*.

To emphasize the stigma further, Orellana called the crew together after vespers, and emphasized the necessity for obedience— particularly in matters concerning the natives.

"We are at their mercy," he said. "So long as we eat, we live. Once they withdraw food from us, we move or die." He laid down three laws for treatment of the Indians from that day on. First, to take nothing from them. Second, to be sure they were generously rewarded in trinkets for their food offerings. Finally, and equally important, to refrain, under the most severe penalty, from touching the women.

"These women," he said, "know nothing of morality. To them one man is as another. But their men think differently and are jealous, and it is from the men that we receive our food. Let no man of this company lie with a woman, even though she be willing—for these savages may be induced into willingness, since they know no better. Do I make myself plain?"

The crisis passed, he summoned his shipmaster Juan de Alcantara, the helmsman Miradero, the woodcutter Diego Mexía and a few others, and put them to the problem of building a new and larger brigantine. The men at first were overwhelmed, although admitting that on two ships the company might make faster progress in better security than scattered in one boat and ten canoes. But no man was there who knew how to make nails.

Finally Alcantara volunteered, with one Sebastian Rodríguez who knew something of charcoal, to attempt the nails. Immediately the entire company, except those engaged in preparing food and mending gear, was put to work. Some made a bellows out of buskins, others wrought crudely the necessary tools, groups of threes made kilns for charcoal, and the remainder cut and hauled timber from a hardwood grove a half-league away. No digging irons were available, and scooping out the smithy pits by hand was laborious and agonizing, especially since no man knew exactly what should be done, or how a nail was made. The work went forward, however, Orellana in the midst of every operation with extravagant praise.

So high was the morale that Father Carvajal, still keeping his journal, wrote glowingly one day: "A wonderful thing to behold was the brotherly affection and obedience and diligence with which we few men who were together there, dealt with one another and aided one another with a comradeship and love heartfelt and bright; but as the angel said to Esdras, 'However much men may love their neighbors, God loveth them more.'"

Harmony restored, Orellana turned again in leisure to his fellowship with Alonso Robles. The two would sit on the river bank, watching the nail making in progress, on guard against Indian attacks, and speak of many things. For each tale Robles told of Spain, Orellana had one of conquest that was new to the Andalusian.

One day, feeling that Robles now unquestionably was his friend, Orellana asked the lieutenant to keep an eye on Maldonado, for he knew the rogue would seek means to strike again. He told Robles of his encounter with Maldonado that had almost ended in swords.

"I would like to know," Robles said, "why Maldonado fled from Spain. The knowledge might be helpful."

"The surest way to death is to inquire into any man's past," Orellana answered. "Scarcely a man in Peru can return to Spain. For all his gold, there is an old murder, a debt, the Inquisition, or a youthful indiscretion waiting to rise and strike. The less said of such things the better."

Robles, thinking of his own indiscretion that had sent him to the New World, was silent for a moment. Orellana knew that this was the nature of Robles' thoughts. Men always became most silent who, when Spain was mentioned, could not return there. Then Robles said, "Forgive me if the question is impertinent, Don Francisco, but if this is true, how do you propose to woo Ana de Ayala?"

Orellana looked up. "I was not referring to myself," he said quickly. "There is no reason why I may not return to Spain."

"You are sure? No woman, not even Ana, is worth the risk of death."

"From what you say of her, she might be worth any price, but don't worry, friend. You can sponsor me with a clear conscience."

The Andalusian smiled. "I wondered," he said.

"Then wonder no more. If we are going to be friends, and possibly even cousins, you should know about me."

"I have lived with you. That is enough."

"It is not enough for me. Ana should know what I have done. You could tell her."

"That I would be glad to do."

So for the first time in his adult life, Orellana turned over in words the pictures of his past. He spoke proudly, conscious that in contrast to most conquistador histories, his was good.

"I was sixteen," he said, "when I left Spain, a long fourteen years ago. I had two good eyes, then, Alonso, and sometimes girls would smile at me. It is the wars of Peru that have put this age and ugliness on me."

Robles smiled a denial of the deprecatory statement, but he did not interrupt, and Orellana went on to describe how he had reached the western world as a page to his Uncle Sebastian, who had good cause to quit Castile.

Their destination was Panama, where a kinsman, Francisco Pizarro, had amassed fame and gold as a captain to Cortez in the conquest of Mexico. Pizarro had been with Balboa across the snake-bitten isthmus of Panama and with his own eyes had witnessed the discovery of the Southern Ocean. Now he was confidante to a governor, and a mighty man. Uncle Sebastian had intended to enroll under his banner, but in Panama he received the crushing news that Pizarro was not there. To the south along the Southern Ocean, after two years of exploration, Pizarro had discovered a new continent where gold was as cheap as iron, and with proof of this fabulous land in his possession, he had returned to Spain to solicit a governorship and charter from the Emperor Charles. To wait for his return might be to wait many years.

Luckily, Uncle Sebastian had in his possession twelve hundred ducats. How he had obtained them was his own business, but because of them he had left Spain. He and Orellana drifted with the crowd to Guatemala on the false scent of gold, and there enrolled under de Soto in the conquest of Nicaragua.

Uncle Sebastian had not liked the rigors of jungle campaigning, the slaughter of defenseless Indians, the discipline of camp life. He had returned, a year later, to Panama. The little town was only seven years old, a humid, pestilential hole inhabited by sickness and riffraff, but with all that a governor's residence, the crossroads of Spanish America.

There also were women there, and where there are women, Orellana said to Robles, there is a magnet. In Panama City had assembled those dregs of the army of Cortez who had not been sufficiently distinguished to have won lands and favors in Mexico. Gambling at cards and dice was the main occupation of the town. A man's life was only as long as his dagger. But Uncle Sebastian, in the midst of cutthroats, was unabashed. He was a caballero of the old school of chivalry; he had fought for Ferdinand in Italy. He knew a few card tricks himself.

For a month Orellana and his uncle lived by their wits, frugally lest anyone get wind of the twelve hundred ducats. There was tilting of reeds on feast days in the square, and other feats of arms which Orellana learned under the schooling of the old chevalier. There was gaming in every house in town and on the steps of the cathedral then being built. There were reminiscences of the bloodshed in Mexico and Yucatán, enough excitement for a boy of seventeen. But not enough for Uncle Sebastian. Chivalry was not yet dead in him. He undertook to place under the protection of his standard a widow of the town. She was ugly and forty, and greasy-fat, but she was Spanish, and for her sake Uncle Sebastian forswore the ancient soldier's obligation to share his fortune in all things. For his monopoly, Uncle Sebastian paid with his life. A dagger in the dark put an end both to him and the twelve hundred ducats. Some said the widow had a one-third interest in the booty, but this Orellana had no heart to prove. He was alone, and penniless, and in Panama; and the one man who might have aided him, Francisco Pizarro, still dallied in Seville.

"I buried my uncle," Orellana said, while Robles listened intently to the tale, "and went with an old soldier named García Tapia, now a resident of Quito, to Nicaragua, rejoining de Soto."

This Tapia, Orellana went on, had been south with Pizarro, and he was not averse to returning again, sponsored by the young first cousin of the mighty explorer. He clung to Orellana, and the boy to him.

One day to de Soto's camp came news. Pizarro had landed at the Atlantic port of Nombre de Dios with many men and great rolls of parchment authorities from His Majesty. Tapia and Orellana set out for Panama at once, taking with them another old soldier of Pizarro's army, Gonzalo Diez de Pineda, who now Robles knew from Gonzalo's expedition. Arriving in Panama, they went at once to the residence of the Bishop de Luque, Pizarro's business partner.

"I shall never forget," Orellana said, "my feeling as we crossed the threshold of that house. For two years I had waited for this day. Yet I had no idea how Pizarro would receive me, and my knees knocked together as I faced him."

Robles smiled. He had often felt the same way before his uncles.

Pizarro was alone, Orellana related, in a bare council room. He was in light mail, with a black cloak brilliantly decorated with the ensign of Saint Iago, and white shoes, and carried a white hat in his hand. He was tall for a Spaniard, solidly built for his fifty-five years, his body responsive and commanding. Tremendous energy shot from him, and there was no doubt that here was a leader, self-possessed, confident, and bold. If his dark eyes were avaricious and impatient, it was the Spanish character and nothing to worry about. Orellana knew that he had not made a mistake in waiting.

He had gaped, and Pizarro, after greeting the others warmly, turned questioningly to him.

"And the lad?" he had said. His voice was deep, his address deliberate.

"Francisco Orellana, Your Excellency. I—I am your cousin."

"My cousin!" Orellana remembered that the words were not so much an exclamation as a question, and the iron, slow voice had not been raised.

"Yes, Your Excellency. Your father's sister Estefanía was my father's wife."

"Francisco Orellana," Pizarro had said.

"My father's name, and mine, too. I came out with my Uncle Sebastian two years ago to join you, but you were not here. I waited."

"Waited two years for me?"

"Yes, Excellency."

Pizarro had not smiled, as Orellana had hoped he might, or speak of the family, some of whom he must have seen recently in Spain. He had merely stared for a moment in silence, then turned deliberately back to his old companions. Not until the interview had ended, and they were leaving, did Orellana understand that he had been included in Pizarro's invitation to Pineda and Tapia to accompany him in the conquest of Peru.

"The rest, friend Robles, you know," Orellana said. "It has been a long road—but I am determined now that the way shall lead back to Spain, to a red-tiled house on the Avenida Teresa where there is a silver bell at a gate, and inside the gate a girl with hair like pale wine and eyes that melt."

"You will be making no mistake," Robles said simply. "My cousin Ana is worth even as long a hike as from Panama to Spain."

19

THE WORK of making the nails sped forward, but now that the men no longer were fighting for their lives, the sick men on the brigantine began to die.

In six days, five new crosses stood beside the grave of Fuenterrabia. The deaths were no loss to the company, rather a gain, for the men had been ill all the way down river. But death is always depressing, and Orellana sought some means of buoying the spirit of the survivors for the immense task of building a new ship.

He sent Robles downstream, with the mountain man Gutiérrez and the fisherman Contreros, to explore, hoping they might return with morale-raising news. Very little work was done in the lieutenant's absence, as the men anxiously awaited his reappearance.

After three days Robles returned. The junction with another river, sought since departure from Don Gonzalo's camp, lay scarcely sixty miles downstream, he reported, and up this other river scarcely a day's rowing lay abundant Indian domains. The men threw down their tools to cheer, to laugh, to rough each other with the exuberance of soldiers saved from death.

Orellana was extravagant in praise of his lieutenant, and made no effort to hide it. Finally Hernández the Portuguese sought him out and suggested that such open-handed esteem was unwise.

"I may say this," he said, "since I am no Castilian. The surest way to arouse jealousy among Spaniards is to favor one over another. Your comradeship with the young man is causing talk. Some even say there is a woman involved."

Orellana restrained himself with effort. That the name of Ana de Ayala should be thrown about the camp like that of a common wench at once annoyed and shocked him. "Thank you," he said. "You are right. I shall be more careful."

He was so much more careful that Robles was hurt. He had fed on Orellana's praise and feasted upon his patronage. Now Orellana began to address him, in company, by the formal title of Lieutenant, and made little effort to seek him out privately. Robles did not understand. And Orellana did not notice the hurt.

Inspired, however, by the great news that food and hope lay down the river, the men sped back to work. In twenty days the nails were made, and so great was the enthusiasm that not even another death— the seventh—depressed the company. The sick bay was almost empty, for aboard the brigantine remained only one critical patient, a ruffian tough from Seville named Alvar González whose bullying words could not intimidate either the jungle or his slowly rotting guts.

Orellana had just begun to lay out, on the sands, the wooden ways on which to build his new vessel, when a strange event occurred that shattered his hope of awaiting Don Gonzalo longer. A native canoe, like all the others that had faithfully brought food to camp day after day, shot to the shore and a warrior jumped ashore. Not to Carranza, custodian of food supplies and dispenser of trinkets, did he go, or to Orellana, who was known to all the natives as their friend. Rather, he strode silently, wrathfully, to Friar de Vera and, seizing him by the chin, barked angry syllables. The friar was perplexed. He did not understand. He attempted to withdraw, but the Indian shook his head persistently.

Orellana came running, but he was too late. The native picked up de Vera and threw him over his shoulder. The friar lit heavily on the ground, then staggered to his feet bruised and querulous. Again he sailed over the Indian's shoulder, but this time he did not rise. He had had enough. The native spoke to him a moment and retired.

Orellana had paused when he saw the friar thrown. He did not interfere. Only one complaint caused a member of this clan to throw another man. From his conversations with the natives that had encompassed many topics, Orellana knew that if de Vera were thrown

181

twice, the anger of the native would be appeased. De Vera had committed the great sin. He had lain with a native woman.

A few companions ran after the native and seized him. They were about to kill him for desecrating the priest, when Orellana stopped them with a shout.

"Por amor de Dios, caballeros!" he cried out. "Leave off and let him go. Will you never learn the folly of murder?"

He ordered the Indian released, then explained the significance of the Indian's action. The men began to laugh.

"It is no joke, gentlemen," Orellana said, "but a tragedy. Wherever we Spaniards go, the natives receive us with open arms, bring us food and drink, and treat us as their guests. We repay their hospitality by rape and murder. Shame, shame upon you all."

Father Carvajal, who had listened intently, now turned on de Vera.

"Dog in priest's clothing!" he screamed at the friar. "Have I not had enough tribulation from you, that you should shame the Christ, too? I will give you punishment that will cause even you to think."

He imposed the most vicious penance within his power. Until released, de Vera was charged to maintain absolute silence, except such questions in line of duty as he might be forced to ask of General Orellana. But this was only the beginning. Until further notice he was forbidden to say the Mass, although as a priest he was obligated to perform the sacrament once each day.

De Vera crossed himself, and went down on his knees to beg mitigation of the punishment, but Carvajal was firm. The friar then appealed to Orellana, who refused to interfere. "Religious matters are between yourself and the chaplain," he said, and turned away.

A few minutes later Contreros walked dejectedly into the camp, his fishing spear over his shoulder.

"¿Qué va?" he asked indignantly. "Just when I am getting some place with these savages, and they are showing me how to fish this purgatory, they run away. Have I the pox, or something?"

That evening not a canoe brought food, nor all the next day. The supply had dried up.

Orellana knew better than to search for the Indians. On the vast expanse of river, in all the lumbering leagues of forest, there was not a sign of them. The Spaniard had offended and would be helped no more.

Orellana refused to break camp, leaving behind his plan to build a new ship, without making one last attempt to reach Gonzalo Pizarro. Calling the men together, he offered a thousand dollars in Castilian gold to each of six men who would take the brigantine, the two Negro oarsmen, and all the cache of food on hand, and pole back upstream under his own command. The rest of the party, he said, could go overland to the large village discovered by Lieutenant Robles, wait there for the brigantine to return with Don Gonzalo aboard, and build a new ship to pass away the time.

Only three men would volunteer to attempt a trip all knew to be suicidal. Gutiérrez responded first, he who had gone once before through the trackless jungle in search of help. Now he volunteered through loyalty to his leader. In shame that none others responded, a young hidalgo named Cristóbal Enríquez who until recently had been on his back ill, stepped forward, on condition that three crossbowmen and all the arrows and thongs of the party accompany him. Then reluctantly Miradero the helmsman volunteered. "Someone must go," he said, "who can handle the brigantine."

Three crossbowmen could not be found.

"How about you, Maldonado?" Orellana asked. "You should be anxious to take help to your friends."

"I am not anxious to die, Captain," said Maldonado.

Orellana next looked at Soria. Even an old man in his dotage was preferable to none at all.

"And you, Soria—our best crossbowman. Surely you will go."

The hoary old man shook his head sadly. "I am on the downstream of life, Captain," he said. "Upstream work is for younger hearts than mine."

"Friar de Vera—perhaps in penance for your sins—?"

"I do not acquit myself well with the crossbow, sir," the friar answered evenly. Under penance, this was his first word in some days.

Orellana shrugged.

"Very well, then, gentlemen," he said, "we must go on downstream. But God is my witness, that were there six men in this entire company who believed there was any chance to go back, I would take them and go. We shall proceed south rather than north, but let no man feel that our duty to His Excellency is discharged. God willing, we shall rescue him by another route."

They set out next morning, after a special Mass by Father Carvajal to celebrate the feast day of the Purification of Our Lady, or Candlemas, otherwise known to the calendar as February 2, 1542.

But they did not go to the abundant village in the land discovered by Robles. At the junction of the Napo and the Río Curaray, the brigantine and canoes were swept into a current so fast, and teeming with a jam of logs so great, that they were pressed to their utmost exertions to prevent destruction of their vessels in the rapids, the maelstroms and eddies that they encountered. Ashore they saw Indians waving to them, and behind them reverberated the welcome of native drums. They could not stop. A wall of water twenty feet high, sweeping down the Curaray at that moment, picked up the brigantine and the canoes as though they were driftwood, and carried them many miles downstream before they reached a lee bank and pulled ashore, so exhausted not a man could stand.

And as far as the sharpest eye could see there was not so much as a native, or a bird, or even a turtle in evidence. The starvation-ridden jungle was there, the river, and nothing else.

20

Owing from dawn to dark, the men drove onward, swept downstream at the pace of the flood-raging torrent. The river channel was less distinct now, for islands lay like trash heaps upon the broad back of the Curaray, stretching out greedy fingers of sand toward the little brigantine. Orellana skirted these shoals carefully, for as though to vindicate Carranza's superstition, the ship's planks were rotting rapidly. Had there been a village handy to provide food, Orellana would have hauled the brigantine from the water for repair, now that the ill aboard had died; but there was no hint of human life anywhere.

Orellana relied more and more, as the days passed, upon the quartet of his company whose loyalty he now believed to be thoroughly tempered by the heat of privation. These men he put in one canoe: Lieutenant Robles, the swarthy mountain man Gutiérrez, the Portuguese Hernández, and the physician Carranza. They, with crossbowman Soria and arquebusier Pedro de Acaray to bring down any game they might chance upon, and five stout men to ply the oars, were assigned to scout ahead while the brigantine and its escort of nine canoes flung along a half league behind. In further punishment for his crime at Aparia, which had brought on this new fight for life, Friar de Vera was one of the oarsmen in the lead canoe.

The friar did not like the assignment. He was unfortunately seated just in front of the acid Carranza, who was not bent, as were the rest of the company, to overlook de Vera's sin out of respect to the frock he wore. League after league down the treacherous stretch of river, Carranza goaded de Vera with strong words, and by evening of the third day de Vera had had enough.

He could not, however, complain to Father Carvajal, for the chaplain's terrible decree of punishment was still in force, jeopardizing de Vera's immortal soul. So the friar went to Orellana.

"Excellency," he gasped, as beaten by hard words as by hard rowing, "I beg you, by the great heart you have, to relieve either that heretic Carranza from the lead canoe, or me."

Orellana did not reveal that he was amused, but knowing Carranza, his lungs swelled with a suppressed laugh.

"You who have inconvenienced and imperiled us all, Father de Vera, and more than any among us has committed mortal sin to the double shame of yourself and your religious vows, need not come to me for relief. I have none to give."

"But Excellency—"

"Enough," Orellana cut in. "If you were to die damned, I should pray for your soul, but alive no suffering is too great for you. You need a few calluses on your hands to match those in your heart."

"I will gladly row out my penance, Excellency," de Vera pleaded. "My sin is great, and I pray God to hear my repentance. But if you have any mercy, call off Carranza, or I am a madman."

"What has he done?"

"He goads me, Excellency, from morning to night."

"You deserve it, Father."

"Not such as I hear from him. I am truly penitent, yet my prayers are constantly interrupted by his vicious talk. How may I recover my soul when my ears are ceaselessly polluted with blasphemy!"

"Carranza utters blasphemy?"

"Truly, Excellency. He challenges the most sacred precepts of our Holy Faith, mocks my fight for redemption and pardon, parodies my prayers, makes lewd gestures in the shape of the cross—and—and quotes obscenities from pagan Latin writers. If I should drown on this accursed river with my ears full of such talk, my soul might be damned forever. Carranza knows it, and gives me no peace."

"You should have thought of that before you risked the lives of us all by shabby sin, de Vera," Orellana said. "But I will speak to him.

It is to all our interests that you are truly penitent and learn to walk as a priest should."

"Thank you, Excellency," de Vera said and retired, not in the direction of the altar that Father Carvajal was setting up on the river bank for vespers, but toward the isolation and silence that had been imposed on him.

Orellana summoned Carranza, who quickly caught the twinkle in his leader's eye.

"I have done nothing to the dog," the physician answered Orellana's question, "except put a crown of thorns behind his ears. If he is a Christian, then I am proud to be a Jew. At least we are faithful to our obligations, and so I've told him."

"You take unfair advantage of him," Orellana said. "Under his obligation of silence, he cannot refute you."

"Exactly, Excellency. It is not often one finds such an opportunity against a priest. It will not happen again in my lifetime. I make the most of it. Besides—it flatters me. His face reads more easily than a prayer book and I know what he is thinking—so I refute his thoughts, too. Ah, sir—you would have such fun yourself, I know you would."

"Not at a time like this, Carranza, when our lives are a gamble. Unity is the thing for now."

"Yes, sir. The sport is wearing thin, anyway. But to be able to scorch a priest—it is a temptation not lightly overcome."

"You should not hate priests so much, Carranza."

"When has a priest merited other than hatred? Do you love them so much, that you defend them before me?"

Orellana looked steadily at him as he answered, "For fifteen years I carried a hate against them in my heart. Then I discovered that it was not priests I hated at all, but men. Priests are men, and men are human. The measurement of the House of God is not to be found in the servant at the door. No servant ever meets the standards of the master. You must judge the home by the head of it, just as you judge the house itself by the architect, not by the artisan who can only try his best to realize the perfection."

187

"My faith would not tolerate such poor workmanship as this de Vera," Carranza said.

"That is one of the differences between my faith and yours, Carranza," Orellana replied. "We seek by tolerance to discover our weaknesses, and to correct them. You avenge the loss of an eye by blinding the offender, and thus neither of you can see."

"Christians have never been tolerant toward me or mine," Carranza said bitterly.

"You confuse men who profess Christianity with men who are Christian, amigo. There is a difference, as I have had to learn. I have always hated Dominicans, Carranza, and with good cause, but Father Carvajal's example is beginning to teach me that what I was really hating were not Dominicans at all—merely men who professed to be what they were not."

The next day the lead canoe disappeared. It was in the channel one moment, cutting across the lee of an island, and the next moment it was gone.

Orellana was watching it at the time, gauging from its action in the heavy current the channel for the brigantine. He saw it scud close in to a sandbar, then the stern pulled out under a sudden whim of the river, and it was gone. At that distance, Orellana could not tell whether or not it had overturned. Ordering full speed at the oars of his own pirogue, and gluing his eye to the spot where the lead canoe had been, he rushed forward. There was no sign of canoe or men.

Gone, at the blink of an eye, his best men. Gone his lieutenant, his physician, his confidant, his scout, not to mention an arquebus, a crossbow, a fisherman, and the cousin of Ana de Ayala.

Scanning the empty river which wound between three islands, Orellana felt suddenly as alone as though every man of the company had disappeared.

He did not have time at that moment to contemplate the full implications of his loss, for Father Carvajal was screaming from the brigantine.

"Merciful God in Heaven, what have I done?" he roared, sinking to his knees and clasping his crucifix in his upstretched hands. "Merciful Father, forgive me for sending a vicar of God to his death a sinner and unredeemed."

He fell prostrate, full length upon the deck, and remained there in prayer and self-abnegation all during the search that followed. It was a feeble search. And lest the men become obsessed by it, Orellana finally gave the order to move on. At least the exertion of rowing would keep the men occupied with muscular rather than mental anguish.

Two days passed. Anxious eyes constantly scanned the river, and canoes were set to exploring the shore on both hands, but the lost boat was not found.

Father Carvajal meanwhile felt himself unworthy to conduct the morning Mass and each day Orellana dragged him bodily to his altar. The rest of the day he punished himself by the sternest measures, refusing food, remaining continuously upon his knees in the ship's prow, his lips in prayer. A hundred pledges he made in those two days, mortgaging the remainder of his life to the most stringent missionary devotions, if only God spared the life of the wretch who, by Father Carvajal's order, had lost his chance of heaven by being denied the privilege of living up to his holy vows.

At sundown of the second day, while Orellana was debating which of two islands should shelter the company that night, Father Carvajal leaped to his feet with praises to heaven. Cutting out from one of the islands was the unmistakable contour of the lead canoe, with eleven men aboard.

The expedition went no farther that day. The men were too excited, their rejoicing too great, for further work.

Personally Carvajal helped de Vera to the brigantine's deck, raised him when the friar would have knelt, and with tears drowning his beard absolved de Vera of his sins and clapped him in his arms.

Orellana was standing at the rail, welcoming his friends with a warm handclasp. De Vera, released from his penance, turned on Orellana.

"I shall never forget and never forgive you, sir," he said, "for allowing the tortures of silence to be imposed on me, and then goading me with that devil Jew. If I die for it, you will pay."

Orellana ignored him. He was too busy receiving friends to bother with enemies. To Carranza, Gutiérrez, and Hernández he gave his rarest gift—a smile. To Robles he gave thanks, and would have said much more had he not been restrained by the memory of Hernández' advice. To prevent a show of affection for Robles, he put the lieutenant to the task of securing the camp for the night.

From the others he learned what had happened. The canoe, caught in a strong wash, had plunged down a channel on the far side of one of the many islands. Thinking to save time, they had pushed on, expecting to rejoin Orellana in a few minutes. Several other islands appeared, and they had become hopelessly lost. All they could do was to cruise on downstream until they outran the islands and emerged again into the main channel. This they had done, and they had been waiting half a day when finally they had seen the slower moving brigantine.

Vespers that night were attended by everyone, including Carranza, with de Vera once again in his familiar role of acolyte. Afterwards, the friar sought out Carranza and shook his fist under the Jew's nose.

"I have pledged God," the friar said, "as part of my penance, to bring you to burning, you infidel dog, for the heresies you have spoken. Now God has rescued me from death—and I shall keep my word."

Carranza was amused.

"Your threats of inquisition do not frighten me, little friar," he said. "How can a Jew speak heresy? Were I a Christian, and recanted, then my fat might fry as well as that of any Christian. But I have not spoken heresy, for I am a Jew, and you cannot touch me."

"I shall find a way."

"Vengeance is mine, saith the Lord," Carranza mocked him.

Maldonado, who had been standing by, took the friar's arm and led him away. They talked to one another for a long time. Then they stood in silence together, listening grimly, while Orellana paid special favor to three of his friends among the lost. Midway in this conversation Lieutenant Robles appeared, but he was not noticed, and after a moment, he, too, joined Maldonado and the friar. Darkness had descended by this time, and Orellana had not seen Robles. The lieutenant had been standing in the lee of his blind eye.

Scarcely half a day later an appreciable slackening of the current foretold a river junction. Orellana went ahead, mindful of the flood that had swept him a hundred miles down the Curaray from the River Napo.

Cautiously, hugging the lee bank, he poked around a bend in the river, and rose to his feet in amazement.

Ahead of him, the Curaray catapulted its flood burden onto the serene breast of a river so mighty that at first it appeared to be a sea. Only the sluggish vein of clear, moving water at least a mile away indicated that it was, in fact, a river at all, so vast and calm it was.

Up and down the course of the river Orellana gazed, and nowhere could he see the farther shore. The flood waters of the Curaray, until now so formidable, sank almost with a sigh of resignation into the body of this new giant, causing scarcely an undulation in its endless expanse.

"Holy Mother of God!" Orellana exclaimed in awe. "It is a river surely, but such a one as no man has ever seen, and without seeing it could believe possible."

Gutiérrez, at the steering oar, crossed himself.

"It cannot be," he said. "Hunger has gone to our heads. It is a mirage, General, and all of us are about to die. Be reasonable, sir; there could not be a river such as this!"

21

IT WAS indeed a river, however. And as though it was a symbol that God had tried these weary men enough, an Indian village soon appeared along the shore, and the natives, amazed at Orellana's ability to converse with them in a semblance of their own tongue, brought meat and fish and information. The village, together with a generous expanse of populated country downstream, belonged to an overlord named Irimara, of the Omagua nation. Irimara had heard of the white man, and welcomed him.

Joyously the company continued now, passing several fair villages of friendly natives. The fourth day was Sunday, and Providence rewarded the men handsomely, for upriver came a delegation of canoemen to meet the white chief who spoke like an Indian. Even more important than food, they brought an invitation from Irimara to visit him.

So handsome was the reception and so teeming the countryside with provision, that Orellana halted and sent Lieutenant Robles on a scouting expedition to discover whether food supplies were sufficiently abundant that the men might remain there during the forty days of Lent which now were approaching, reorganize their effort, build a new brigantine, and repair the old one which was in perilous disrepair. On such a river as this, another ship was imperative.

Robles' report was thorough and confirmed the native stories. Food, both game and vegetables, was abundant. Calling upon the men to recognize this sign from heaven, Father Carvajal excitedly went ashore and set up on a hillock, in the presence of the entire company, the Cross of Christ. The day was Ash Wednesday, February the twenty-second. Fifty-nine days had passed since the company had left Don Gonzalo Pizarro—two months during which they had navigated the Río Napo and the Río Curaray and now were lost upon an even greater river that flowed eastward rather than toward the north. They were five hundred leagues—eighteen hundred miles—from their starting point. Seven who had set out now were dead, and one was dying. Now, as though miraculously with the arrival of Lent, they had come upon rich country and friendly savages. There was reason, indeed, to be thankful. Every man except Carranza knelt as Father Carvajal set up the Cross, and the savages were impressed.

The chief, who was delighted by Orellana's gift of the silver bells lately recovered from Maldonado, cleared the village of its inhabitants to provide shelter for the white men, and the next day brought twenty-six native overlords to see the Cross and receive presents. Orellana took the occasion of their presence to summon the scrivener and take possession of them and their lands for God, His Holiness the Pope, and the King of Castile. They didn't mind in the least, for they comprehended nothing of what had happened.

Exhaustively Orellana questioned the chiefs for a clue to his whereabouts, and his men, as curious as himself, marveled at his agility with the native tongues. They admitted, as Father Carvajal inscribed in his journal, that without this gift of Orellana's, they would all have perished along the banks of this vast expanse of forbidding river that now confronted them.

Orellana confirmed that the river continued east, and his heart sank. He could only conclude that it emptied, not into the Northern Sea, but into the Ocean Sea, and that each day's journey would take him farther from Peru. All hope of rejoining Gonzalo Pizarro was at an end.

His leadership, then, likewise was ended. He had failed in the task to which, on the figure of the Madonna, he had pledged himself. His investment of forty thousand pesos was gone. For having failed to rescue the Marquis Pizarro's brother, he would be an outcast in Peru. And before him in failure lay a fearful wilderness of savage tribes, one of which, the natives said, was ruled by a woman named Queen Coñorí. These aborigines must be met and conquered. And then?

193

Orellana projected his problem to the mouth of the river. Old Pinzón, navigator to Columbus, had recorded fresh water forty miles offshore and had called it Mar Dulce, Fresh Water Sea. The phenomenon was caused by the flow of water from a river sixty miles wide at its mouth. Surely this must be that river! Surely no other river, in this world or the next, could be so wide and deep!

Assuming this proposition to be correct, Orellana was in deep trouble, for the nearest settlement of white men was fifteen hundred miles from the Mar Dulce, across almost the whole expanse of the Northern Sea, at Cubagua. Granted that the rustic brigantine and its companion about to be built might navigate this stretch of open sea by hugging the shore, they would never get past the dread Gulf of Paria with its dragon mouths which had wrecked every Spanish ship that had ever passed by.

Orellana felt suddenly as he had felt the first day he had put on full armor. The weight crushed in upon him, too heavy a burden for his frame.

He had no stomach for the enterprise before him. He had lost hope. He had no desire to go on. Physical weakness ran through him like the beginnings of fever. He sat down beside a smudge fire and, reining his spirit by the snaffle bit of will power, considered his situation. He was weary, but it was nothing new; he had been fagged for many days. He was ill, but fevers he had come to live with by natural compromise, as with cousins. And he was despondent. The bald fact was that he did not want to return to Spanish country. He had failed, and nothing is worse than a Spanish failure.

For him, reunion with Castilians was more terrifying than the jungle. Facing the accusations of survivors of Don Gonzalo's expedition who would charge him with saving his own life at the expense of the welfare of a hundred men under a great hidalgo, and, more monstrous, the hopelessness of emerging into the bright light of Spanish society a miserable wreck, once again at the mercy of Spanish law, Spanish custom, and Spanish superstition, was too much for him. Rather the honest stench of the jungle than the dishonest reek of civilized culture; rather the simple, honest dignities of these savage chiefs than the complex rottenness of the white man's society. After the jungle, he could not face a world that condoned a de Vera in the garb of a priest, persecuted Carranza because he was a Jew, enslaved a Nogal because he was black, burned a Castilian because to him God was a Spirit rather than a gold idol mounted on a superstitious fundament. Life in such a world was tolerable only if you were rich enough to humble priests, honored enough to ignore convention, and loved by a woman of such delight that merely the thought of her buoyed a man to faith not even a whole vile world could shake.

Ana de Ayala. There was such a woman, and now she would not have him. She was ripening for a conqueror, not for a grotesque, one-eyed failure.

No, better to stay along the river. He had talked to the chiefs often enough to feel real affection for them. They accepted him for qualities of manliness and honesty considered liabilities in the Castilian world. Their jungle, for all its mazes and amazements, was decent. Even the habits of its vipers were predictable, and a smudge drove off its insects. Its natives killed only for food, and a man made of his life what he cared to build with his own hands and his own heart.

Considered thus, the jungle was no longer oppressive. It emerged, in comparison with civilization, as desirable as a hot sun to a man who has lived long underground. The jungle gave to every man and every living thing, from the chigger and adder to the mightiest jacaranda tree, an opportunity to live according to individual strength. The weak fell, yes; but each had his chance.

Orellana became conscious that he was no longer alone, and looked up from the fire. Before him, waiting to be recognized, were Lieutenant Robles, Friar de Vera, Maldonado, and a half dozen others of the company. Behind them, anxiously on the fringe like unsheathed swords alert to trouble, were the mountain man Gutiérrez, the Portuguese Hernández, and Carranza the Jew. Immediately Orellana shook off his despair and stood up.

"Yes, gentlemen?"

"Excellency," de Vera answered, "there is an ugly rumor in the camp that we hope the Captain will disperse."

Orellana could not resist looking at Maldonado, the instigator of all trouble. There was no visible message written on his face that gave Orellana any clue to this strange new union: Robles and de Vera in league with the devil.

"Name the rumor," Orellana said.

The direct challenge was too swift for the friar who, fearing reprisal, passed responsibility for the charge to Robles. Orellana rewarded the friar with an open laugh.

"Well, Lieutenant," he said then, "it appears that the act of courage falls to you. I know you to be a man of courage, so speak up. What is it?"

"It is nothing, really, sir," Robles replied, uneasy and regretting his participation. "Some of the men have noticed your great free-handedness with the trinkets and think they should be consulted before wealth is given these savages."

"You mean the silver bells? Are we back to that again?"

"Yes, Excellency. Maldonado still feels that articles of value should not be given as personal gifts by the commander to the native chiefs."

"God in heaven! Personal gifts indeed! In return for your cheap bells this chief has cleared an entire village for us, that we may have shelter and rest. In return for a few silver shells, bracelets set with gold medallions of Our Savior, and strands of mother-of-pearl, I have learned where we are, where this river flows, and what's ahead of us. Is that a personal gift?"

Robles was abashed. "We do not know," he said, "of what you speak to the chiefs. We do not understand the tongue, and you never tell us. It is natural that the men should resent the disappearance of our treasures—particularly since you are not leading us to any other gold."

Orellana gasped. Robles' tone was edged. No one had so addressed him since the start of the expedition. If he knew why Robles now attacked, he might answer prudently, but he did not know.

He was saved from answer by his friends. With Gutiérrez and Hernández at his back, Carranza stepped forward. The grim commotion likewise had attracted Father Carvajal, who was always everywhere at once, and he came now to join the group, his pointed beard jutting forward and his eyes beady with alertness.

"The question is one of propriety," Carranza said hurriedly, to cover Orellana's hesitation. "Since you ordered the men to turn in all community property some time back, a few of them——" his sardonic gesture included Maldonado and de Vera——"feel that they should be consulted over their disposition."

Orellana relaxed. "So long as I am leader of this expedition, I shall do what I have to do. When I am no longer of use to you, someone else may lead you. That's all."

He turned his back, but the blunt Gutiérrez had to face the issue. "Sir," he said, "that does not dispose of the rumor."

Again Orellana turned. "Of course," he said, "the rumor." His mind was still fogged with his own personal turmoil, and he wanted time to place Robles' allegiance to Maldonado. So his words lacked emphasis. Fortunately the tone was construed only as indifference. Gutiérrez pressed his point.

"The rumor is that while you give away valuable gifts from the common stores—and I wish to emphasize that I do not myself claim any responsibility for the story—you might better bestow personal gifts from the personal treasure that is said to be hidden by you."

Orellana's eye flamed.

"Excuse me, Excellency," Gutiérrez fumbled. "I do not speak very well, and I bungle, but I mean well."

Orellana nodded. "I know you do, friend Gutiérrez. Thank you." And turning directly to Maldonado, "And what may this personal treasure be?"

He could only hope that Maldonado had not found out about the emeralds, which certainly did not belong to the expedition, and which had never left their hiding place under his breastplate.

"A certain gold cup of immense value, Excellency," said Maldonado. "The men feel that if rare gifts are necessary for heathen savages, your treasures should be used, as well as ours."

Orellana laughed aloud.

"I have a cup," he said. "It was part of my share of the Inca Atahualpa's ransom. It is finely wrought, and heavy, and pure gold. But I have only one such cup, and there are twenty-six chiefs. Do you wish me to excite the envy of twenty-five by bestowing such favor on one? . . . As usual, Maldonado, your reasoning is faulty."

"But the cup is yours," Robles insisted. "If all of us are required to put our treasures in a common store, all articles of value should be there."

Orellana turned on his lieutenant. "How long would it stay there?" he challenged. "How long would a gold cup worth twelve thousand pesos remain common property in a company of Spaniards? How many men would die fighting to steal it from each other? How many hatreds would rise among those who knew who had hid the cup? How long would our company maintain any unity with one treasure that could not be broken up?"

He turned toward the brigantine in a fury.

"Even though it is not rightly common property, you shall have the cup," he said. "You shall have it with the envy, the murder, the deceit that go with gold. As for me, I thank God that gold is no longer precious to me. What can you buy for twelve thousand pesos? Your freedom from the selva, perhaps?"

He went to the hold, now vacant of its dying except for one man, and from the bag of his personal effects drew forth the great gold cup of Atahualpa. He returned to the deck, where the splendid workmanship and glittering brightness of the cup gleamed out in the dullness of the jungle with luster that brought avarice to every eye.

"I give you the cup," Orellana said again, holding it high for all to see, "and with it a curse on every man who touches it. May you die in agony and rot in hell, all men who covet this gold above their own souls."

The cup slipped from his hand and fell to the hold, where dying Alvar González rolled his weak body over on top of it.

"Thank you, Excellency, thank you," he croaked. "I accept the gift—and the curse with it. Indeed, with such a cup for physician, I shall outlive you all." He laughed long.

Orellana stepped off the brigantine and walked away, Father Carvajal trotting after him. But the rest of the men stood on the deck of the brigantine, looking down into the hold, where Alvar González continued to laugh as he cradled the great cup in his emaciated arms.

Orellana stomped to the fire, and was about to sit down when Father Carvajal spoke.

"You are a greater man than I thought, my son," he said.

"Because gold no longer interests me?" Orellana invited the priest to sit on the only seat free of biting insects, a large boulder.

"Partly. And partly the maturity of mind that has led you to such a—shall we say—uncivilized point of view. You know the saying, 'The Spaniard who loves not money is like a woman who scorns her own child.' Freedom from covetousness is not often found outside the clergy."

"It is not often encountered among the clergy," Orellana replied.

"Not often enough, I admit. When the natural son of a Pope can himself become Pope by claiming descent from Saint Peter, we have fallen on evil times within the Church. Evil is evil, no matter where it is encountered. But, as with the present extremity of our little expedition, so with our Church—things cannot get worse, therefore they must get better. The standard is what the Church stands for, not what men make it."

Orellana grunted, but said nothing. Carvajal did not know, of course, that Orellana had used the same argument upon Carranza.

"And—" Carvajal went on with a slightly querulous overtone, "with such leadership as you have just displayed, so free from avarice, I would say that we are, by God's will, in good hands. Tell me, son, what has brought you to this remarkable display we have just witnessed?"

"Men," said Orellana.

"Men?"

"Yes, men. When I compare men, and the way men live, with the naturally upright savages, I cannot help but prefer the savages."

"Suffer the little children to come unto me," Carvajal said in Latin, "for of such is the Kingdom of Heaven."

"Which makes me doubt that any adult man has a sow's chance of paradise."

"Something is on your mind, son. Confess to me. I am, after all, your vicar and chaplain. Unburden your soul. It may help you."

"I do not unburden my soul to priests," Orellana said. "God may pardon my sins, but you cannot."

"You have been listening too much to your friend Robles."

"No, Padre," Orellana contradicted him. "I have seen too much of Brother de Vera, and Maldonado, and civilized men generally."

"They have disillusioned you? The men of Galilee crucified their own Savior, but He was not disillusioned."

"He would be now, were He to return to earth and see what use men make of His teaching. . . . No, Father, leave me alone. My torment is of the intellect, not of the soul. You cannot help me."

"You do not want help, then, son?"

"No, I don't want help. This I must fight out myself."

"And meanwhile?"

Orellana smiled. He did not realize that it was his second smile that day.

"You need not worry for your own safety, Father. Someone else will lead you. I know where you are going, now. It is a thousand leagues, more or less, to the Ocean Sea, then four hundred leagues to Cubagua."

Father Carvajal was not impressed.

"I am not interested in where we are going, only in where you are going."

"I don't know."

"I wish I might help you find your way. Mine is a feeble lamp, but there might be a little light in it."

"Thank you, Father. I shall not need it. Only the civilized man walks in darkness. The savage knows how to use God's sunlight."

Father Carvajal sighed. "What are you going to do?" he asked, hoping that a call to action might release Orellana from his depression.

"I am resigning my command."

"Son, son! You are ill."

"No longer, Father. I've had enough of leading men—and to what? To all the things I despise, away from all things that are good. I am not going back. I am going to stay here on the river, which is as near, I guess, as I will ever get to the New World I have dreamed of. . . . Call the men, if you please, Father. I am going to resign."

"But son—"

"For the love of God, call the men."

Father Carvajal bowed.

"Very good, Excellency."

22

ORELLANA sat in the bow of the brigantine, watching the men ashore. When everyone else was busy, he always guarded the ship, for in case of sudden attack, the ship was the one asset of the company that must not be lost.

The men were indeed busy. In clumps of twos, threes, and fours they discussed Orellana's resignation, with much running back and forth, converging and reforming into new groups, all to the accompaniment of explosive epithets in the virile Castilian tongue.

Detached from the excitement, Orellana was able to watch impersonally. Oddly enough, although he knew that he was perhaps the sole person under discussion, he was not concerned in it or by it. He could sit aboard the brigantine, guard the water lane against attack, and leave the men to the perplexities of their problem.

He had made quite clear why he was resigning. At least the motive he had given them was logical, for they would not have understood his real feelings. Inasmuch as they had refused to follow him back up the river, he had said, his commission from Don Gonzalo had expired, and therefore the lieutenancy was thrown back upon the entire expedition, which must select such a leader as it chose, in the name of the King. He had added that he chose this moment for his action because until that day's talk with the chiefs he had not understood clearly that they were on a river called by navigators the Marañón, which emptied into the Ocean Sea. He had hoped this long time to come out in the Northern Sea and to be able to succor Don Gonzalo. Now such a course was impossible. He could not, he had pointed out, delay his resignation, inasmuch as his leadership had that day been challenged, and military leadership that was obstructed was futile. They must therefore elect as their captain a man in whom all had confidence, and he himself was not a candidate.

The result, he noticed from his vantage point aboard the brigantine looking down upon the shore, was unquestionably sympathetic to him. First, Father Carvajal had talked for a long time to Friar de Vera, and in his gestures and the sunset redness of his face, the chaplain revealed his anger. Second, Maldonado was not a part of any of the little discussions that now went on with much fever. Maldonado and de Vera stood aside, uncomfortable in isolation, awaiting the outcome. This time they had to deal with the men themselves, and the experience was not to their liking.

Orellana observed also that Lieutenant Robles was active. Far from shut out, he appeared to be drawing up some sort of a document, for the scrivener was at his elbow, and Robles was dictating, halting now and then to consult one or another of the many groups. He appeared to be aided by Orellana's triumvirate of friends, Carranza, Gutiérrez, and Hernández. Occasionally one or the other would look toward the brigantine, as though they wished to consult with Orellana, but Orellana gave them no encouragement. Rather, he pointedly looked away.

Every man of the company was on the beach, save the two Negro slaves and Alvar González, who, despite the tonic of a twelve-thousand peso gold cup, still lay in the hold. The slaves, of course, had no part in any election concerning Castilians. They were aft on the brigantine, fishing from the stern.

Orellana caught the eye of the slave called Nogal, and beckoned to him. The brawny black jumped lightly afoot and came forward. He was a big man of no particular accents—just big all over, well suited to the task he had performed so faithfully of stroking the stern pole of the brigantine during the entire voyage.

"Tell me, Nogal," Orellana said, inviting him to sit on the deck, "what you think of all this?" He swept his hand toward the turbulent beach. "If you had the chance, would you not rather stay here than to return to civilization a slave?"

"No, master, by your leave," Nogal said, squatting Indian fashion on the deck, "I have not rowed these groaning leagues to die in the wilds."

"But you came from the selva! I should think you would feel at home here."

"The selva I came from, master, was not like this. It was a good little river, and the fields beyond were small and fertile. My people are there, master, not here."

Orellana pointed beyond the sand beach to the native village.

"Out there," he said, "you would be free. Here you are a slave. I should think you would want to be free."

"I do," Nogal said. "Freedom is very precious to me, since I do not possess it. But I should not be free long among people who do not know me. At least here I am alive, not in a stew pot; and with you, master, I feel free."

"You—feel free?"

"Yes, master. When I belonged to Don Gonzalo, I was a slave. I was beaten, clubbed, the dogs were turned on me. Then I should have paid any price for freedom, even death. You are different. I have not felt a lash from you, or a cruel word. I have felt that you are working toward something, and that what is good in it, I shall share."

"What do you think I am working toward?"

Nogal thought a moment.

"I do not know, master. Whatever it is, it will be good, because you are good. I do not think there will be any slaves there."

"You delude yourself, Nogal," Orellana said. "Our way can lead to only one of two places, back to Spanish country, or to death."

"I do not fear death, master."

"But Spanish country—that is something else?"

"I should not even fear that, with you."

"If we return, I should be obligated to return you to Don Gonzalo."

"No." Nogal was emphatic. "You would not do that."

Orellana smiled, and this time was conscious of it, and liked it.

"No, I wouldn't do that," he admitted. "You are as much a companion of this company as any man here, Nogal."

"Thank you, master."

Orellana scanned the water for possible enemies, then turned genially to the slave.

"Tell me, Nogal. Suppose I stay here. Would you wish to stay?"

"You alone, master?"

"Yes. Suppose the rest go on down the river, and I stay here. Would you stay with me?"

Nogal drew up his creaseless forehead until the skin across his cranium was tight and pale.

"I do not understand, master," he said. "You would not stay here."

"Why not?"

"For the same reason that I would not. As long as men are slaves, I must be with them. And you, too."

"But I am not a slave."

"As much a slave as I, master," Nogal said, rising at the approach of Lieutenant Robles. "Is it not so?"

He retired to the stern. Robles waited to be recognized.

"Come aboard, Lieutenant," Orellana said. "You have as much authority here as I."

Robles came forward. "Excuse me," he said. "I wish to speak to González."

"He won't give up the cup, Señor Robles," Orellana said. "Not so long as there is a breath in him."

Robles winced. "I wish to see him on another matter," he said tensely, and went below. He returned a moment later, in his hands the paper that he had been dictating to scrivener Isasaga. "You might like to see this," he said.

Orellana did not take it. Even to Robles, who knew it, he could not confess that he could not read.

"Does it concern me?"

"It does, sir. It is a petition, signed by all of us, begging you to be our captain, in the King's name."

"It is a gracious compliment."

"It is not meant to be a compliment. It is a summons which we will submit to you shortly."

"You are wasting good ink," Orellana said. But he was not so sure. After Robles had departed, he warmed to the possibility. Nogal was right. Man, like the ostrich, gained nothing from hiding his head in the sand. Out in the world where men were slaves, there was work to be done, not in the jungle where men already were free.

Unless— He leaped to seize a hope. Unless enslaved men came to the jungle and there founded a free land, where generations now and after might meet and speak and act as freely as now Nogal, Carranza, Hernández, and he himself could speak and act, where Carranza's children, and Nogal's children, and Hernández' children, absorbing the simple dignity of the jungle savage, might grow up free of the superstitions, hatreds, jealousies, and prejudices of the old world. Where there would be no Friar de Veras. It was a fantastic dream, but no more fantastic than the actuality of the present, the bitter miles that lay behind them, the perilous miles ahead. God must, indeed, be preserving this company for some useful purpose known only to Him. Was this the purpose? To see this jungle, to course the full length of it eye to eye, to select upon it the site for a new world in which there were only free men?

He put his hand before his eye. He must be feverish, he thought.

When he looked up, four familiar figures stood before him. On the beach everyone was looking his way. He shook himself.

"Yes, gentlemen?"

Robles stepped forward.

"Sir," he said, "for my part in this morning's challenge to your authority I apologize. I was led astray by a very bad ear."

Orellana nodded. "Forget it, Alonso," he said. "I should be the last man to condemn another for accepting bad advice, since I am so guilty of the same weakness."

"But I should like to explain," Robles said. "When we left Don Gonzalo I felt closer to you than anyone else. The feeling of being in your confidence is very heart-warming."

"Thank you, amigo."

"Then—when I saw others replacing me as time went on, I was jealous. Particularly when we returned, after the canoe was lost, you had affectionate words for several, but none for me."

"Ah," said Orellana, "but you, my dearest friend, were also my lieutenant. I took you for granted. It was unforgivable of me, but forgive me, anyway."

Robles bowed.

"And now," Orellana said, "what have my four friends to say?"

"We have been sent," Carranza said, "to wait on you."

"Is my affection for you so obvious, then, that of all the company, you four should be sent?"

"I am afraid it is, Excellency," Carranza said. "Or perhaps we four have spoken of your favor so often that now men call upon us to prove it. We are proud of your confidence, sir."

"Thank you."

"And that is why," Gutiérrez rushed in clumsily, always a man to come to the point, "we have been chosen to present you this petition. They—they think maybe we have the best chance to persuade you."

"Who is 'they'?"

"The entire company. The petition is signed by everyone except the scrivener and the two priests, and they are witnesses for all the others."

Orellana glanced across the water to be sure no hostile canoes were in sight.

"What assurance have I," he asked, "that if I accept this petition and become your captain, I shall be obeyed?"

"We shall make our mark on it," Hernández said.

"Maldonado, too?"

Gutiérrez' eyes gleamed. "Maldonado also. From this day on he is my special charge."

"No more than mine," Robles said.

"I would have no man intimidated on my account."

"It is not a matter of intimidation," Robles answered. "He has felt the weight of unanimous opinion against him, and knows that any further conspiracies will be answerable to the entire company. After all—" he smiled—"one man cannot be a conspiracy by himself. Like love, evil requires two persons."

"And Friar de Vera?"

"He has been placed on probation by Father Carvajal," Carranza said, "threatened with excommunication, interdiction, repudiation, ostracism, proscription, and other mercies of his charitable religion. And I have added a threat from my own—circumcision. I think you need worry no more about de Vera."

Again Orellana smiled, and again was conscious of it.

"Doubtless he fears your punishment the most, Carranza," he said. "He has lived with the others too long to fear them." He looked about the group. "You have thought of everything, then?"

"We hope so, sir," Hernández said.

"And what does our chaplain say of all this?"

"It was he who urged it," said Robles. "He believes God has called you and that you will not refuse."

Again that phrase, Orellana thought. The jungle was driving him mad. He must put aside these delusions. And yet, perhaps—

"Why have you chosen me?" he asked. "I do not feel any longer capable of leading you. Someone else, someone who has not been worn down by these responsibilities, might do the job better. You, for example, Robles?"

"I, Excellency?" Robles protested. "It is impossible."

"We have considered everyone," said the untactful Gutiérrez. "There is no one but yourself. Either you lead us, or we die."

"Why so?"

"Excellency," Carranza said, "may I say a word? We know you honestly do not wish this assignment. You would not have resigned, otherwise. But in this crisis you must consider the welfare of fifty men, even at the expense of your own desires. You are the only man among us with experience in leading so large a group. You are the only one who can keep us all together. Time after time we should all have died, but you renewed our hopes and our strength. Your resourcefulness, in

selecting good camp sites, in organizing searches for food, in anticipating perils, in navigating these swollen rivers, in keeping peace among
us, are all of a measure not found in many men, and certainly not in
any of us."

Orellana said nothing.

"I might add," said Robles, "that your charity and understanding,
your feeling for leadership that inspires us to work and to love you, is
as important as anything. None other has that faculty."

"And the way you handle these savages," Gutiérrez said. "That's
the clincher so far as I am concerned. You are the only one who can
talk to these heathen. They'd slaughter us, without you."

Again Orellana looked out across the water. The depression that
had been upon him, that had made the jungle so attractive, was gone.
Now he wanted only to get on, to get out of the wilderness, and then—
to come back again.

"So you see," he heard Carranza saying, "it is impossible to consider
your personal wishes in this matter. All our lives depend on you. You
have no choice but to lead us. Leadership is a gift of the gods, given
in times of crisis. This is a time of destiny, and you are the man."

"You ask much of me," Orellana said, rising. "Now it is time I
asked as much of you."

The four men waited. Orellana put his dream to the test.

"You four," he said. "You know how I feel about you. If I accept
this commission, and if by God's will we reach civilization, will you
four return with me to Spain and help me organize a new expedition
up the river, to colonize this land permanently? I do not ask you to
come back here again with me; that is asking too much. Merely that
you help me in Spain until the new expedition is ready to sail. In details
of organization I have little wit, and need help."

Robles, thinking of his own family's vengeance that he faced if he
returned, nodded assent.

Hernández, wondering to what possible use a Portuguese might
be put in Portuguese-hating Spain, and remembering his own sins in
Estremadura, also nodded.

Gutiérrez, recalling a murder for which he might die, pledged his word.

And Carranza, for whose return the price was undoubtedly death, likewise nodded, though sadly.

"Very well, then," Orellana said. "Let Father Carvajal bring his cross to the deck, and let every man kneel and swear that he will follow me. And I will kneel and swear by the cross to be true to the obligations of my command."

Robles waved his arm, and the men rushed forward, shouting.

23

AKING advantage of the unity born of desperation, Orellana
moved swiftly to solidify his command and repair his equipment. He was as restless now as the river itself to be off
downstream, and he drove the men hard.

They liked being driven, for now there was purpose in their sweat,
and a goal in view. For the first time they knew what they faced, and
where they were going. And their Spanish hearts were cheered by the
possibility that they might encounter diversion in the realm of Queen
Coñorí, which reportedly was populous with exotic women. Brightness returned at once to every eye.

After the ceremony of assuming command as captain of the expedition in the king's name, and free of allegiance to Don Gonzalo Pizarro, Orellana ordered Diego Mexía, the woodcutter, to build a new
brigantine half again larger than the *San Pedro*, and to haul out and
repair the rotten planks of the existing vessel. Now that they were on
the large river, the sail and oars could be used, at last. Fortunately the
moon was in the proper quarter this time for cutting trees. Heeding the
warning of Carranza, Orellana took no chance with superstition. To
sail four hundred leagues of open sea, stout boats would be required.

Duties were assigned to everyone. The nails, already made, were
brought out. The men were organized into teams, each with a particular duty. One group made the frames and futtocks, another the
keep, another the stem pieces, another sawed the planks. Since good
wood was two miles from the beach, a party under Gutiérrez was organized to guard all the woodcraftsmen, lest they be ambushed by
hostile Indians.

As the work progressed another duty became imperative. So bad
were the mosquitoes that Orellana broke the carpenters into groups

of two, and over each pair set a man with a fan made of toucan feathers to ward away the insects.

In thirty-five days, at the beginning of Holy Week, the brigantine was launched, caulked with cotton and tarred with pitch, and christened by Father Carvajal with a name unanimously agreed upon: *Victoria*.

The *Victoria* was a trim ship of nineteen joas, or ribs, about twenty cubits in length overall, equipped with a stout centerboard forward that could be raised in shallow water or for beaching, but lowered to provide sufficient lateral resistance for windward work upon an open sea. At shipmaster Alcantara's insistence, she was gaff-rigged, correcting a weakness of the square-rigged *San Pedro*, which maneuvered heavily in river current. The new ship also had four oars, rather than two. Since Orellana expected trouble from warlike Indians downstream, he was grateful for Alcantara's design which was to save the lives of all of them on two occasions later on.

All during the work, the Indians remained friendly, bringing food each day. Orellana personally dealt with them, asking endless questions about the river, and by the time of launching, he had made a rough chart of the river downstream as far as the domain of Queen Coñorí, a fierce people none of the chiefs ever had visited, nor their fathers before them.

During the first two days of Holy Week, the *San Pedro* was repaired and fitted with new sails and ivy rigging. The two brigantines floated easily offshore, and every man of the company looked forward to the prospect of the five-day climacteric of Lent, during which they would labor only with the purification of their souls.

In all the days of boatmaking, only one incident dampened the boisterous spirits of the company. Alvar González, who had been moved ashore when the *San Pedro* was beached for repairs, lay in the shade on a knoll overlooking the river, the gold cup of Atahualpa clutched tightly to his body. Carranza took food to him three times a day and Father Carvajal visited him each morning after Mass; but otherwise he was ignored in the bustle of heavy labor.

He appeared to be improving in health. At least Carranza thought that González might, had he the will for it, assist the company by waving a mosquito fan a few hours a day. Father Carvajal was convinced that González had gained sufficient strength to rise in the morning and attend the Mass, and demanded that he do so, at the risk of his soul. González, however, refused to move. Life was easy so long as he was ill, and he was better able to guard his cup in idleness than at work. So he lay upon the knoll in the shade. Orellana said nothing; he was too busy to deal in trifles.

One morning, when every man except the beach guard was away cutting wood, and Orellana was in the village showing the natives how to twine vines for rigging, a fierce scream lifted from the beach and reverberated across the water.

Juan de Alcantara, who as ship's master was aboard the *Victoria*, rushed to the knoll. There was no evidence of Alvar González. He was gone. Lying on the reed mat was the blazing cup of Atahualpa, its condor-head handles caught by a ray of sunlight.

Alcantara picked up the cup and smiled. Stealthily he went to the beached *San Pedro*, tucked the cup under a breastplate and covered it with a pair of breeches. Then he gave the alarm.

González' body was found twenty yards away, under a shelf in the river. He was dead. Obviously he was the victim of a crocodile. Father Carvajal was summoned, but he was too late. And he could not, in his own conscience, administer absolution to the bloody corpse. He remembered that González could have attended the Mass, but did not. Grimly he turned from the body and left it to be buried without church offices. Orellana's curse had been fulfilled.

No one knew what had become of the golden cup. Alcantara was suspected, but because his work kept him constantly in sight of his ships, none of the company was able to search his luggage on the sly.

During the boat-making, there had also been one moment of uneasiness. Contreros, visiting among the Indians and trading with them his knowledge of fishing for theirs, had brought into camp an Indian taller by a span than the tallest Christian, and as white, with long black hair that reached to his waist. The Spaniards noticed immediately the golden bracelets on his wrists, the anklets of gold faced with toucan feathers. But Contreros called their attention, not to the gold, but to the weapon the strange warrior carried.

It was a blowgun of pukuna caspi wood, eight feet in length, with a quinilla wood mouthpiece attached at the thick end of the barrel. Even woodcraftsman Diego Mexía marveled at the precise workmanship, particularly the glass-smooth round bore in the center of the shaft.

Contreros made known to his companions that he had not brought the savage to display woodcraft. By signs he coaxed the Indian to exercise his gun. The Indian nodded, took from his headdress one of a dozen fine darts, moistened the cotton shaft wrapper with saliva, and placed the dart into the mouthpiece of the gun. He waited a moment until he saw a parrot high in a tree and then with lightning speed raised the blowgun to his lips, drew a deep breath, swelled out his cheeks under enormous pressure, and expelled the compressed air into the gun. The dart shot true, a good twenty-five yards, and the parrot fell.

The Spaniards, who could appreciate marksmanship in any weapon, applauded and asked for another demonstration. Asking Carranza to release a wild turkey from one of the food pens, the Indian waited until the turkey had run twenty meters or more into the brush. Again he went into action. Not one, but three shots spat from his gun in such rapid succession that the Spaniards did not see him reach into his headdress for the darts, or moisten the cotton. But he had done so. The turkey fell to the third dart. The men ran to it. It was alive, but paralyzed. They kicked it, and it merely blinked its eyes. In a few minutes it was dead.

Like a good exhibitor saving his thrill for the finale, Contreros called attention to one of the darts as he took it from the dead turkey. The dart was tipped in poison.

Orellana, who until then had watched from the sidelines, now came forward swiftly.

"Where are you from?" he asked the Indian.

"Far down," the Indian replied in a reasonable likeness of the

Aparian tongue. "Far away. Came to invite white chief to visit my country."

Orellana examined the dart. It was poisoned, of that there was no doubt. The Indian said the poison was prepared from cooking down to syrup the bark, fruit, and young shoots of a certain tree.

"Do your people shoot their enemies with this dart, or only game?"

The Indian nodded.

"Just game?"

The Indian assented.

Orellana and Robles exchanged troubled glances. They had feared poisoned arrows all the way down the river and now, with fourteen hundred miles to go, their fears were crystallized.

The visit from the Indian was not without its agreeable side. Contreros, in exchange for a mother-of-pearl necklace from the common stores, learned a fishing trick that was to save more lives than the poisoned darts threatened to destroy. In the river were many fish the natives called payshi, a sort of codfish, some of which were ten feet long and three hundred pounds in weight. Contreros had tried unsuccessfully to land these big fish, but his spears or lines always broke. The Indian had a more subtle method. He selected some roots of the barbasco, a wild cinnamon tree something like the dogwood in appearance. He clubbed these roots on a hardwood stump and wrapped the crushings in wide fresh leaves. Then, accompanied by Contreros, he went into the forest to a place where the river had overflowed during the rainy season but now had receded, leaving a large pool. Into the pool the Indian tossed a few crushed roots. A milky sap oozed across the surface of the water while the Indian calmly sat down and waited. In a few minutes a small payshi, and a few tasty gamitana, floated stupefied to the surface, white bellies upward. The Indian gaffed them ashore before the astonished eyes of the ardent Castilian fisherman.

On the eve of Tenebrae Wednesday, with both ships riding to anchor and only a fortnight of last-minute preparations required before the expedition would be ready to set out again, Orellana formally ordered a five-day fiesta in honor of the Resurrection, and asked Father

Carvajal to climax the occasion by a High Mass and a special sermon on Easter Sunday. The company owed this obeisance, Orellana said, to the God who watched over them so generously.

Father Carvajal set about his duties with gusto. Since the men would not be working, he imposed for the fiesta the fasts usually observed on Tenebrae Wednesday, Maundy Thursday, and Good Friday, although due to circumstance the men had eaten whatever there was to eat, be it flesh or acorns, on all preceding fast days, and thus far in Lent. Now, however, Father Carvajal wanted to bring the men back to the fast as a real sacrifice of Holy Week.

Here, however, he ran into a snag. The men balked. "Let us eat while we may," they said, "and save our fasting for the day when there is nothing to eat."

Father Carvajal did not know what to do except to pray. Tenebrae morning arrived, but not the friendly natives who for the first time in fifty days failed to send fresh meat. Not an Indian appeared all day. Not a partridge, or parrot, or turkey flew overhead. No peccary grunted in the forest.

So there was no meat. Contreros, however, practicing his new art of fishing by poison, hauled in a catch large enough to feed the entire company. The men grumbled but fasted, and dined on fish, because there was nothing else.

Father Carvajal quietly breathed thanks to heaven that his prayer had been answered. He did not expect the miracle to be repeated on the two succeeding days, but it was. Even Carranza the Jew joined the Christians in their imposed fast, which caused much joking in the camp.

On Saturday the Indians came again, with game in such abundance that part of it was thrown away. When Orellana asked why they had not come on the three fast days, they replied that, though they had scoured the forest for many miles, not a bird had flown.

Father Carvajal crossed himself devoutly, and with unusual awe began to prepare his Easter sermon. If ever the presence of God had been more clearly manifest to man, the priest was unaware of it. He was inspired, but he was also humbled. Twice he began to compose his sermon in his mind, and twice rejected his ideas, although each time he felt that his subject was good and his reasoning sound. Now, after two failures, he became afraid to begin again. He felt a peculiar hold on him, such as had never before beset him—an intoxication as of strong wine, that flushed his blood and beat against his head. He could not drive it away, though he tried by prayer and meditation. Something seemed to urge him to think about Orellana. Finally he arose from the solitude of his Indian tent and stepped out into the blinding, humid sunshine of tropical springtime. The first person he saw was Francisco Orellana, sitting alone upon the afterdeck of the *Victoria*.

Quietly the priest sat down before his tent, his eyes on the leader of the expedition. It was God's will, he now knew, that he think about this man. The question of why God wished him to think of Orellana, when he should be writing his Easter sermon, flipped across his mind, but he did not try to answer it, for Father Carvajal was not a man to challenge Providence. God directed him; that was enough.

He relaxed, letting his thoughts tumble as they would. Orellana had his map across his knees, and was copying it elaborately with a charcoal, his whole taut body cooperating with his unlettered fingers. Obviously, thought Father Carvajal, the Captain was not satisfied with the sketch of the river he had drawn from conversation with the Indians. He was beginning to chart the river, marking upon it the contours of the shoreline. The logical leap of the priest's mind took him to the utility of such a chart. Since it was not needed for the downstream trip, it could have only one use—a guide to anyone who might return.

Return! There was the key. There the meaning of the Divine benevolence which had become so manifest. There, too, the Easter sermon.

He smiled, and smilingly recalled, easily and without taxing his brain for it, the beginning of the Thirty-Ninth Psalm. Why that Psalm? "I said I will take heed of my ways." It did not make the sense he expected of Divine revelation. God should move with forceful strokes to paint a sermon picture for a humble priest, should He not?

Carvajal's mind cut swiftly forward across the poetry of David, probing for inspiration. Suddenly he began to understand. "Lord, let me know my end, and the number of my days. . . . For man walketh in a vain shadow, and disquieteth himself in vain; he heapeth up riches, and cannot tell who shall gather them."

Father Carvajal bowed his head. His mind was clear, now. He knew what he must preach. And after Easter, he knew what he must do, during the remainder of the voyage, to add his own feeble skill to that of Orellana in completion of the chart, that those who came afterward should know what these few had seen, and knowing should conquer. *In hoc signo vinces.*

He also wondered, as he attacked the sermon again, whether God had revealed to him more than He intended. God did not make mistakes. No, He must have meant for the priest to know, that he might be better equipped to perform his duties.

But, merciful heaven, could it be?

He found himself interceding, begging his Creator against the irony of the revelation, the while his charcoal stick ran across paper building a sermon upon the Psalm. Even when the sermon was completed, the irony dallied in his mind.

"Beloved Father, guide me," he begged.

But he received no further guidance. Finally he put aside his fears meekly, and went to lead his vespers.

Of course, he thought, and the thought was enough for him, God does not reveal his whole intention to any man. He has kindled a light for my feet. Who am I, to know the whole of God's intent, or to question what I know? Enough that I may see my way, I do not need a light also upon my right hand.

He felt better, then, and put the matter from him, though sadly, with the tug at his heart that always tore him in the presence of death itself.

24

A T DAWN on the Eve of Saint Mark, with the holds of the two brigantines food-laden and the company awaiting the command to be off, a bird none had ever seen before, nor could identify as common to the jungle, perched upon a treetop near the beach, screaming like a crow.

Its cry was ominous.

"Hui, hui!" it said. "Flee, flee!"

As though to confirm the warning, the natives that morning did not come in with food.

Carranza called Orellana's attention to the double phenomenon, interpreting the signs as an omen the expedition could not ignore. Orellana shrugged.

"We are ready to go," he said, "and we are leaving. I would stay another day, just to prove the omen wrong and dispel the fear it is causing among the company, if that were possible. The food, however, will rot soon enough as it is. We leave. Summon the men."

There was a rush to the ships. The native village that had been home for two months was stripped of Castilian belongings as the company boarded the brigantines with the gusto of men who, having rowed out their spines so long, now would sail instead.

Orellana placed himself upon the *Victoria*, designated as his flagship, with Juan de Alcantara as master. Helmsman Miradero was promoted to command of the *San Pedro*. The men took their allotted places, as assigned by Orellana who, with forethought, had placed his two trouble makers, Maldonado and Friar de Vera, upon the smaller ship.

When all was quiet and the men were listening, Orellana called Father Carvajal to his right hand, and spoke.

"I do not need to remind you, gentlemen," he said quietly, "that we are going to run a gauntlet against all the keepers of death. If we encounter half that we fear, our souls as well as our bodies will be sorely tried."

He paused, to be sure all were listening.

"My commands—and you have sworn on the cross to obey them—are brief. They are brief so that none of you may forget them. Listen well.

"Stay together. The *San Pedro* shall maintain not more than a crossbow shot distance from the *Victoria*. Do not land for any reason without my express command.

"Do not quarrel. Unity is our only hope, after the help of God. I shall hang any man who causes trouble.

"Conserve the food. What we have now appears to be generous; but remember that the mouths of fifty-two men are a large cavern and we may not find anything fresh but fish henceforth. Death is ordered for any man who exceeds his ration. Lieutenant Robles will again act as second in command, and his word is mine."

Again he paused, this time for effect.

"I have only one other thing to say," he went on, "and I have left it to the last to impress it upon all of you. These Indians are our friends. They may one day be Spaniards—do not abuse them. I propose to return to colonize this river, if God be willing, and the friendship of these native peoples will, on that day, be more valuable than any treasure we may find. Let them remember us with pleasure, not with hatred; with happiness, not with pain, that when we come again they will open their hands to our service and their hearts to our God. In this way only will God and our king be served. A people inspired by kindness will fashion their lives after ours, but a people reduced by force to obedience will live only for a chance to disobey. Remember, as we go forward, that we shall come again. Fight only in self-defense, and then only at my command. And may the Holy Trinity, the Blessed Virgin, and Saint Iago accompany us along our way."

He knelt, and all with him on both the ships. Father Carvajal raised his hand in the sacred sign and commended their souls to heaven. The priest remained on his knees as the two ships cast off and pointed their blunt, efficient noses downstream.

They had not gone a hundred yards before Orellana, standing in the bow of the *Victoria*, was distracted by a sharp spatter at his back, like hard-driving rain. On the deck lay a half score of blowgun arrows.

Ashore, savages were bursting from the erstwhile deserted village to the shore. Carranza bared his teeth in a grim smile.

"The little bird was an omen after all, Señor," he said.

"Perhaps," Orellana admitted, "but these natives of Irimara are our friends. If they have become warlike, it is because they are driven to it by fear of someone stronger than ourselves. May God help us when we reach the lands of Queen Coñorí."

Four days passed in alert uneasiness, the brigantines keeping wide of shore except at night. Each day at sundown Lieutenant Robles and a small party went cautiously to land, reconnoitered for possible enemies, and gave a clear signal before Orellana permitted the ships to be tied up.

Some members of the party were so frightened by the unknown wilderness that confronted them, by the vast interminable stretch of murky river bounded by impenetrable ivy-thicketed trees, and by the warning of the mysterious bird, that they advised spending the nights in travel. This Orellana would not permit. Anxious as he was to reach the sea, he was obsessed with his chart of the river, which he kept up-to-date from day to day. Also, he knew that the men, constantly manning the oars and tending the rigging of the little vessels, needed rest at night; and always there was the danger that a sudden shoal might wreck one of the ships.

Such Indians as appeared were friendly. Occasionally a pirogue scudded out from the shore, its occupants inspecting the brigantines and offering to trade in turtles or maize. A few villages were passed, but Orellana did not risk an encounter ashore.

On the fourth day the chief of the domain came aboard and invited Orellana to spend the night at his village downstream. Orellana was wary, but he was also anxious to discover why the Irimarans, after two months of service, had attacked on the morning of his departure. So, posting a stout guard, he went ashore, taking with him Robles, the swordsman Gutiérrez, the crossbowman Soria, and the arquebusier Pedro de Acaray. His bejeweled dagger was loose in his belt, and his right hand remained casually but vigilantly near the hilt of his sword. There was no ambush, however. The chief even apologized.

"But you," he said to Orellana, "are leaving. The Machiparo, the Omagua, and the women of Coñorí are always with us. Defend us against them, and we shall be your friends."

Orellana promised that one day he would come back, but the chief shook his head.

"You will die," he said, "at the hands of the Omagua. Their warriors are as many as the trees in the forest. Big men, with shields that cover their legs and trunks. They have heard about your canoes that carry many men, and to seize them they will kill you. I am sorry, my friend, for I like you."

"We can defend ourselves."

"Not for three turns of the moon," the chief replied. "They will be mosquitoes at your heads night and day. You may kill many, but many more will seek you out. If not the Machiparo, then the Omagua who are a greater nation, and if not they, then you will be weak by that time and easy for the women, who are the strongest of all."

Orellana arose and embraced the old chief.

"I shall come again," he said, "and build a city among you and make you strong. Together we shall humble Queen Coñorí and release the Omagua and Machiparo from their slavery. Tell the Omagua and Machiparo chieftains so, that they will let me pass in peace."

The chief fingered his blowgun sadly.

"I shall tell them," he said, "but it is natural to fear the reptile at your door before the jaguar in the forest."

He waved his hand and turned away. There is no word in the Omagua tongue for "goodby."

No Indians appeared thereafter along the shore for many days. The food, so carefully treasured, disappeared into the bellies of the company or rotted away. By the sixth of May, the Day of Saint John Ante-portam-latinam, hunger had again become a reality. Two weeks had passed since leaving the village of Irimara. There was a guarded cache of maize, but little else.

Orellana turned inshore, hugging the bank so that his bowmen might shoot at game along the bank. Only the bowmen could be used, for the arquebus powder was so damp from humidity that it would not fire.

Diego Mexía, as the crack shot of the company, spied a parrot in a tree, and carefully taking aim so that his arrow might be recovered from the body of his victim, he fired. The arrow sped true, but there was no rejoicing over the meager bird, for in shooting, a nut sprang from the stock of the crossbow and fell into the water, where a fish that had been following seized it with a mighty leap.

To replace the nut was impossible. With the arquebus powder wet, the company was reduced to three crossbows, small comfort against the formidable enemy that was expected at any moment. The tragedy quickly communicated itself, as army rumors will, to the men aboard the *San Pedro*. Tension gripped all the men.

In mid-afternoon a strange thing happened. Contreros, fishing as usual from the *Victoria*, hauled in a large fish, and gleefully ripped it open to provide food for the hungry crew. To the astonishment of all, the crossbow nut was found inside the fish.

Father Carvajal proclaimed that another miracle had occurred, and considering the condition of the arquebus powder, all except Carranza were inclined to believe him. At least, fortified with a generous fish supper, the men attended the chaplain's vespers that night with impressive piety.

Another week, passing without food of any kind, inclined the men to believe that at last God had forsaken them. True, as Father Carvajal said constantly, no storms had beset them, not even a drop of rain, and no savages had appeared. To this, Carranza had a ready reply.

"The belly, good Father," he would say, "is not a good Christian.

When it is full, it believes; when it is empty, it is inclined toward heresy."

The stress of hunger day by day became more acute. At Orellana's request, Carranza attempted to cheer the men. One night, around a mosquito smudge, when the fare had been six kernels of maize and what leaves and grass the men could stomach, Carranza broke into song.

Los mis cabellicos, maire,   *My little hairs, mother;*
Uno a uno se los llevó en el aire.   *One by one the wind carried them off.*

¡Ay, porbrecitos,   *Alas, poor things,*
Los mis cabellicos!   *My little hairs!*

The veterans of the conquest of Peru smiled even through their hunger. Before their eyes again were the great days, when Pizarro the conqueror was looting the Inca nation. Before them again were their own great fortunes heaped up upon the body of the Inca— enough ducats of gold and marcs of silver to set them up in idleness, had they nursed their pesos instead of pursuing greater treasure.

Before them especially was a memory of the venerable wit of Pizarro's infantry, Sancho de Carbajal, as wily a soldier as was ever trained for warfare. At the age of eighty, he was by far the oldest of the conquistadores, but in spirit he was as young as any of the beardless boys who listened to his profane stories of the Italian wars, of continental conquests under Ferdinand, of a captaincy under the great Gonsalvo, a lieutenancy under the sapper Navarro, of ensign duties at the battle of Ravenna, what he had said to the face of the French monarch when Francis I was captured at Pavia, and his gleeful, unholy description of the sack of Rome, when he had with his own eyes seen the doting old Clement VII flee the Vatican with little protecting him from the night air and the eyes of Rome except his long white beard.

Many could see Carbajal now, a six-foot giant with a chest as broad as that of a horse, throwing off his helmet and cuirass in contempt of the Inca's mercenaries, storming and capturing their positions with his own hand.

They could see him, recouping his ancient frame after every battle with a licentious orgy that none other could match, relaxing in his wine, rolling his hand over his balding head, lamenting the departure of his remaining hair: *"Los mis cabellicos, maire."*

Those were the days! Every man who had accompanied Pizarro had won a fortune in treasure. In addition, the Peruvian mines yielded six million ounces of gold and twenty million ounces of silver a year, much of which sifted, by theft, murder, and gambling, into common circulation.

There was grimness, too, in the song. Spreading from Sancho de Carbajal to the soldiery, it was a favorite of the gaming table. Nearly every man, having lost many ducats at play, gazed ruefully upon his diminished fortune and sang, *"Los mis cabellicos, maire."*

Soria the crossbowman smiled upon Carranza.

"If ever we get out of this cursed forest," he said, "I am going back to Peru."

There was silence among the hungry men. Until now, none except Orellana, and the four who had promised to return with him to Spain, had given thought to their future.

"Why?" asked Juan de Illanes bluntly, tightening his stomach muscles against a hunger cramp. He was always first to tease the feeble-minded old man.

"Why, because there is still gold there. I know where—but why should I tell you? You might get there before me. But there's more. Lots more."

"There must be," someone said. "I've heard tell that the pagan dogs hid most of it."

"Of course they did," Soria said. "What would you do if someone came to rob you? You'd head for the hills. That's what the savages did. I know."

"As for me," Juan de Illanes said, "I'm going to marry a rich widow and settle down to a life of ease. No more of this rooting like a pig in

225

the wilds. I'm going to be smart. I'll pick me out a long-legged widow, with an income and a good twinkle. It's better than grubbing."

"Who wants to be tied to a widow's purse?" Soria disputed him. "I tell you there is still gold in Peru. I have made a study of it."

"Sure," Illanes said. "You have a map with the places marked. Two hundred thousand ducats under the stump of a sycamore tree in the valley of the Huancavilcas. Ten thousand ducats in the north wall of the temple at Charcas. I myself know personally eighteen men who have seen these treasures with their own eyes. But I ask you: if they ever saw such sights, why did they not bring them out?"

"They feared the law," Soria said. "The Marquis and his tenth, the crown and its fifth. Every robber had his hand in a percent. It is better to go back later. Like me."

"If you know so much," Illanes taunted him, "then you should share your fortune with all of us. Are we not brothers? Have we not starved to death together?"

"We have, by God's truth," said Soria. "We are brothers. I will tell you what I know."

"But it won't be as good as a rich widow with a twinkle, eh, Soria?" said Friar de Vera.

"Twinkles can be bought for a maravedí, amigo," Soria said. "I shall keep the gold then, and buy the twinkle from Illanes' woman when she sends him on errands."

The men laughed.

"Let Soria speak," Friar de Vera said. "After all, he may know where there is gold."

"Gold enough even for a friar," Soria answered. "Even enough to satisfy the appetite of a friar, and that is a great deal indeed."

"We are listening," said Juan de Illanes.

"Well, then," Soria went on, "you remember that at Pachacamac, Pizarro did not find the gold. It was spirited away while King Atahualpa was collecting his ransom. In two hundred litters, each borne by four men, the gold and silver was carried away."

"Where to?" the friar asked.

"To the mountains. I had the story from an Indian girl whose husband bore one of the loads. First they went to Potosí, then northeast over the mountains to the River Urubamba. It is easy to find, for the valley is guarded by a great fortress known as Ollantay. Sixty miles you follow the river toward its mouth, then cross at a deep canyon where a river begins to cut a ridge into the side of a vast mountain called Salcantay. There is a stone house there, with steps leading under a waterfall, and then upward nine hundred steps cut out of the native granite to a city. Beyond this city the road leads still upward, through another city on top of the mountain, so high that the clouds are always below it, hiding it from view. From here the roads lead across the divide, through a tunnel cut from the granite, to another city even higher. There the treasure of Pachacamac is buried. I would not even dream what it would melt down to, but if it is not a half-million gold pesos, then I will give it to you, and take no share."

"Generous of you," said Illanes. "But it is too far to climb. I shall stay with my widow."

Soria smarted.

"Very well, then," he retorted. "Lazy dogs find the least meat. Hidden in the sand ten paces south of a double-trunked tree a league north of Apurimac is an idol worth not a cent less than ten thousand pesos. I know, because I put it there. I give it to you."

"You can send the widow to bring it home," someone said.

"And I heard of another," Soria rushed on, stinging under the ridicule, "and as God is my witness, it is true. The royal treasures of the Inca are hidden at Vilcacampa. I do not exactly know where, but I can find out."

"I believe," Friar de Vera said, "that he is telling the truth."

"Of course I speak truth," Soria said. "And the gold of Prince Huascar is in a cave at Hilcaconga. I could take you there."

"Tomorrow, then," Illanes said. "Tonight I am too tired."

Carranza, noticing the avidity with which de Vera listened, and seeing Soria becoming hysterical under the lash of sarcasm and the gnaw of hunger, rose to his feet.

"Come, friend Soria," he said, "I need help with the grain bags."

"They think I lie," Soria said, sobbing. "But these things are true."

"Of course they are, friend," Carranza consoled him, giving him three grains of maize, half his own supper, "but why give your secret to those thieving dogs? Do you want them to murder you when you return to Peru?"

Soria smiled.

"I have not told them enough to do them any good," he said slyly. "I still have a head on my shoulders. You and I will go back and get the gold, Antonio. Just you and I. We will be princes, richer than the king. Won't we, Antonio?"

"Yes, amigo," Carranza said, "richer than the king."

25

ROM that time, Carranza and Soria were brothers. To the crossbowman, the companionship was the grip of an old man upon a stanchion that held him upright. The two men were the oldest members of the party, and Soria's fifty-year-old body, having withstood so much hardship, now was crumbling. The evidence of physical failure, manifesting itself through increasing emotional instability, was understood by physician Carranza, who took Soria under his special care, encouraging the old man with comradeship, the only prescription that medicates the infirmities of age. The younger men of the expedition, with no perception for any ills except their own, were inclined to laugh as Soria's mind cracked. But Carranza, with the understanding of both physician and sufferer, led the old Valencian patiently by the hand. Carranza saw in the disintegration of Soria the mirrored reflection of himself. He, too, was weakening. But whereas Soria's breakdown was evidenced outwardly by acute sensitiveness and failure of the mind, Carranza's was internal only, manifest by a pounding of the heart, and an increasing sluggishness of mind.

As day after day passed without relief from the exhausting debilitations of hunger, Soria clung more and more to Carranza, his mind more tightly clenching the memory of his buried treasures. Within a few days he could think of little else, and it was evident now that he expected to die, without ever reaping the golden harvest he had so carefully planted. Minutely and endlessly he acquainted Carranza, in whispers, with the exact location of his treasures, swearing the Jew to secrecy again and again. And after each such conversation, to which Carranza listened as diligently as though he expected tomorrow to return to Peru, Soria would relax and smile.

"There," he would say. "Now I may die in peace. If I cannot have the gold, amigo, my soul will rest knowing it is yours."

Always Carranza would reply, "You are not going to die, García. You will see. Together we shall go back and get the gold."

But every day's sailing took them a hundred miles farther from Peru. Tempers became sharp again throughout the company. Great stress cannot support brotherhood indefinitely.

Worried as much over the condition of his crew as over the threat of attack from the Machiparo, in whose domains they now must certainly be trespassing, Orellana watched with growing anxiety a petty feud upon the foredeck of his own flagship, an altercation that revealed starkly the hunger-ravaged collapse of his men.

In the prominent forepeak, tolling at times his lead line and constantly charting his mileage, stood Juan de Alcantara, master of the vessel. Even Orellana deferred this position in the ship to his fleet commander. But Father Carvajal, who grew more stubborn as he grew hungrier, refused to do so, and furthermore, was unreasonable.

The cross, the chaplain insisted, must be put first. It was a maniacal obsession with him. So great was his own physical suffering, that he became unbending in literal devotion to the duties of his office. This had become evident first when he castigated, with all the fury of his practiced tongue, the crew of the *San Pedro* who at night could not find strength to come aboard the flagship for vespers. The outburst was out of character for him.

Next, Orellana noticed that the chaplain was spending more and more time washing his vestments. All down the river he had fought against great odds to keep his white robes spotless. Somehow, on the new brigantine, he had acquired an ugly brown stain that dripped from his left shoulder straight downward almost to the waist. Nothing would erase it. He brooded. My faith, he would say, is clean and shining. My clothes must be the mirror of my faith. But he could not exterminate the spot. He began to believe this a sign from heaven that within himself there was a streak of sin, and that when the error of

230

his heart was rectified, the stain upon his vestment would miraculously disappear. Probing with merciless cruelty his own shortcomings, both of commission and omission, he concluded finally that his sin had been one of indulgence. He had permitted the suffering, hunger-wracked men to relax their devotions to their Creator and Protector.

He became stern, threatening eternal misery upon all who refused strict compliance with the religious services. Like a fanatic he hawked the individuals of the company, searching their souls and exacting penance.

To symbolize his stern devotion, he fashioned from wood a large cross and nailed it to the ship's bow, that every man, looking downstream, would see the cross and understand that God was constantly going ahead of his flock into the terrible unknown.

Juan de Alcantara objected to this position for the cross, since it interfered with his navigation. For several days the ship's master and the chaplain excoriated each other to no other purpose than rousing one another to fury. Finally, one morning Alcantara, who could submit to no more, and who must, after all, navigate his ship, seized the chaplain by his shoulder and presented him to Orellana, demanding a showdown.

Orellana declined to interfere.

"You are in command of this ship, Alcantara," he said, "and this is a ship's problem."

In a fury, Alcantara raged to the prow of his ship, and began to tear down the cross.

Father Carvajal was struck speechless by this blasphemy. He could only kneel and, watching the desecration, mumble to himself, "May God have mercy on your miserable soul."

But God that day was not showing mercy. Unable to dislodge the base of the cross, which had been securely nailed, Alcantara leaned overboard and tugged with both hands. The cross came loose suddenly, spilling Alcantara overboard, and as the ship sped by, one of the oars caught Alcantara's head and cleaved it. His body sank like a rock, leaving the cross buoyant upon the waves.

The body was not recovered, and Father Carvajal refused to ease the dead man's soul.

"God exacted His own vengeance for the desecration of His cross," Carvajal said. "Who am I, the least of miserable men, to interfere? God has cursed him, and may God have mercy on him, for I cannot." He nailed a new cross to the *Victoria's* prow, and there it stayed.

The men all came forward to witness this ceremony. Taking advantage of the distraction, one Mateo de Revolloso, a goatherd from North Valencia who until now had done nothing to distinguish himself, slipped into the hold to loot Alcantara's luggage. Like everyone else, he suspected that the ship's master had found too many excuses for keeping his baggage within sight.

While every other man knelt on the deck, paying humble homage to the triumphant standard, Revolloso found what he sought, the golden cup of Atahualpa. He held it aloft to let the sunlight play upon its craftsmanship, and to caress it with tender hands. At that moment the consecration of the cross was ended and the men, rising, saw the cup. A gasp went up. Father Carvajal turned sternly to discover the meaning of this profanation of the sacred moment. He, too, saw the cup.

In a rage such as none had ever seen, he pointed his finger at Revolloso, and screamed, "Is it not enough that two men already have lost their souls for that filthy piece of pagan gold? Must you, too, lose yours? On your knees, swine! On your knees to the cross, and give *me* the cup."

Revolloso laughed and went back to his duty post where he sat mending the rotting ivy hawsers, the cup of Atahualpa between his knees.

Father Carvajal would have enforced obedience, had not Orellana led him away.

"Come, Father," he said, "the man is damned enough. Have mercy. Our lives depend on our sticking together."

"I show no mercy to such a dog," the priest answered, but he turned away. "God will destroy him, in His own time."

Action put an end to squabbling on the next day.

It was the twelfth of May. No man had eaten solid food for three weeks. The arquebus powder was still too damp to shoot. In any collision with the Indians, the crossbows would be the Spaniards' only defense. On this the men still worried.

Late in the morning there appeared, on a knoll along the river bank, a village gleaming golden yellow in the sun. While the Spaniards gazed at it, still two miles away, a horde of canoes swept out from shore, gaily colored and heavy with bows and spears.

Orellana noticed quickly that the natives were equipped with some sort of shields overlaid with stout lizard skins and the hides of manatees and tapirs, which Orellana knew would resist the arrows of the crossbows. He signaled the *San Pedro* to draw close. Lines were run out, lashing the brigantines. Orellana shouted to his men.

"We must fight," he said. "But we do not fight alone. What if the powder is wet? Did not God recover for us the bolt of the crossbow as a sign that with bows alone we can conquer this enemy? Take heart, and follow me."

"Saint Iago," shouted Father Carvajal. The lashed brigantines swerved toward shore, into the midst of the enemy, every man attired in full armor against the Indian arrows.

The crossbows fired steadily at a bee swarm of canoes that attacked from all directions. Indian arrows swept the decks and ricocheted from the armor, but Spanish steel repelled boarders. Foray after foray the natives attempted, accompanied by fierce taunts and the hammer of drums, and some might have succeeded except for the brilliance of Lieutenant Robles. As a canoe touched the brigantine's side, he seized an iron hook and rushed forward, arrows rattling like rain from his breastplate and closed helmet, caught his boathook under the attacking canoe, and overturned it. The Indians could not swim. After a half dozen such disasters, the Indians held off a dozen paces, belaboring the brigantines with spears and arrows and defiant shouts.

As the brigantines touched land, Robles, accompanied by twenty-five of the stoutest swordsmen, cut his way ashore. Immediately the

Indians, as is their custom, withdrew, for the savage, when his first plan is frustrated, invariably runs away until a second impulse again drives him into the fight.

Orellana had counted upon this characteristic of the jungle men. Speedily he organized a food search, charging his companions to hurry. Reconnoitering, Robles discovered some turtles alive in a pool, and stores of meat, fish, and a supply of lumpy balls of cooked manioc. He sent a runner to report his find.

Orellana dispatched Maldonado, as the only powerful swordsman at hand, to take ten men and round up the food. Maldonado sped away with the zest of a youth anxious to show by prowess his right to the full fellowship of warriors. Now having no ship's master owing to the death of Alcantara, Orellana remained to direct the fight against canoemen, should they return, and sent another score of men to the assistance of Lieutenant Robles, who by now was a half-mile away in the upper reaches of the village.

Seeing the Spaniards dispersed into three groups, the Indians attacked again by land and water. One force pressed upon Maldonado as he and his ten men had their arms full of provision. Another swarmed on Robles, cutting off his retreat. Two hundred canoes beset Orellana from the water side.

At that moment the expedition would have ended in the death of all the Spaniards, except for the protection of the armor. The Indian arrows were as futile against it as hailstones. Spear thrusts were turned aside as easily as though they were tree branches in a forest. Sheer weight of numbers, taking the Spaniards off their feet, was their only vulnerability, and they knew it, combating it by forming a Roman square through which the Indians could not break. Those savages who attempted it, and there were many, were impaled on long Spanish swords.

Even so, the issue was in doubt. Seven of Maldonado's men were tripped off their feet, and Indians were on their backs before they could rise. Maldonado himself was clubbed across the face with such force that the visor of his helmet was shattered.

234

"We are dead men," someone cried.

Maldonado rallied his men coolly, re-formed his Roman square, and lifted his voice to accompany the thrust of his blade.

"Die then, knave," he shouted. "But not I. This is the first food I have seen in weeks, and I shall live to eat it."

His men responded. The Indians could not break the square. Maldonado did not budge, neither did he attempt to retreat. He stood his ground as though he was the guardian of the food stores and the Indians the interlopers. So intrepid was his defense, so disorganized the Indian attack, that the Indian arrows began to wound their own men, and seeing this, the savages at a signal fled into the forest.

Maldonado was about to relax when he saw a strong force sweep out of the woods close to shore and attack Orellana and the boats from the landside. Orellana was occupied with the canoes, and did not see this new danger, thinking his rear was covered by Maldonado. At once the danger to the boats was apparent and Maldonado, summoning the last strength of his men, only two of whom were uninjured, crashed into the backs of the Indian attackers. The surprise and drive of his rush scattered the Indians who again, at a single instant, gave up the fight. The canoemen followed their example and swept around a bend in the river.

For the first time since the expedition had left Don Gonzalo Pizarro, Orellana turned a pleased eye on his former equerry.

"Thank you, Maldonado," he said. "You have saved my life."

"The greater pity," Maldonado replied. "I assure you that I came to the rescue of the ships, not you."

There was no time for further words. Risking everything in a gamble for food, Orellana left the brigantines unguarded by so much as a man, and rushed ashore with the entire company to collect the foodstuffs that Lieutenant Robles still defended in the upper village, and to rescue eighteen men who lay upon the ground here and there, stunned by war clubs.

The Indians did not take advantage of their opportunity. Instead of attacking again by water, they waited until the entire party was in the upper village and struck there. Orellana was in a storehouse with most of his leaders, so that the Indians were in among the Spaniards before any knew it.

Cristóbal de Aguilar, who had come up with Orellana from Guayaquil, gave the alarm after he was struck in the back by a spear. He arose tottering, and unable to find his sword, used his dagger with such fury that the savages were for a moment disconcerted. The pause was fatal, for Orellana with sharp orders formed a battle square. Once again the discouraged Indians broke off and disappeared.

Now Orellana moved the food quickly to the beach. Sundown approached. The running fight had lasted more than six hours, and the men were so weak they could scarcely stand. Orellana surmised that the Indians would not attack again until dark, unless they realized the weakened condition of himself and his men. To mislead them, he trussed the wounded like grain in sacks and carried them aboard the brigantines as though they were so much yucca. The ruse worked and the wounded were saved. Some food also was captured, but enough only for a few days.

Orellana was tempted to remain another hour, salvaging more food, but Carranza rushed to him and pointed to a tall tree.

In the topmost branch, facing away from the Spaniards toward a gully that ran from the southeast, sat the bird of omen which had appeared to them at Irimara.

"Hui! Hui! Flee, flee!"

Orellana shook his head. Food was his only concern.

"But Captain," Carranza said. "The omen! You dare not defy it."

Impatiently Orellana called the little Portuguese Hernández and asked him to go, with fifteen men, and scout the gully to which the bird called such noisy attention. Orellana went on gathering food.

Hernández was beset almost immediately by an attack of such fury that one of his best men, Pedro de Empudia, had a leg ripped off, and he sent back a runner to inform Orellana that the full body of savages was assembling, to much exhortation from the chiefs, in the gully which led by another outlet to within two-score paces of the beached ships.

At this news Orellana recalled Hernández and retired. The men dragged to the ships and cast off. Almost immediately the bird of omen left its tree, circled the brigantines silently, and flew off over the forest. Before the ships were fully in the channel, the Indians swept out of the gully a stone's throw from the spot where a moment before the brigantines had been.

The men were about to set up a cheer at their delivery, when around the river bend again came the canoe armada. So tired were the Castilians by now that many wept unashamed at the sight of this new peril, which none had the strength to parry.

Orellana rushed about the brigantines, which were still lashed together, exhorting his men to a final effort, and pointing out that soon darkness would rescue them from further attack. Inspired, Pedro de Acaray, the arquebusier, seized his weapon suddenly and loaded it.

To the amazement of all, the powder that during the morning had been damp now was dry. The weapon fired. The leader of the enemy navy toppled from his canoe into the water. Consternation attended his collapse. His crew hauled him back to his boat, but he was dead. The Spaniards could see the puzzled natives examining a round hole in the dead warrior's shield. Two other arquebuses soon fired, with equally deadly results, and the native armada sheered off to discuss this new weapon. In the confusion, Orellana cast off the lashes that bound his ships, and piling on all sail and all strength at the oars, he fled down the river into the gathering night. Carranza ministered to the eighteen wounded in the hold.

One of the wounded was the wood carver, Diego Mexía. His right hand was horribly crushed, a heavy Indian club having smashed his hand between his sword and his breastplate. He refused Carranza's services.

"Sooner would I lose an arm than be cured by the pagan witchspells of a Jew," he spat at the physician.

"What would you do without an arm, now?" Carranza said. "Could you carve wood again? Could you swing a sword? You could not even lift the food to your mouth. Think again, Diego. There are worse things than Jewish magic, one being a one-armed man."

He slipped a blanket under Mexía's head, and took the wounded hand in his. Lithe, gentle fingers explored the broken bones. A thrust here, a push there, reset the fingers. Mexía cried out in agony.

"You are killing me, dog! Leave off, before I kill you."

Calmly Carranza put his knee on Mexíca's chest, immobilizing him, and went on with his work. A mass of mud, scooped from the river bottom by old Soria, was padded around the injured hand.

"Now be quiet," Carranza said, "or I will hit you over the head, and put you out blacker than the night. Tomorrow, keep this mud in the sun. Let it bake hard. Then you will feel no pain."

Already the agony was easing under the cool ministry of the mud, and Mexía lay back exhausted.

"I do not thank you, Carranza," he said. "I will not be under obligation to a Jew."

"You are not," Carranza answered. "I am indebted to you. This expedition has few hands with which to save all our lives. We cannot spare a one, especially yours that fights so well."

Two nights and two days Orellana ran the gauntlet of determined savages. Eighty leagues, as Pedro Miradero Domínguez measured their flight, the expedition raced downstream under almost ceaseless attack. Miradero had been promoted, at Alcantara's death, to command of the *Victoria*, and Mexía would, when he was well, take the *San Pedro*. About three o'clock of the third afternoon, the attack ended and the last canoe disappeared upstream.

"I think," Orellana said to Robles, "that we have reached the boundary of the Machiparo nation. If we have as good luck against the Omagua, we shall have reason to thank God."

"We have reason enough, anyway," Father Carvajal said.

They sped on down the endless river, cleaving within a crossbow

238

shot of the north bank, not daring to cross to the other shore, which was not visible. There was no change whatever in the monotony of the bank which remained a mass of tangled greens and forest, which even in bright sunlight a monk's hood of heavy sweet clouds overlay.

The men ate and slept. The wounded began to emerge from the hold, cured by Carranza's charms, since he had no medicines. Pedro de Empudia, who had lost his leg, finally was the only patient. Diego de Mexía, going about carefully in his mud cast, cheered Empudia.

"When my hand is well," he said, "I shall carve you the finest wood stump in the world."

He looked sheepishly, as he said it, toward Carranza. He would not express his own gratitude to a Jew, but Carranza understood. That a Castilian should be sheepish before him, and anxious to help another maimed Spaniard, was gratitude enough.

The quiet of exhausted men lay as heavily as the humidity over the two brigantines when a shriek arose aft on the *Victoria*. Mateo de Revolloso had leaped to his feet and was tearing out his hair.

"The cup," he screamed, "the cup of Atahualpa is gone. A thief has taken it."

He ran up and down the deck, a madman. Orellana tried to calm him and was rewarded with a slash from Revolloso's dagger.

"The cup," he shouted, "the cup!" He threw aside whatever caught his eye, seeking the hiding place. Not a man moved.

His eyes were bloodshot. He was obviously in fever. Orellana spoke, and two men tried to take Revolloso by force to the hold, but he tore loose. Weeping and muttering, he turned like a bear when anyone approached him.

Attracted by the commotion, the *San Pedro* drew close to discover the cause, and on the deck Revolloso spied Friar de Vera.

"You took it," he shouted across the water. "I remember now. While every man was fighting off the cursed savages on the river, you crouched beside me. You took the cup."

He plunged into the water and struck out for the *San Pedro*. The current was swift, Revolloso was in armor, and within a few seconds he was far astern. Orellana started to order the *Victoria* about, but Carranza was immediately at his elbow with a whisper.

"For the love of God, Captain, let him go. He has typhus. Would you kill us all?"

Orellana watched the struggles of Revolloso for a moment, until the mailed head disappeared. "I hate to see a man die," he said.

"I wonder," Carranza replied, "if that black-hearted friar really took the cup? I will wager ten castellanos it is even now under his frock between his legs, tied with a rope."

Orellana turned his gaze down river.

"A good place for it, then," he said. "And may God have mercy on poor Revolloso. I am his murderer. Fool that I was not to destroy the cup."

26

DESPITE the attendant hazards, Orellana's curiosity finally impelled him across the great river to explore the south bank. The risk from warlike savages was no greater there than along the north shore, however, and across the water there might be rich lands that should be entered on his chart.

To his amazement he found no jungle, but a rich savanna that stretched back from the banks across well-tilled fields to a low ridge of wooded hills.

Summoning Robles, he put ashore at the first village. At his approach, the natives fled without a fight. Orellana walked into the village, accompanied by Robles and, as an afterthought, by Maldonado. For some time the equerry had attempted no mischief. After the fight at Machiparo he had been accepted again by the men, and Orellana had been for some time searching for a way in which, without undue emphasis, he might express common agreement in this matter with his men.

The town was laid out in squares, as were the streets at home in Castile. Rush-thatched houses were set down in orderly rows. The natives evidently were tall men, for the doorways were high though not wide, and the slung hammocks were twenty inches longer than those used by the Omagua. At the edge of the town, bordering a hard-packed, man-built roadway, were cassava and yucca plantings, avocado and plum orchards, and, to the wonder of the explorers, a fine field of ripening oats.

"Oats!" Orellana exclaimed. "White men have been here!"

Robles gazed speculatively at the blue-green stalks that rippled in the wind like a gentle ocean swell.

"It is not likely," he said. "Oats might grow anywhere."

"Where there are oats, there is beer," Maldonado said hungrily, and left them to forage farther on. Orellana and Robles resumed their walk. Soon Orellana paused again, and pointed. Behind each house, concealed in a small brake, was a latrine.

"They are civilized people," he said. "They have order, and cleanliness. It would not be difficult to establish a colony here."

Robles agreed. They were gazing at the latrine, which to them summarized the vast difference between savage and civilized man, when they heard an excited shout from Maldonado farther up the street.

Drawing their swords, they ran toward him, but he was not under attack. Rather, he was waving and holding something aloft. It was a porcelain bowl, finely manufactured and beautifully decorated. Orellana took it, ran his hand over it carefully, feeling the excellent texture of the glazing. He saw many other pieces of pottery manufactured with equal skill all about this particular house, inside and out, and examined the kiln, the tools, the paints with which this wonder had been performed.

"Not even in Minorca," he said, "is there pottery like this. Robles, think of it! Who knows—it may be more valuable than the mines of Potosí. This is the site I have been looking for. Here I shall build my first city when I return."

He selected three of the best examples of the porcelain to take with him. They walked circuitously toward the ships, on fine clay-packed roads which were part of a system stretching inland.

"We should take a large party and explore," Maldonado said. "Surely there must be gold here, too."

Orellana shook his head. "We must not risk war with these people," he said. "Life, not gold, is our objective. The gold will still be here when we return."

But he was troubled by the appearance of the oats. His restlessness and excitement increased mile after mile as they resumed their journey. He had dubbed the town Loza—Porcelainville—on his chart, and now he paid even more attention to his clumsy map. Many villages were passed, with roads tangenting behind them. A few cattle resembling the llama of Peru grazed in open spaces. Of natives, however, they saw few. The populace blotted into the hills at the approach of the brigantines.

On the Eve of Holy Trinity they came to a large river which emptied into their own from the north, its current so black as to leave a streak a mile wide upon the surface of the larger current. Orellana was elated. Here was an unmistakable landmark that no colonizer could miss. He called the tributary Río Negro, and so inscribed it on his map. Two days later he passed the mouth of an even larger tributary, coming in from the south. He called it the Río Grande. He was now, by Miradero's reckoning, more than five hundred leagues—eighteen hundred miles—from the camp at Aparia. He had been separated from Don Gonzalo for one hundred fifty-four days, more than five months. The men were rested and strong again, and able to grumble against the food and the river. Even the grumbling was a favorable sign, Orellana thought. Only hale men protest; sick men whine. Carranza's belly, long thin, was growing fat. Father Carvajal's sternness had relaxed, and the men were able to escape vespers on slight excuses again, though the chaplain was as unyielding as ever concerning attendance at his morning Mass. Apparently, Orellana thought, the chaplain had grown accustomed to the stain upon his frock, for he had given up searching the villages for soapstone.

On Wednesday, the Seventh of June, the eve of Corpus Christi, Father Carvajal plied Orellana to stop, that the holy day might be celebrated ashore. Orellana demurred. "In the last hundred leagues," he said, "we have not talked to any native. We do not know how warlike these people may be."

"They have shown no resolution to fight."

"That's why they are dangerous. At some point they are waiting to attack us. We have not slept at anchor in the river these last ten nights to be beset from ambush now."

Carvajal insisted that Orellana's duty, as captain, was to heed the spiritual needs of the men, and Corpus Christi was not a feast to be ignored.

"We must get on down the river," Orellana said impatiently. "I have reason to believe there have been white men here. We might be attacked by Portuguese. Wisdom holds us to our course."

"The only course to which any man must hold is the road to the Cross," said the priest, growing angry.

"All right," Orellana said, "we shall go ashore, but it is unwise."

They went ashore, and Maldonado, who remembered the oats, this time found a bitter fermented drink that he jestingly called beer. The feast of Corpus Christi was celebrated in high style, in a large house with two entrances. Even the guards that night were a little drunk.

They were ambushed in the night. A quick noose over the necks of the guards and the two men were dead. Orellana and his men were all asleep. One guard at each door had appeared to be enough.

The Indians were in the cavernous darkness of the hut before the beer-heavy men awoke. Suddenly all around them were shrill-shouting bodies. The Castilians did not know who was friend and who enemy.

Friar de Vera screamed, "Blessed Madonna, I beg you, do not let me die among these heathen."

Orellana arose from his hammock with a roar that cut across the confusion of savage shouting and the despairing invocations of his men. Slashing his sword with one hand and his dagger with the other, he fought his way toward the starlight at one end of the building.

"Shame, shame, gentlemen," he called. "They are nobody; at them."

"Saint Iago," Robles shouted, and followed his leader. Blindly the men rallied in the wake of Orellana's voice and the encouraging flesh-clash of his steel. The Indians could not defend the door against Orellana's attack, they who were naked and spear-armed, he armored and strident with two sharp blades. They slipped away into the night, leaving five of their number trapped in the hut.

Stunned by the nearness of the catastrophe, enraged that his better judgment once again had been overthrown by bad counsel, smarting with shame, Orellana ordered the five captives to be hanged in the center square. He did not know exactly why he did so. Impulse, perhaps, or anger at Father Carvajal, or anger at himself. It was fierce, inflamed anger that must be appeased.

Father Carvajal protested the hanging. Orellana had known that he would. Perhaps, he thought, that's why he had given the order. He turned on the priest.

"You got us into this, Father," he said, "and two of our company are dead. If Corpus Christi must be celebrated with death, then let it be heathen dead, that can do us some good, and show these savages the penalty for attacking Spaniards."

Orellana remained grim as two weeks passed. Not even his friends Robles, Carranza, Hernández, and Gutiérrez could pacify him. Father Carvajal left him alone. As though to atone for the deaths of the two men, Orellana imposed rigid discipline on the company and refused to listen to suggestions even from Robles.

As they passed one large village, Miradero, the ship's commander, pointed out an ideal spot for a landing, that they might replenish their food supplies and perhaps find fresh fruit.

"Don't be a fool, Perucho," Orellana snapped. "See that break in the foliage along the shore? A clearing of some sort is behind the trees. Perfect for ambush." They sped by without pausing, and in their wake a swarm of savages burst from the woods, daring the Spaniards to stand and fight.

Orellana set his teeth in vindication, and resumed work on his chart. Robles, who had been standing by, walked to Orellana and placed a hand on his shoulder.

"Softly, Captain," he said. "You grow short and your temper strains. You have not had enough sleep for many nights. Stretch out on the deck and rest. I will wake you if there is any need."

Astonished, Orellana looked up. "Am I short, Alonso?" he said. "Forgive me. It is just—I don't know." He held his hand before his good eye, and sucked in his breath.

"We understand, Captain," Robles said. "The responsibility is too great for any man—especially on this incredible river, in this tight air, among all this death. You cannot hold yourself responsible that two men died. You have led us well. Relax. We want you to lead us farther, not crack up and leave us without a commander."

"Am I so far gone, then?"

"You punish yourself. The Orellana we know and love does not hang Indians, or speak harshly to the commander of his flagship. Rest a little."

"I cannot rest," Orellana said. "These cultivated fields, these roads, these villages, fruit trees planted in rows on hillsides—I must be able to tell the King of them." He shook his head. "I would be a friend among them, amigo, yet I bring them only death. I would love them; I bring them hate. I would teach them more than the use of the gibbet. If I could only talk to them, as I talked to the chiefs at Aparia. Then they would understand us, and we would know more of them, and when I come again, they would be my friends."

"Perhaps if we captured someone with whom you might talk, it would relieve you."

"How can one capture these devils?"

"A quick sortie ashore. There is always a straggler."

"Good," Orellana said, not realizing that for the first time in two weeks he had accepted advice. "But mind—just one prisoner, Alonso. Not two, for two must show one another hatred against us. One has no need for heroics."

"I understand." Robles smiled as he turned away. What the captain needed, he thought, was more than conversation, and that, too, might be remedied by a captive.

They landed next day, at a miserable hut attending a field of grain. Robles made his capture. The men with him found a store of native liquor, and brought it along as well.

Proudly Robles led his captive to Orellana and smiled broadly, watching his captain's face. Oddly, Orellana did not soften.

"This?" he asked, stupefied.

Before him stood an adolescent girl, fairer than most and spare of frame, with white teeth and a wide smile. Her black hair was cut off abruptly at the level of her ear lobes, her eyes were satin black, alert without cunning, nose rather Roman. She looked quite Spanish, her lips no thicker than those of a Moorish woman. Around her neck was a necklace of woven reeds but otherwise she was unclothed except for an armlet of polished nutshells. Her entire body was dyed a dark cinnabar red that gave off a pungent smell not unlike pomegranate. Her hair, which was clean, had an odor of its own, a highly exotic perfume from the leaves of a forest plant in which it had been washed. She stood on flat feet, shoulders squared, eyes amused, as she looked at her one-eyed captor.

Orellana turned away from her eyes.

"Is this the best you can do?" he asked Robles.

"She can talk," the lieutenant said, "and perhaps have other uses? The captain has tensions that only a woman can relax."

He was anxious, his face drawn. Orellana stared at him a moment, and then he understood.

"You do think I'm losing my grip, don't you, amigo?" he said.

The girl stood serenely, impishly, waiting. Behind her on the deck of the brigantine were thirty pairs of lustful eyes. Orellana turned to her.

"What is your name?"

Her eyebrows, so fine that they might have been plucked in the manner of the Florentine women, went up.

"It is Lalah. You speak my language!"

"A little," Orellana said. "Only a little. You are not afraid?"

"Why be afraid? I have seen pale men before."

Orellana froze. He tried to be indifferent.

"Of course," he said.

"Many seasons ago," she went on. "Chief Apuna brought six of them to show my people. It is a legend among us. He had caught

247

them, like fish, in the river, after their boat sank. He brought them to prove they were men, not gods. They were weak little men, afraid. They only chased the women." She was archly scornful.

"Where are they now?"

"Three died. Three others Chief Apuna gave as husbands to women they had made heavy with child."

Orellana's face brightened. Now he would learn what he must know.

"The children—how big are they now?"

The girl regarded the question as trivial. Mischief flashed in her eyes.

"Almost warriors now. Grown boys."

Orellana nodded, relieved. Then there was no colony on the river. Diego de Ordaz or some of his men, undoubtedly. Spaniards. Scarcely Spaniards now, after fifteen years in the wilderness. For a moment he was tempted to discover exactly where these white men were, and rescue them. The whim passed immediately. Kinder to leave them to the forest. It is unfair to the living for the dead to return. Unfair to the dead to rip open their tombs and expose them again to the decay of living.

He knew what he had to know, and his spirit eased. There was no colony along the river. The fear that had gripped him, that had found outlet in tenseness within and rage without, evaporated.

"You got—" he paused. He did not know any native word for oats. "You got grain from the Spaniards?"

He pantomimed the growing stem, the threshing, the quenching of thirst with bitter liquor.

"They planted it," she said. "They planted it and it grew. They made drink and gave it to our women. Our women would do anything for them then. Now all of us have grain."

Orellana smiled, and Robles, standing rigid alongside the girl, eased the weight upon his insteps. Everything was all right, now.

Orellana ordered a pallet spread for the girl on the foredeck, close to the position in the ship's bows where he usually slept. The word of this command scattered swiftly among the men.

But that night, while many eyes watched the girl stretch out upon her litter, Orellana did not go to her. He called Robles, and they talked for a long time of the next day's problems. Finally Robles excused himself.

"I think I'll go over to the *San Pedro* for a while," he said. "You have need of this space upon the deck." He looked down at Lalah. She was wide awake, listening to the strange, unknown syllables. She was awake and waiting. The lot of captive girls she understood. So it had always been among her people, and among the women her own warriors brought home. She was not the least dismayed, or even resistant. Her eyes reflected curiosity which both Robles and Orellana saw. She was not averse to the novelty of lying in the arms of the white man some of her people thought might be a god.

"I leave her to you," Robles said. "God, what I would give to trade this night with you."

Orellana watched him go, and looked again at the girl. The stars and a three-quarter moon wrapped her in a shadowy wraith. The ship rocked gently at anchor, answering the wooing murmur of the river beneath its hull. The girl stretched languidly. Her knees were graceful in shadow, her gesture was one of invitation.

This was the first such gesture, Orellana thought, since he had lost his eye. He remembered how the women of Guayaquil had spurned him, suggesting he solace himself with a native girl from among his slaves. As though easement was all he required of an embrace! Taking a slave, who must submit, was a repulsive thing he could not bring himself to do. Love was a consecrated act, unfulfilled even in fulfillment unless there was tenderness as well as passion.

A girl in Panama had taught him that, he recalled, before he had lost his eye. She was Spanish, having come from Cuba with her mother.

Orellana was seventeen, the mother was seeking a husband for her daughter, and here was a cousin of the Pizarros. Orellana fell in love. He courted the girl with idealistic fervor, and she encouraged him. One day when he called to see her he found the mother away. Alone with the girl, the manhood that was nascent in him welled up in response to her seductive guile. He took her in his arms and experienced the excitement of his first embrace; the earthquake rapture that comes only once to any man.

In that sacred moment, when he looked into her eyes and began to blurt his endless devotion, in that moment when his adult sun burst over the horizon in warmth and glory, when he knew that now life had begun, she turned aside his lips and said, "My, my, how serious you are!"

Even now, thirteen years later, Orellana could hear her mocking voice, and the answering groan of his own heart.

He went to Lalah, covered her with a blanket against the mosquitoes, and returned to the bow of the ship. For a long time he stood in the starlight, trembling, not daring to look behind him to the pallet on which, he knew, the girl still lay awake and waiting.

27

Robles returned from his night on the *San Pedro* with sparkling eyes. Lalah was eating a generous breakfast, with Orellana at her side.

"Well?" the lieutenant asked, "how was she?"

"I don't know," Orellana said. "I didn't touch her."

"You didn't touch her! When every man on your ship went ashore that you might have privacy? Why, in God's name, did you not take her?"

"I think," Orellana said slowly, "that I will wait for Ana de Ayala."

"God in Heaven!" Robles said.

They sailed on down the river, Orellana too absorbed with his chart to notice that his men were getting out of hand. Lalah might have told him and even explained the cause. Hungry eyes followed her wherever she went, especially those of the man who wore a skirt. Several times this one came over from the *San Pedro* and touched her in an unmistakable way, but she understood that she belonged to the one-eyed man, and resisted the friar.

One night she awoke under the morning stars, to feel clumsy hands upon her. She lay very still until the friar felt certain of his conquest and then, catlike, her fingernails reached out and tracked a bloody course across his face. Without a word, lest he wake the sleeping Orellana nearby, the friar crept away and she heard the lisp of water as he swam back to his own vessel.

Next day, she noticed, the men were laughing more than usual. The friar's face was hideously streaked. The men would look at him and cackle, and turn to look at her. One man particularly, the one called Illanes, who sat often among the men with colored boards in his hands, kept going back again and again to flush still higher the streaks of fire in the friar's face. She knew, instinctively, that he was the next among the men who would seek her out.

He came that night, and she was ready for him. Orellana had left the bow, going ashore as he did every night before retiring. The man Illanes came to her crouching, the ship's rail between himself and the shore. He was not clumsy like the priest. He sat beside her, babbling in the unknown tongue. The tone of his voice, however, was the same in her own language. He kissed her outstretched toes, one by one, talking, alertly watching her. She did not move. He smiled; she did not respond. She knew that aboard the other ship eyes were watching, and among them the eyes of the man who wore the skirt. She waited.

Suddenly the man was upon her. He was agile, and knew what he was doing. She did not cry out. At the right moment, with all her strength, she drove one knee upward.

He moaned and rolled to the deck. She leaped up quickly, came down knees bent with all her weight upon the spot he was clutching with his hands. He cried aloud and then, seeing her poised again, he rolled over and over along the deck away from her, tumbling down the foredeck steps to the safety of amidships. She stood defiant, watching him, while harsh laughter rippled to her from the *San Pedro*.

She was not bothered again. And she observed that the red-bearded man so often in attendance on her one-eyed master, next day became her special protector. By day he did not wander from her sight, and by night he slept at the foot of the foredeck steps, his sword close to hand.

She noticed something else, too. Two men there were of a color unlike the rest. They were black and all day long they pulled the oars of the ship on which she rode. One of them was tall and strong and sad of face, and before she had been two days aboard she knew that he was in love with her. His name, she discovered, was Nogal. He would watch her as he stroked his oar, hour after hour, day after day, his face a bliss that erased the hardships of his physical labor.

Robles saw this, too, and for a day was alert, until he saw that

252

toward Nogal, little Lalah had no eyes whatever. She was, he thought, like a paying passenger on the *Victoria*, whose pallet was attended for her, whose meals were served, whose company was sought by the captain at mealtime. And she was modest. The provocation in her eyes was not that of Spanish women. It was amusement, superior amusement, the duchess among her minions.

From Lalah, Orellana learned a great deal concerning the organization of her people, their clans and nations, their subjugation to Queen Coñorí. The warrior women, she said, had built the roads, set up idols, established the system by which they lived. She had never seen any of them herself. Not in her lifetime had the women come among her people. She did not know how much farther the river coursed before it reached the sea.

Orellana, in turn, told her a great deal about Castile, and its women. His descriptions were those of gentlewomen of the grandees and hidalgos, not those of the goatherds and swineherds. He wanted her to see the brighter side of Christian civilization, that she might tell all her people, in advance of his return, what Spaniards were like. She told him she was surprised that he took no interest in her womanly function, and he explained that among real men, in contrast to those who had come among her people previously, the bearing of children was a sacred rite and an obligation under God.

She did not understand this at all, but her attitude was not that of a woman scorned. She was a woman and therefore meant to be used. It was her role, her reason for being. Children were the inevitable result, like purgation after feeding, accepted and natural. How uncomplicated, Orellana thought, how civilized, was the approach of the savage to the cycle of reproduction in comparison with the mantraps which so-called civilized man had lain across the simplicity of life. Again he felt the call to stay along the river, but he put it aside. He would return.

One day he knew that he had told the girl all that she could absorb of the Spaniards, their ways and their God, and that the time had come to put her ashore. The river now surely must lead through the domain of Queen Coñorí, and he wanted these warrior women to know that when he came again, it would be in peace. Lalah should be his ambassador.

He was about to communicate this thought to Lieutenant Robles when Father Carvajal approached. He stood at a distance and waited to be recognized.

"Yes?" Orellana said. He was still unable quite to forgive the priest.

"If it pleases the Captain," Carvajal said, "it is the eve of the feast of Saint John the Baptist. Saint John, beloved disciple, favorite of Our Lord. It would be fitting to spend tomorrow ashore, if it can be done without risk."

"Very well," Orellana said. "We must put ashore soon anyway; I shall look for a place."

An hour passed. The surface of the broad river was choppy, kicked into little waves as in a salt sea inlet, revealing in restless surges the vast breadth and depth of the water. Orellana leaned over, scooped up a little of the water and tasted it. No salt. He arose. The brigantines were rounding a bend. On the left bank a mile away, shining in the humid sunlight, appeared the first village of the warlike women. It was neat, laid out with streets, giving evidence of order and empire and power. Orellana did not like the look of it.

He would have given orders to pass the village without stopping, but the natives compelled him to stand and fight. A hundred large war pirogues put out from shore, intent on crowding the brigantines toward a landing on a strip of sand. Orellana called to the nearest, making the signs of peace, and avowing friendship. The natives—they were men, not women—laughed and taunted him.

Once more the brigantines were lashed together, to drift slowly toward the beach. No man fired his weapon. Arrows hailed down upon the ships with such fury that the oarsmen were driven from their seats. The missiles were tipped with what looked to Orellana like poison, but he was not sure. Five of his men went down with face wounds before they could close their visors. The *Victoria* crunched into the sand, the three arquebuses fired a brave volley, followed by the deadly beehum of the crossbows. Lieutenant Robles and a landing party stormed ashore through a thundershower of arrows. The enemy were tall and strong, and obviously from several tribes, for some wielded spears, others fired arrows, and others brandished clubs. A few, taller and stronger than the rest, were armed with heavy sticks with which they felled any of their fighting men who retreated. Under the goading of this death from behind, the Indians crowded out into the water up to their waists, clutching at the ships, and one strong young man, more hardy than the rest, jumped to the deck of the *Victoria* over the shoulders of another. Hernández clubbed him with a mace, and he fell unconscious, forgotten in the fury of the fight.

After an hour, Orellana saw that he could not win a hold upon the beach, for now his rear was menaced by an armada approaching from across the river. Also, he dared not put Lalah ashore, lest she fall either to the savage arrows or the volleys of his own men. Robles' weary party was hauled aboard; the brigantines, cut loose, began to drift downstream, oars and tillers unattended as every man pressed the fight.

They had not drifted far when Father Carvajal pointed ashore. A village lay there, unprotected, its inhabitants obviously in attendance upstream. Here, the chaplain said, was an opportunity to seize food for Saint John the Baptist Day. Orellana demurred, but others insisted, pointing to the small quarry of provision still remaining, reminding their leader of the many miles to come. Orellana put ashore.

The deserted village was a trap. No sooner had the landing been made, with Father Carvajal in the van as an example to all, than Indians rose up from the cover of the jungle. Father Carvajal was struck by an arrow and went down.

Immediately Orellana sprang from the *Victoria* and cut his way to the fallen chaplain, shouting for assistance. With Robles and Gutié-rrez, he formed a shield behind which others dragged the priest aboard the ship. Orellana retreated slowly, yielding inches in minutes, careful to maintain his Roman square. At last the *Victoria* was reached, the fighting men hauled bodily aboard, and the company made off again across the choppy water, drifting past a solid rank of villages and beautifully tilled fields.

Carvajal had been wounded in the right eye. The tip of the missile projected two fingers' length behind his right ear. Carranza went to him, dexterously broke the shaft, pulled out the arrow, and cauterized the wound with a hot iron. He could not save the eye, however. Not once during the operation did the priest cry out.

Then began a chase that lasted for three hundred miles. Day and night the company was oppressed. Islands began to encumber the river, from which without warning canoes would dart, fling a death rain of arrows, and retreat again.

All that time Orellana tended his chart of the river. To each village he gave a name, to each a description. The land was temperate, but lush. Strong stands of orchard sliced the hillsides, below which grain fields were being burned over for spring planting. Grassy meadows admirable for livestock thrust to the water's edge, thick with marjoram and thistles and rich herbs. Evergreens, oaks, and cork trees swathed the islands, and at times behind the hills ashore appeared glimpses of rolling savannas vegetated with lespedeza and knee-high herds' grass. Cities and villages were as plentiful as along the Tagus, and as gentle in the bright sun.

Orellana could not yet put the girl ashore. The Indian whom Hernández had clubbed was chained in the hold, undismayed by his cracked head. The chaplain was delirious for two days, so that Carranza or Soria remained constantly with him, scattering insects from his festering wound. Finally Carranza found some maggots and put them on the eye, and the priest began to mend.

As if hunger, weakness, and despair were not enough, a tumult arose one morning upon the *San Pedro* just as Orellana was devoting his attention to a canoe, containing two savages, that had put out toward him from one of the now innumerable islands.

"What is it?" he asked impatiently as the *San Pedro* pulled alongside. Miradero, the ship's master, merely pointed. Annoyed, Orellana turned. Maldonado, the former equerry, stood widely grinning in the bow of the smaller brigantine, holding something in his hand, which Friar de Vera threatened to take from him with a dagger. Orellana squinted and saw the golden cup of Atahualpa.

Maldonado leaped aboard the *Victoria,* followed by the screaming vicar.

"I knew he had it, the dog," Maldonado said. "He has been gambling too heavily with Illanes lately not to have a cache somewhere. I waited until he slept, and lifted his robe and cut it out. What a prize! Now it is mine."

De Vera made a furious pass with his dagger, which Maldonado disdainfully warded with a twitch of his body that took the point on his breastplate.

"Enough!" Orellana roared, his eye darting toward the two savages who still approached. "There has been enough death over that miserable gold. Give it to me."

Maldonado snarled.

"Give it to me!" Orellana reached for his sword. Maldonado hesitated a moment, watching Orellana's wrist, then casting a glance at de Vera who was coming on again. Outnumbered, he shrugged, and threw the cup at Orellana's feet.

"Tie them both and put them in the hold," Orellana said. He picked up the cup absently, his attention again upon the encroaching canoe. The two natives came on, until they were within arquebus range, then turned and began to cruise parallel to the ship. Orellana called to them. They did not answer, nor did they deviate from their course off the starboard beam. Orellana called again. They came closer to listen, alert, but unmenacing. Orellana still held the cup of Atahualpa in his hands.

"If I could just tell these men that we come in peace," he said to Miradero. His eye lit on the cup.

"A gourd," he said quickly, "a large gourd."

While the company of both ships watched, Orellana placed the golden cup in the gourd and launched it over the starboard side. It gleamed gloriously in the sunlight, its fine intaglio work catching and throwing back like prism reflections the hard shafts of sunshine.

The Indians held their course. The gourd fell behind the *Victoria*, behind the *San Pedro*. Not a man on either brigantine moved or spoke. Nor did Orellana, in the bow.

Now the gleam of metal attracted the men in the canoe. The smooth cadence of their oars faltered, their heads turned. Digging deeply, they turned and darted to the gourd.

The taller Indian reached out cautiously, touched the gourd and withdrew his hand. He reached out again, took the cup from the gourd and looked at it.

"It is a great treasure," Orellana shouted. "It is the golden drinking vessel of a great king. I give it to you to prove that we come in peace."

The men understood. Now the seated Indian took the cup from his companion and examined it, holding it in both hands, his paddle between his knees. He stood upright then and looked across the water.

"It is a priceless gift," Orellana called.

The Indian turned toward his comrade. He stared again at the Spanish ships. Then contemptuously he tossed the cup into the water and did not even watch it sink. He took up his paddle and departed.

Aboard the *Victoria* and the *San Pedro* a groan arose like the lamentations of Israel at Atonement.

The Indian girl went to Orellana. "Are you surprised?" she asked. "Of what great value is a drinking vessel, when one may drink from the palm of one's hand?"

"It is difficult to explain, little Lalah," Orellana replied.

28

THAT night the brigantines were moored under the overhanging branches of an island grove. Most of the exhausted men fell asleep at once. Fearful of surprise attack, Orellana remained watchful, his friends Robles and Carranza beside him on the foredeck of the *Victoria*.

The night was snowy with stars, and humid. The men were silent, ears alert to detect the stealthy creep of alien paddles. A large meteor spilled its molten shaft over the sky, splashing out of the east.

"It points at me," Carranza said. "My people have a saying that when a shooting star looks at you, it has chosen you for death."

"You don't believe such a thing," Orellana said.

"Yes, I believe it. In the past half year I have become an old man, and I am about to die, that I know."

"Nonsense. You are coming back with me to Spain."

"The stars do not lie."

"It is just a superstition," Orellana insisted.

Impatiently Carranza answered, "Where would we be now without my superstitions? The charms that healed the wounded, the conjures that fattened the lean pot, the ship's plank sawn in the first quarter of the moon. These things are the accumulation of man's knowledge. Without them civilized man would die."

"Man is not so civilized," Robles said.

"No," Carranza agreed. "He is merely shaved by the razor of custom. Remove the razor for a day, and the cruel beard of his inner nature returns again to blacken his face. Civilization is a house with a high wall that conceals what used to take place plainly in the open. We have built the wall so high that we can no longer see into our own souls. We cannot even understand what goes on within us."

The stars were close, as always they are on a clear night in the tropics. A husky wind fanned away the mosquitoes. The brigantine churned somnolently at its hawser as though it too was asleep after the trials of the day.

"You feel more than most men," Orellana said.

"Civilization was built for the unfeeling," Carranza said. "The restlessness of men like ourselves, who pioneer an unknown world—what causes it? Why do we leave snug beds and gentle women and come out here to die on a stinking river no one before us has ever seen?"

"I have asked myself that question," Orellana said.

"It is because we feel," Carranza said. "We feel the yoke of custom about our necks, but we are not pulling to any purpose. We feel the pestle of precedent grinding us to dry powder in the mortar of stupidity. We must not think, we must not act, save as the laws of civilization may direct. And what are those laws? To serve in the king's wars, to kneel in the Pope's church, to be swineherds because our fathers were swineherds. The wars are not of our making, the church is not of God's making, and our fathers did not want to be swineherds. But the law is inexorable; we obey it or die."

"It is not as bad as that," Robles said. "We advance through defiance of custom and customary thought. Had Columbus obeyed the law, we should not be here, for the law placed no land here. Now in Germany Martin Luther preaches that God is in the heart, not in the prayer book, and men gain new hope. The measure of civilization is change, not constancy. You struggle, that your children may have better."

"My children!" Carranza said.

"You have children?" Orellana asked.

"No, thank God, I have not. I would not impose the afflictions of my youth on any child. I leave such cruelties to you Christians."

"Was it so bad, then?" Orellana did not ask any man about himself, but somehow he felt that tonight Carranza wanted to be led back over the thorns his feet had trodden.

"My people," Carranza volunteered, "lived in Granada, which then was Moorish. My father was a physician, and venerated for his knowledge. He taught medicine and astrology to the sons of noble families, holding classes in the Alhambra. At these classes I, too, sat.

"Then came the Spaniards. They took the city at last, scattering the Moors, enslaving them, slaughtering them in the name of Christ. Our family, however, was not touched. My father's father had lived in Valencia, where he had embraced Christianity to escape humiliation, and therefore my father had been born a Christian—through no fault of his own, of course. It was useful to him, like a cloak, but unimportant since we were well-seated among the Moors. What if we did, in the shadow of our homes, dress meat in oil instead of in lard, keep the Passover, and eat beef on fast days? Were we less observant of the faith than the Christian clergy? The Moors understood, but not the Christians."

He stirred. Bitterness sharpened his voice.

"Ferdinand and Isabella came to the fallen city and set up their court in the Alhambra. My father, with certain other Jews, wishing to show respect to the conquerors and win their favor, called upon the Queen and offered her a gift of thirty thousand ducats to help defray the expenses of the conquerors. The Queen seemed to favor them, when into the room burst her confessor, the insane bigot of the Inquisition, Torquemada. He saw what the Jews were doing. Stripping the crucifix from his waist, he shouted, 'Judas sold his master for thirty pieces of silver. Your Highnesses would sell Him again for thirty thousand. Here He is, take Him and sell Him.' He threw the crucifix on the table.

"That was the end of us. An edict was issued, expelling all Jews from Spain. I shall never forget the date—the thirtieth of March, 1492. My twelfth birthday. By July all Jews must be gone from Spain. Three months in which to prepare for exile! To make matters worse, all Jewish property was confiscated by the crown, and we were forbidden to take gold or silver with us. How could one finance flight?"

He paused, not expecting an answer, swallowing hard. Soon he resumed.

"My mother, my sister, and I must share this exile—but not my father. Remember that he had been baptized a Christian. Rather than separate from us, he renounced his Christian faith and prepared to go with us. The act proved fatal. Within a night he was taken by the Inquisition. A Jew might flee, but an apostate never. For renunciation of the Christ of mercy, he died on a Christian rack, torn apart by priests."

He looked up at the clear stars as though in wonder that they could shine upon a world so unclean.

"My widowed mother traded a vineyard for an ass on which her children might ride, her costly furniture for our clothing. Yet we did not know where to go. By luck we were able to hide some rubies from the king's men, but they would not buy anything, for all Spaniards had been interdicted from sheltering or feeding us along our way.

"We set out westward. Some said Portugal would receive us, but it was only a hope. I remember the long line that crossed the Roman bridge and climbed into the hills that day we left, the sick, the helpless old women, the little children. My sister and I were lucky; we were on the donkey, led by my mother afoot. Few were so lucky. The line of emigrants reached from Granada to Málaga, a distance of four hundred miles. Some say farther, I do not know. Six weeks we journeyed, without shelter, or any food except what we could steal in the fields by night, constantly beset by priests who exhorted us to confess our sins and become Christians. What sins? What Christianity?"

He shook his curly hair sadly.

"In Portugal we exchanged a ruby ring for the privilege of using the king's highway from the border to Lagos, on condition that we would not remain in the land. Another ruby paid our fare by boat to Tangier. But rubies do not last forever. Along the hot desert, walking now toward Fez, my mother was stripped naked by brigands searching plunder, and when they found none, they looted her body and left her dying along the road. In her defense I lost consciousness and never saw my sister again. There was nothing in Fez except starvation. I begged passage aboard a ship to Naples. It was filled with refugees who, like myself, had no place to go. Black pox hit the fleet and more of us died than arrived. There we were not permitted to land. We were unclean. Three days we remained in harbor, eyeing the free gray shore, then went on to Turkey, where at last in an unchristian land, we were received. The refuge of homeless men, however, is but the prelude to death; it cannot be called living. I think I have not lived since."

He had finished.

"How many of you were exiled from Spain?" Robles asked huskily. He was too young to have remembered all this.

"I do not know," Carranza said. "A half million, more or less. What does it matter? They are all dead."

Later, Orellana went to the hold to talk to Father Carvajal. He had expected to find the priest suffering sleeplessly, but found him sitting up, talking quietly to Friar de Vera, who was still trussed in ivy ropes.

"What are we to do with this outrage?" Carvajal asked Orellana.

Orellana sat down upon a baule of ship's stores, and shrugged. He thought of Carranza, and knew that if de Vera were shown mercy, he himself must decree the clemency, for the chaplain would not. The mercy of Christ was not reflected in the stern priest.

"Let him go," Orellana said. "He can do us no further harm."

"He has sinned and he must suffer."

"That is your problem, then, not mine," Orellana said. "My captaincy ends with the body. I try to ease suffering, not to cause it."

Father Carvajal turned away. He had no desire to match wits with Orellana, particularly before the friar.

"Your Indian captive," Carvajal said, changing the subject, "has come around. I think he is hungry."

"Yes," Orellana said. "I have brought him manioc and water. I want to talk to him." He addressed words to the savage in the Aparian tongue but drew no response. Slowly, by trial and error, a rudimentary vocabulary was worked out between them. Orellana, who had probed so many tribal tongues, soon understood, and was understood in turn.

The Indian was pleased and responded. Tactfully Orellana interpreted his words to Father Carvajal, who listened raptly, and once burst out, "Orellana, my son, you are given the gift of tongues. When this voyage is finished, you must become a missionary priest. It is your duty."

"I have a greater duty," Orellana replied, turning back to the Indian. His name was Cuenco, son of the overlord through whose territory the Castilians then were passing. They were subject peoples of Queen Coñorí.

Orellana asked about these female warriors, and whether they were the tall savages who clubbed the cowards in the fight.

"They are indeed women," Cuenco said with a grave face, and in answer to the chaplain's questions, which Orellana relayed, Father Carvajal received astounding information. Cuenco's replies were mainly brief affirmatives to Father Carvajal's queries, but in sum they drew the picture of a race of women who inhabited seventy large villages. None but women inhabited these towns, and none was married. When they desired children, men were captured as consorts until the women became pregnant, after which the men were killed or sent home again. Male children were destroyed, females were reared as warriors. Their queen was a giant of pure white skin, who ate only from gold and silver vessels and dressed in the finest wool except during battle, at which time she appeared naked with her troops.

Orellana knew that the story was not true. He had observed many times that the savage will respond affirmatively to any leading question, for in his code it is ill-mannered to contradict anyone. Therefore Cuenco confirmed the theories Father Carvajal expounded, scarcely understanding them, but Orellana did not interfere. Father Carvajal, the literal man, was too greatly impressed.

"Justinus writes of a savage race," Carvajal said to Orellana, "a nation of warrior women called Amazons. The word in Greek means 'having no breasts.' They cut off their breasts lest the protruding surface interfere with aiming the bow. Ask this man if these women do likewise."

But Orellana phrased the question this time to suit himself rather than the priest. "Do the women," he asked Cuenco, "have two breasts?"

"Yes," the captive said.

"And they shoot accurately?"

"Yes. Their breasts are beautiful, likewise their aim."

"Remarkable, remarkable," Father Carvajal exclaimed. "I must enter it in my journal. The learned men of all Europe will be impressed."

Orellana smiled. Before long, he knew, Cuenco's story would be in every historical chronicle in Europe. Carvajal would put it there. Sometimes, he thought, the learned man is simpler than the savage. Down the entire span of the river Father Carvajal had seen that in every tribe the women worked, the men fought. It was the jungle law. It was natural that Cuenco, the son of a chieftain subject to another, should make the subjugation convincing. Man who is subject to another man is a coward, but man dominated by a woman is merely in the hands of fate.

"What will you do with me?" the Indian asked.

"Return you to your home," Orellana answered. "We have no quarrel with you."

Cuenco was amazed. Orellana took the opportunity to instruct the Indian carefully in the Castilian faith. This lad, he thought, may well be a chief when I return, and I shall need him.

"I could kill you," he said, "even as you have killed my men. But we Christians do not like to die, or kill. We would prefer to live among you, when we come again."

"And when will you let me go?"

"In my own time," Orellana said. "I have further use for you."

He was thinking of the many islands in the river. This lad would know the channel through them, and could act as guide.

Next day the savages attacked again, and Father Carvajal could no longer stay below decks.

"Now I know," he said, joining Orellana in the bows, "how it feels to be only half a man, and see in one direction only."

"Don't grieve, Father," Orellana replied brightly. "Stay close beside me. Keep always on my left. Then with my good right eye, and your good left one, we shall each have a pair, and shall see as well as any man."

The priest rallied. "If you can jest about it, my son, it must not be so bad."

"No, it is not bad," Orellana agreed. "It just makes a man ugly, and that is no concern to you. You are not interested in pretty girls. You will learn in time to see better. Lack sharpens appreciation. Anyway, what is the loss of an eye to what you have gained?"

"What is that?"

"Why," Orellana said, half mocking, "did you not go ashore in the interests of the feast of John the Baptist? Was it not in his service that you lost an eye? Have you not won his eternal gratitude? There is nothing he will not do for you, now. Save for the intercession of the Virgin, whose patronage could one wish in heaven above that of Saint John?"

"Ah!" Father Carvajal gasped. "God forgive my sins. I am unworthy of such sponsorship. And yet—who knows, who knows?"

Cheerily he hurried away and began to wash his robe. To the ominous black streak upon his cassock now was added a mass of bloodstains from his gory wound. He set to work with a holystone, dipping water from the river. The spot was stubborn. Finally forsaking modesty, he doffed the robe, rubbed it well and hung it to dry in the fiery sun. Then he went below and fell asleep.

When he awoke, hours later, and appeared on deck, he could not believe his sight. The robe was spotless.

He took it in his hands, fingered it, pressed it to his lips. With zealous awe he donned it as though it was a sacred relic, and slumped to his knees.

"Good Saint John," he prayed, "herald of Christ, I am unworthy of such intercession. My sins were heavy. Now I am as white as snow. From this day my miserable talent is dedicated to your special service, after that of God and His Son. I shall try to be worthy of your benign protection."

The miracle was heralded upon the two ships and all came to see the miraculous robe. Most of the men kissed it. Kneeling before it, Friar de Vera again received absolution from his sins.

But Carranza the Jew was not impressed.

"By the God of Abraham," he exclaimed to Orellana, "there is a powerful bleaching agent here somewhere. . . . Let me see. He washed the robe in river water, and hung it to dry in the sun. If the tide came this far upriver, there would be salt in it, and the action of salt and this tropical sun would bleach anything. Do you suppose—?"

He hurried to the ship's side, scooped a palmful of water and lapped it with his tongue. He arose beaming.

"Orellana!" he called excitedly. "Captain—come here! There is salt in the water. We are near the sea!"

29

Tidewater in the river made imperative a new landing for supplies. Now drinking water must be laid by, as well as food. Forty-five hundred miles the little company had traveled since leaving Don Gonzalo Pizarro, and now at last, after one hundred eighty-five days of torment, there was salt water—salt from the same ocean that kissed the shores of Spain.

The river was gentler than before, the climate more temperate, the humidity at last bearable. Chiggers no longer tormented the men, although mosquitoes and black flies followed after the ships in a cloud. The shores were high land with hills and valleys thickly populated.

Canoemen still attacked, but the physique of the natives had changed. The men were giants, taller even than Cuenco, but not pale like Lalah. Their hair was short-clipped, and they ventured upon the river covered with black dye, and gayly decked in coral.

Seeking Cuenco to ask about these people, Orellana found him in coquettish conversation with Lalah. He watched them for a moment. She had opened like a mariposa under the sun of Cuenco's company. He was a prince among her people, son of the overlord of her own tribe. The magic of her deep feminine arts beckoned to him, and he responded. They did not see Orellana. He withdrew quietly, and left them to their play. Love was everywhere. It was the one indestructible. Neither savagery, captivity, nor war dismayed it. Like the cactus of Andalusia, it prospered on desert soil and made fruitful the barren plain of existence. On the deck of a Spanish brigantine two captives, man and girl, of different tribes and different dialects, could still respond to love.

He returned to the bow, where Robles chafed.

"Captain," Robles said, "you'd better pry those pagans apart or there will be trouble."

Orellana saw that he was jealous. "Let them be, Alonso," he said. "You do not want her."

"I cannot work for thinking of her," Robles responded. "The sight of her, rolling her eyes at that savage makes my sword itch."

"Let her be. She is under my protection, and she will not be defiled here."

"I do not mean to defile her, Francisco," Robles said. "I wish to take her back to Spain with me. You can understand what it means to a man to want a wife."

"Nombre de Dios," Orellana exclaimed. "You, an hidalgo, would marry this savage?"

"Yes."

"You would take her to Spain, to live among civilized people, among gentlemen? She who has never seen a knife and only once a cup?"

"Yes."

Orellana shook his head. "No, friend. If you love her, forget her. It is the kindest thing."

"I cannot forget her, any more than you can forget my cousin Ana, whom you have not even seen."

"How do you know you love her? You cannot even talk to her."

"I love her."

"Have you touched her?"

"No, by God's mercy I swear, I have not touched her."

"Then how do you know you love her?"

"I have seen her."

Orellana put his hand on his friend's shoulder.

"Anything I have I would give you gladly, Alonso," he said, "anything in the world. But this I cannot. It does not belong to me."

"You do not have to. I will find a way to win her."

Orellana looked at Lalah, still embraced in conversation with the tall prince. He was everything she could ever want. Were Robles even Philip, son of Charles of Spain, he would have nothing to offer her

269

in comparison to what she now had, in the middle of a jungle river.

"You must forget her," he said. "It would not work. She is too sweet to be defiled by civilized people."

He turned away, knowing that this day he must put her ashore.

A little later he called Cuenco to him.

"I would give you your freedom, Cuenco," he said, "in return for a favor."

The Indian nodded.

"Our little Lalah is far from home. We took her from a village of three huts attending a field of oats, one day's journey upstream from the domain of the Paguana. If you row hard, that would be twelve days from here."

"I know," Cuenco said. "I can find it."

"I will give you your life and your freedom today—if you will take her home."

The Indian nodded again, more gravely.

"You must protect her from all evil, including yourself."

"Yes."

"You must deliver her to her own people."

"Yes."

"You will do this for me?"

"I will do it for myself and for you," Cuenco said.

Steadily Orellana looked at him. "What assurance have I that you will keep your pledge, and will not stop off among your own kind before you take her home?"

Cuenco thought a moment. From his head he took a corona of canary yellow feathers with small green feathers at its base, and handed it to Orellana. Gravely Orellana received it.

"By the mark that shows you are a chief's son," he said. "I could ask nothing more. Go now."

A canoe was lowered overside. Cuenco jumped into it, in his hand a cloth containing every scrap of food that remained to the campany.

Lalah went to the ship's side and turned. Orellana was watching her.

"When you return," she said, "you will find us?"

"Yes, Lalah, I will find you."

"You will live among us?"

"Yes. I will build a Spanish city at the town that makes the porcelain."

"Then do not search for me among my own people," she said, giggling. "Find Cuenco and you will find me."

"Go with God," Orellana replied. She understood the phrase now, after eleven days in the company of white men.

"Hasta luego," she replied, delighted with her Spanish, and was gone.

Robles stepped to Orellana's side. "It was unkind of you, Francisco," he said, "when you knew I wanted her."

Orellana pointed upstream, where the man and the woman equally shared the burden of the oars, two tiny figures fusing slowly into a single silhouette.

"Could you give her what he can give her?" he asked.

Robles looked long at the receding canoe.

"No," he answered bitterly, and went below, where he could not see the river.

They tried for two days to find safe landing, but could gain no foothold among the fierce giants. Twice they were furiously repulsed.

On the evening of the second day there was no water, and no food save Father Carvajal's horde of manioc dough that he had prepared for the Host. The men eyed the food, but none touched it.

Father Carvajal observed their covetous glances, and at first was horrified. Then, as hunger continued to gnaw at his own belly, his horror waned. Why not? he thought. We must land tomorrow, and tomorrow we shall all die. What more fitting death, then, than blessed with the Holy Ghost?

He took his precious manioc and went on deck. The brigantines had been lashed together and anchored for the night. The men had assembled for vespers.

Father Carvajal took the Host, knelt and prayed, asking Christ to forgive him if what he was about to do was sacrilege. Then he began the Mass. At the passage "Domine, non sum dignus," he paused, walked among the men and fed to each a morsel of the Host, taking intricate care that not a crumb dropped upon the profane deck.

When he came to Carranza he paused. The man was kneeling. Father Carvajal had believed him to be a Jew. Yet it was incomprehensible to the chaplain that any man, even in hunger, should receive the sacrament profanely. Still he paused, fearing that the Lord might open up the earth if Carranza received the Host. The starry heaven, however, was serene. Carranza ate.

At dawn the spell of the Host was still upon them all. Almost before they were adjusted to the oars, a little village appeared upon a sharp bluff, overlooking a waterfall.

"May God have mercy on us," Orellana said. "We land here."

"Amen," said Father Carvajal.

They went ashore. The Indians were fierce, but thirst and hunger were fiercer. During the landing Carranza was nicked in the leg by an arrow. The wound was insignificant. He continued ashore, fought with the rest, drove off the natives long enough to secure food and many casks of water.

But that afternoon, safe again upon the river, Carranza noticed that his leg still bled. He touched the wound with a finger, and smelled the blood, recoiling from its stench. He recognized the vile odor at once. He, the physician who had healed so many bodies and so many hearts, knew that his time had come. The evidence of blood poison was unmistakable. There was no cure for it. No cautery, no unguent, no spell. In the whole pharmacoepia of his knowledge there was no antidote for it, nor had constant quest among the savages for fifteen hundred leagues discovered any. He was dead. For seven months he had feared that one day a victim might be brought whom he could not cure. Now that victim had come. It was himself.

He knew what to expect: a heavy chill during the night, a high fever subsiding by morning. A few hours of peace, then fever and delirium,

272

another short peace, another fever. By then the wound would reek, the flesh about it would crackle to the touch. Bubbles of air would ripple up his leg from the wound, blackening the skin. Then another agony of delirium, followed by peaceful death. Three days.

He said nothing to anyone, lest they conclude he had been wounded by a poisoned arrow and be unduly alarmed. He knew by now that the Indians never used poison on human beings, lest they destroy the charm of the drug that brought down their meat. Rather, he thought, he was an accidental victim. Once he had seen some natives leave their arrows in a peccary until the cadaver was rotten. Such arrows would carry a poison for five or six days. The arrow that had struck him perhaps had been used for hunting not many days earlier. In any event, he was as good as dead.

He could not hide his affliction from old Soria. The aging man, who now followed Carranza as a little child its father, could not be deceived. He saw the black death rising, noticed the first fever.

"Amigo," he said, "you are ill."

"Soft," Carranza answered. "An arrow scratch. It will pass."

Soria was terrified. Carranza was his life. He ran babbling and crying to Orellana, who came at once. Carranza was chagrined.

"No peace," he said. "All my life, no peace. I cannot even die quietly."

"You are not going to die," Orellana answered, and called for help. At the risk of the brigantine, a fire was built on deck to heat an iron. Tender hands applied the torture, but it did no good. The black bubble crept up the leg like a living thing.

Father Carvajal meanwhile was in panic. Carranza had received the Sacrament—would he likewise accept extreme unction? He bent over Carranza, now weak from the ordeal of the iron.

"Do you receive the Father, the Son and the Holy Ghost?"

"Away!" Carranza shouted. "I need no intercessor to reach my God. He is with me always, even to the ends of the earth."

Father Carvajal went at once. Carranza was forgotten as the chaplain begged God to forgive his own terrible sin.

Downstream the brigantines plodded, feeling definitely now the rise and swell of the tide. Carranza felt it, too.

"It surges up in me," he told Soria, "like a caress from my mother's hand. Mother! Mother! What has become of thee?"

He slept. Orellana came, bringing water to Soria, who would not leave the ragged litter, or allow anyone to relieve him of the devotion of fanning away mosquitoes with a palm branch.

Carranza awoke during the night.

"Little sister," he cried out, "little sister, can you hear me?"

He listened a long time, but there was no answer.

By morning he did not know anything more. Soria sat beside him, without food or water, two days until he died.

Father Carvajal came at once.

"Overboard with him," he said, "he died in terrible sin."

Orellana put his hand upon his sword.

"Father," he said, "go to the *San Pedro* and remain there until I tell you to come again."

The priest flushed.

"Do as you are told," Orellana said sharply. "I am in command here."

The priest went.

Orellana and Soria wrapped the body in the sailcloth that once had been a horse blanket, and over the humble bier erected a canopy against the cruel sun. Orellana went on deck.

"We must land," he said to Robles.

"It is impossible. The enemy is all about us."

"Put ashore at once," Orellana said. "I will go alone if there is so much danger."

"If you go, I follow," Robles answered, and gave the order putting the *Victoria* ashore. The *San Pedro* was to stand off, guarding the water way.

Diego Mexía, who was on the *San Pedro*, asked permission to follow. None knew why; he had not been Carranza's friend. In the hand that Carranza had healed, Mexía carried a knife. Hernández, the Portuguese, whose king had taken a ruby ring from Carranza's mother, appeared quietly with a digging iron.

"It is on your own heads if you give him Christian burial," Carvajal screamed from the *San Pedro*. No one listened.

Orellana, Robles, Hernández, Soria, these four carried the body ashore, while aboard the *Victoria* the arquebusiers and crossbowmen stood alert, their eyes on the shoreline. Diego Mexía also went ashore, but did not stay with the others.

"Dig deeply," Orellana said. "He must not fall to wild beasts."

The pit was deep. Soria cried unashamed. The body was lowered tenderly into its grave, quickly covered. The men stood back. Absently Soria gathered flowers and sprinkled them upon the new earth. Something, however, was lacking, and none knew exactly what it was.

Soria stepped to the grave and looked down.

"By the God of Abraham and Isaac and Jacob, who is also the God of Jesus and Mary, I swear to avenge you, Antonio, if it costs me my life, I shall avenge you."

"Amen," said Robles, "rest in peace."

Orellana stepped forward.

"You will not be lonely long, friend Carranza," he said. "We are coming back. We are coming back here to this shore. One day you will see, along this bank, a rich nation in which your children and Nogal's children, and all children, for your sake, will live in security and peace. Your name shall be revered throughout the land on that day, Antonio, and we shall put over you a mausoleum of marble. I swear it."

"Goodby, friend," said Robles.

They were about to go. There was no time left. The Indians might come at any moment.

From the woods hurried Diego Mexía, the wood carver, touching wood with his knife. In his hand was a fresh jacaranda stave. He had started to hew a cross and then, instead, had scratched hurriedly a single word.

"Amigo," it said.

He placed the stake upright, and struck it home firmly at the head of the little mound of dirt.

They looked at it a moment, reading the simple epitaph.

"Thank you, Diego," Orellana said huskily. "You are the noblest Christian of us all."

30

ARCÍA DE SORIA was lost. He wandered about the *Victoria* as though he were forsaken in a vast green jungle. The other men ignored him; they were implacable trees in the forest, covered with thick bark. He could not talk to them. The deck, cluttered with coils of ivy rope and stretching sheets, was a wood alive with pendant parasites. Of course there were mosquitoes everywhere, but Soria was alone.

None now listened to his tales of treasure buried in Peru. He had told them too often for credence; they were the delusions of an old man's dotage. Friar de Vera had been careful at first to listen and mark upon a paper the location of these treasures. His crucifix was of poured lead, hollow on the inside, and the head, affixed to an inch-long spike, could be removed. In this sanctuary de Vera could secrete objects upon which his church might frown, but which were useful or necessary to him. The paper, marking the treasures, went into the crucifix to keep company with three stolen emeralds, a lodestone talisman once taken from the body of a Magyar necromancer, and a bright red curl of woman's hair.

García de Soria did not know about the secret chamber in the crucifix. Yet had he known, had he realized that the black priest planned one day to return to Peru and unearth these fortunes in Inca silver and gold, he would not have cared. What good now were a million or so pesos? They could not buy dreams, and they could not buy life. Carranza, with whom he would have shared both life and dreams, was gone. He tried, in a bumbling way, to explain this to a few of the men, but they said, "Go away, old man, you are crazy." They, who bought friendships and gambled them away, were the crazy ones, Soria thought. Carranza had taught him that. Man was enriched,

Carranza had said, by the golden glow, twenty-four carats fine, in his own heart; it was an inexhaustible treasure that grew in proportion to the amount of it that was spent. Not like gold. Gold was an inflationary, fickle friend, untrustworthy; the heart remained undebased until one died.

The brigantine was astir with unusual construction. Heavy planks up to the height of a man's chest were being nailed along the decks, and similar work employed the companions on the smaller vessel. Soria watched.

"What's that?" he asked at last.

"Go away, old man, can't you see we're busy?"

"But what are you doing?"

"Putting up a barricade against poisoned arrows."

"Why?"

"Do you want us all to be killed?"

"What difference? You are dead already."

At an abandoned village the company landed. Soria was first ashore, ignoring the leadership of Lieutenant Robles, and in a panic sought Indians, that he might kill them. He found none. Neither was there food. The water casks and gourds were filled, but the men remained hungry. Orellana would have explored the country inland for edible roots, but he was stopped by a strange high cry from the top of an oak tree.

"Hui, hui! Flee, flee!"

The warning bird. Soria thought of Carranza. "Yes, amigo, we will heed your bird of omen. Do not disturb your rest. You are still with us."

The bird dipped low over the *Victoria*, wheeling softly like a hawk without a wing flutter, and for the first time Soria could see its golden head and its body with an azure tuft and neck.

Soria waved his hand. The bird seemed to look at him for a moment, hanging motionless in the hot sky. Then it dipped its wings, once more circled the brigantine, and made off upstream. It was never seen again.

Now Soria could see the nature of the bird's warning. Up river, in fine formation, came so many pirogues that they jammed the channel. They were larger than usual, heavier, more substantial, more menacing.

"Dogs," Soria muttered, "dogs of murderers, she swine, goats; pox, cankers, festers, offal. Where is my crossbow? Where is it, I say?"

He found it. A great calm bathed his face. Affectionately, tenderly, he fitted his arrow and drew the bolt. The chief in the lead canoe was standing, directing the rest to circle the ships and close from all sides.

"Watch this, Carranza," Soria said. "You will admire this."

He fired. Straight and true the arrow whined across the water, deep into the leader's throat. He toppled into the water.

Soria laughed, "How was that, Antonio amigo?" He bent double with delight. "He will not recover from that. He will not even complain of his sore throat."

Coldness seized him again. The savages were closing rapidly. Like a precision machine Soria began to move, the crossbow a part of him. Left hand back to the right shoulder, withdrawing an arrow from the quiver. Right hand under to the stock. Flip for the arrow, tug for the stock, up with the elbows, steady now, hold the breath—fire! The arrows were not wasted.

He did not know when he fired his last arrow. The machine went on working. Right hand up, seizing the arrow that was not there. Tug for the stock, up with the elbows, hold the breath—fire! The arrow that now was only in his mind sped true. Men fell. He did not know that all about him others of the company were firing too, and that the arquebuses were roaring. Of course men fell. But he was alone; he killed them all.

Suddenly he realized that he was not alone, and that his quiver was empty. He looked about. A pirogue containing twelve Indians, all of them coated with black dye, was about to crash the *Victoria*. He drew his sword. Lieutenant Robles was ahead of him. At close range, Robles fired an arquebus with such effect that the bow of the canoe was blasted from the water.

"Bravo!" Soria shouted, and mounted to the cross for a better view. He could not see well behind the new waist-high barricade. An arquebus in the hands of Pedro de Acaray dropped two Indians with a single shot. Diego Mexía duplicated the feat a moment later with a crossbow. The Indians were so close now that the Castilians could not miss.

"Bravo," screamed Soria, and fell, an arrow in his throat.

The Indians could not withstand the two double deaths among their warriors. Enough was enough. They fled. The only casualty among the Spaniards was Soria, who had left the protection of the new barricade.

He died of the wound. He was gone before dawn, having commended his soul to God. This time, however, Orellana could not risk a landing. The body was trussed in a woolen shroud, weighted and dropped overboard. Father Carvajal lifted his eyes to the first gray of dawn.

"Merciful Saint John," he begged, "cannot you help put an end to this dying? Just this one favor I ask you, and never another. Intercede for us, if you have any love for miserable men, and lead us out of this madness."

Two days later, without again having been seriously attacked, they veered out from a nest of islands and saw the sea.

31

WITHOUT compass or pilot or navigator, the brigantines set out upon the open sea.

They did not set out bravely. In all the company there was not one experienced seaman, now that Juan de Alcantara was dead. There was no physician, for Carranza was gone. There was little food. Aboard the brigantines, to begin a fifteen hundred mile ocean voyage in ships that had been built to ply a river, were a few snails, crabs and frogs scavanged from the islands, and sufficient maize to give each man ten grains a day.

Just before the departure, each man filled his water jar at a fresh spring. The day was the twenty-sixth of August, Saint Louis' Day, the two-hundred-fifteenth since the parting with Gonzalo Pizarro. Orellana commanded the *Victoria*; Miradero resumed his old stand in the bow of the *San Pedro*, with Robles as his second in command.

More than six thousand miles they had rowed and sailed the meandering rivers. Fifteen men had died. There was scarcely a man among them whose mother would have recognized his whitened hair, the scar-creases in his face, the haunted fever in his eyes. Strong men were frail, the frail were weak, the weak had died. Fat Juan de Penalosa was gaunt; lean Francisco de Isasaga, the scrivener, was cadaverous. Philosophical fisherman Gabriel de Contreros had become a cynic, and cynical Diego Mexía, the woodcarver, now was sentimental. The youth Blas de Medina was a man, and at last had a beard. The seven months of suffering had put on each man a mark according to his humor; starvation had robbed every man of his digestion. All had known fever, dysentery, the torment of chiggers, despair, and the stench of death. Only the two priests were untouched. One of them remained, for all the suffering he had seen, the blind believer, confirmed in his faith by many miracles, worshiper according to the Dogma; the other was a rogue, and remained a rogue.

Even Maldonado, the intriguer, was changed. From open villainy he had progressed to secret hate. He was taking with him from the river an intense deeply buried singleness of purpose: to bring Orellana low. De Vera to some extent shared this with him. Maldonado did not want to kill Orellana; that was too easy. He wanted to disgrace him, humble him, shame him, break him. Nothing else was of any importance to him. He had felt the isolation of scorn, the loneliness of contempt, the living death of segregation. For the damnation of the past seventy days, in which no man of the company had sought his companionship except the friar, he blamed Orellana rather than the blackness of his own character. In a situation in which sixty-three men, dwindling under duress to forty-eight, were in fact the entire world, alone together on a river, suffering hardships of such intense fire as to fuse individuals into a united brotherhood, Maldonado was an outcast. De Vera did not count; the frock already had isolated him. Maldonado had not been fused, he was no brother, and he hated it. The hatred solidified against the person of Francisco Orellana.

For four days the brigantines were in sight of each other. Then, on the night of the Beheading of Saint John the Baptist, they became separated in the darkness.

On the fifth morning, from the deck of the *Victoria*, Orellana saw no sign of the *San Pedro*. He cruised the *Victoria* close inshore, in the hope that if the *San Pedro* and its crew of fifteen had been washed ashore, he might attempt a rescue. In three days there was no sign at all. The only effect of the search was that the *Victoria* was driven, before anyone realized the danger, into the dread Mouths of the Dragon in the Gulf of Paria.

They had feared this passage, a narrow strait through which the wind drives constantly landward. Sailing vessels poking alongshore without maps are in the strait and driving downwind before they discover their peril, and once inside, even the sturdiest sailing ship cannot beat to windward on a close enough tack to push to the open sea, so narrow is the channel.

Seven days Orellana and his companions fought the Dragon of Paria. Riding the outgoing tide, rowing like madmen, they would gain half a league, until sometimes they could see the tantalizing green water beyond the Dragon's mouth. Then the tide would change and the wind would sweep them in again, exhausted and forlorn, destroying in an hour the work of a day. The last drop of fresh water disappeared on the fourth day. On the fifth, Orellana inventoried the remaining grain and established a ration of five grains of maize per day. On the seventh, some among the company wanted to put ashore and attempt an overland passage. For once Orellana steeled himself against the advice of his company, and again turned the prow of the *Victoria* toward the sea.

"God did not bring us this far to perish," Orellana said, and Father Carvajal agreed.

Half the company now lay prostrate from thirst and hunger. The outward tide began an hour before dawn. Orellana himself took a place at the forward starboard oar, the Negro Nogal opposite him on the port side. Father Carvajal, hoisting his frock above his knotty knees, mounted the oar behind Orellana with Gutiérrez to help him. Hernández and Contreros, and all others who could stand, attended the sails.

Taking their stroke from Nogal, who lifted his voice in a wild, primitive cry, they began to move. Revolted by the pagan chant of the blackman, Father Carvajal roared out, in Nogal's rhythm, the strongest counteractive words he knew.

"Credo in unum Deum."

The men picked up the familiar words, accenting them with the stroke of their oars.

"Patrem omnipotentem, factorem caeli et terrae, visibilium omnium, et invisibilium. Et in unum Dominum Jesum Christum, Filium Dei unigenitum. Et ex Patre natum ante omnia saecula. Deum de Deo,

lumen de lumine, Deum verum de Deo vero, genitum non factum, consubstantialem Patri, per quem omnia facta sunt."

"We are moving," sang Blas de Medina, acting as helmsman. The chant swelled.

"*Qui propter nos homines, et propter nostram salutem descendit de caelis. Et incarnatus est de Spiritu Sanctu ex Maria Virgine, et homo factus est.*"

"We are gaining way," Blas de Medina called.

Father Carvajal lifted his face toward the wet morning, heavy with humid dew, salt spray and wind, and faith rang out of his throat like a clear church bell.

"*Crucifixus etiam pro nobis, sub Pontio Pilato passus, et sepultus est. Et resurrexit tertia die, secundum Scripturas. Et ascendit in caelum, sedet ad dexteram Patris. Et iterum venturus est cum gloria judicare vivos et mortuos, cujus regni non erit finis.*"

"The wind fails," Blas de Medina sang, "now is our chance. Row, brothers, row." He leaped down from the helm to stroke with Nogal, the proud Castilian hidalgo bending his back with that of a black slave, to the rhythm of the Christian Credo.

Tears bathed Father Carvajal's pointed beard.

"*Et in Spiritum Sanctum, Dominum, et vivificantem, qui ex Patre Filioque procedit. Qui cum Patre et Filio simul adoratur, et conglorificatur, qui locutus est per Prophetas.*"

"How are we now?" Orellana panted.

"In a flat calm," came from the deck. "The wind has completely died. Row, for the love of God."

The men clenched their teeth and gulped with their heavy oars huge bites of the stubborn sea. Father Carvajal, his voice triumphant though broken with emotion, chanted on alone.

"*Et unam sanctam catholicam et apostolicam Ecclesiam. Confiteor unum baptisma in remissionem peccatorum. Et exspecto resurrectionem mortuorum. Et vitam venturi saeculi.*"

"Amen," said Orellana. The priest did not join him. He had slumped unconscious over his oar. Clumsy hands hauled him topside and swilled salt water on his face. The *Victoria* plied on, more rapidly now on the outgoing tide, plodding inch by inch toward the luring green-haired siren of deep water.

Father Carvajal did not revive until the sun was high. The oars still creaked. New men now were at the locks, and they were not breaking their backs.

"Did we make it?" he asked.

"You know we made it, Father."

"Of course I knew," Carvajal said. "God forgive my doubts. Water, Orellana, water, I beg you."

"There will be water shortly, Father," Orellana said. "It is beginning to rain."

They reached Cubagua, the genial little island of pearls, two days later, on Monday, the Eleventh of September.

Hauling with shouts of joy, forgetful of hunger, into the shallow harbor that sheltered the town of Nueva Cadiz, they saw riding at anchor the familiar outline of the *San Pedro*. It had arrived without incident two days earlier. Alonso Robles leaped six feet of open water from the dock to the *Victoria* to clasp Orellana in his arms.

32

THE AGENTS of Bartholomew Welser and Company, German bankers, were delighted to give Francisco Orellana a letter of twelve hundred dollars' credit for an emerald of priceless quality. The Welsers had an office in Nueva Cadiz because of the pearl trade. Not often did an emerald reach their delicate hands for appraisal, and being bankers they appreciated not only its true worth—six thousand dollars—but the desperateness of Orellana's situation. They had heard, for traders hear everything, about this one-eyed explorer late of Peru and the River of the Amazons, and how he intended to return to Spain with three companions to tell his story to the king. Adding rapidly in their minds the cost of the passage and second-rate clothes for the quartet, the bankers concluded that twelve hundred dollars would be acceptable to this emaciated Castilian.

Francisco Orellana took the money, although he knew as well as they the true value of his gem. It was not the best of his collection, but it was flawless and of ten carats' weight, roughly cut in a pear shape by Inca workmen. Under the hand of a Flemish artist it would emerge a pendant of near eight carats which would undoubtedly delight some favorite of Francis of France or Henry of England, or even the fat fingers of a merchant's wife.

There were other odd and curious gems in Orellana's vicuña sack, including one he hoped would please Ana de Ayala, but they remained hidden. Orellana did not want the Welser agents to see, for example, the twenty-carat emerald in the shape of a fish eye, nor the fourteen-carat stone modeled like a water jar. The Incas had loved emeralds, particularly the northern branch of the family at Quito, which had developed a technique for shaping and polishing them to adorn the vessels and persons of the royal family. Many of the best examples of the royal gems had been smashed with hammers by the Spaniards in tests of their quality. In his explorations that led to the founding of Guayaquil, Orellana had profited by Pizarro's lesson in destruction. He had hoarded what stones he found. All had come to him legitimately, from his share in the spoils. Pizarro and the crown had taken the largest. Sometimes, however, the largest were not the most precious and where Orellana had seen magnificent smaller stones, he had claimed them.

Thus the fish eye, the water jar, and most beguiling of all, seven emerald roses, exactly alike in the finest Inca craftsmanship, of exactly the same weight, nine-and-three-fourths carats, which for precision, luster, and perfection were of unbelievable beauty. One alone of these roses carried away the breath; the seven, laid out together so that they traded their perfections back and forth among themselves like precious secrets, would bring a fortune in Spain. In Spain, Orellana knew, he would need such a fortune to finance his return to the New World. He was even sorry, now, that he had cast aside, with such contempt, the cup of Atahualpa. Among civilized men, wealth was everything. Only the savage gave true value for his barter. Refined men drove hard the bargain, and offered half of what a thing was worth. The sharper the trade, the more elegant the credit of the usurer. To the height of his pile of gold man had climbed above the savage, there and no farther; yet only the savage was truly rich.

He returned to his companions. They shared quarters in a wooden house alongside the wharf, their one window facing the narrow entrance to Cubagua's roadstead. Should a ship enroute from Panama to Spain drop anchor, two of the four were constantly on hand to put out in the *San Pedro* and solicit passage eastward.

Gutiérrez and Hernández were on watch when Orellana returned from the House of Welser. Robles was scouting the settlement for clothing. Between the four of them they were able to muster one pair of boots, a doublet, cuirass and casque, and they had traded one of the *Victoria's* horse-blanket sails for that most important item of hidalgo clothing, a good cape. At the moment, Orellana was wearing the community ensemble. It had been thought best that a beggar should not look like one. Robles, foraging, wore rags.

Orellana had not told his companions about the emeralds. He was going to the Welsers, he said, to seek a loan, not exactly an untruth.

"Look you, amigos," he said, spreading the letter of credit before them. "Who says I am not a bargainer? Juan de Illanes with his loaded dice could not have done better."

The eyes of Gutiérrez and Hernández were on the window.

"And look you, General," Gutiérrez said. For all the trials of the river, for all the intimacies of starving days and nights upon a tiny craft, for all the sharing of heartache and death, Gutiérrez could not be informal with Orellana. He respected his leader too much to cheapen the relation with casual friendship.

Orellana looked over the shoulder of the wizened Portuguese, Hernández. A caravel was reefing sail and rattling anchor chain in the roadstead. Already at anchor, low in the water, lay a larger vessel well-fitted and prosperous, such as was only seen in the New World on her maiden voyage from Spain.

Quickly Orellana took off his armor and hurled it to the bed, boots and all.

"You, Gutiérrez," he said, "put on our elegance and meet the long boats. Find out who they are. And here—tuck my jeweled dagger in your belt and mind you don't cover it with the cape." He and Hernández helped strap the mountain man into his harness.

"I cannot wear the cape, General," Gutiérrez said. "I am no gentleman."

"As fine a one as ever married the daughter of a grandee, my friend," Orellana replied. "Perhaps finer, for you have a quicker sword and therefore no one can argue the matter. Go quickly. We can't stand naked long."

Gutiérrez left, awkward in the cloak. Orellana sat back on the bed and laughed.

"I have always wondered, Antonio," he said, "why the Spanish gentleman is so attached to his cape. Now after two years without one, I have discovered why."

"And why is it, Don Francisco?"

"To hide his sins, of course."

Orellana could see that the Portuguese was astounded at his light-heartedness. Somehow for the one-eyed man to laugh seemed incongruous. At least Hernández' face indicated so. Orellana sobered.

"Forgive me," he said, "if I am exuberant. Money in hand to take us home, and if I am not mistaken, a ship to carry us there. Think of it, Antonio—home to Spain!"

"I am thinking of it," Hernández replied gravely.

Orellana looked away. His friend did not desire to go to Spain. This might be understandable in Castilians, but why in the Portuguese? Surely no danger might possibly await this meek, quiet little man in the land of Charles. Robles and Gutiérrez, now, might well have reasons for avoiding Castile. Most of a man's companions in the New World were exiles, for one reason or another, even the priests!

He was saved further awkward conversation by Robles, who at that moment came in empty-handed, his clothing in rags, but with his fiery beard and goatee as always clean and sharply trimmed.

"I had forgotten," he said in disgust, "how avid men are. Money, money. Nothing speaks but money. Charity—fah!"

"Softly," Orellana said. "If money talks, then let us speak in ducats." He proffered the letter of credit. "We can go home now, Alonso lad. Home—to find a husband for your beautiful dotless cousin Ana."

Closely he watched Robles' reaction to the realization that Spain at last was possible for himself, but Robles, too, turned away.

"There are two ships in harbor," the Andalusian said.

They could see, through their window, Gutiérrez questioning the sailors off a longboat that had come ashore from the caravel. Even at the distance of two hundred paces they noted the awkwardness under which he wore the cape, the boldness with which he displayed the jeweled dagger. Gutiérrez would never be an hidalgo, Orellana thought, even were he made a Knight of Saint Iago. He would always be the direct, blunt mountaineer whom Orellana loved. But did he, too, fear return to Spain?

Gutiérrez returned. As always, his information was brief and accurate.

"The caravel is the *Colón*, of fifty-five tons' burthen, from Panama en route to Santiago de Cuba, her master a Portuguese named Fernão Martins. The ship is the *Natividad* out of Seville, destination Panama; of her I inquired no further."

"Good," Orellana said. "We shall break a bottle with Senhor Martins, and Hernández here can bargain for us in the rascal's native tongue." Again he watched for reaction, but this time there was none. If Gutiérrez had no heat for Spain, his temper was not apparent.

"There is just one thing of which I would speak," Orellana said then, "and now is as good a time as any. Hernán, remove the cape if you are uncomfortable—you do not need to prove to us you are a gentleman."

Robles sat on the window sill, moodily conning the anchored ships. Hernández slumped in a chair, his chin in his chest and his short legs sprawled. Gutiérrez lay aside the cape, fouling it in his scabbard, unbuckled his cuirass and lay down on the bed. Orellana alone remained standing.

"Whatever happens now," he said, fumbling a little for words, "we shall be friends. Is that not true?"

"Yes, it is true," Robles agreed for the three.

"Nothing that could happen to any of us would make one think ill of the others, is it not so?"

"Yes, it is so."

Orellana paced for a moment. He realized that the men appreciated the labor to which he was putting his mind, unaccustomed to fine phrases.

"Well, then—here we are in Cubagua. There are ships sailing in both directions. If you have no heart for Spain, in God's name do not feel bound to come with me. A promise made under deep stress need not be kept. That is the law. It also is the law of the heart. You have said you would come with me, but that was long ago, and all of us had died. Now we live again. What is past is dead. The living cannot pay death's debts. . . . I beat around the bush, friends. I cannot help it. . . . What I mean is—you are under no obligation to return to Spain. Wherever you go, we shall be friends. I release you from your promise."

There was silence for a time, then Robles spoke.

"I'm glad you said that, Francisco," he said. "When I was obliged to go, I had no stomach for it. Now you could not stop me. I may become a burden to you, and you may wish before we're through that I had stayed away, but go I shall."

Orellana looked gently at him. He could not say what he desired. All he could do was to ask, "Are you sure that's wise?"

Robles understood the question. He turned from the window.

"You may as well know the worst of me," he said, "if we are to be companions in Spain. I did not leave bright Andalusia willingly, my friend. I left for prudence's sake."

"It is of no consequence."

"Until now, no. Now it is, for it may lead both you and me to danger. I am a poor cousin of the Sidonia branch of the Medina family. This I assure you I have not told to proud Blas de Medina, who is perhaps my distant cousin. He might have murdered me. Under this red beard there is a hot temper—or was until the jungle took the fire from it. We Robles may be poor, but we are proud, and we resent the taunts of richer men in our connection.

"As you may have suspected, I am a Lutheran, and this became known to a certain Knight of Calatrava among my wealthier kin. To avenge the family for my sin, and to prevent my falling under the Inquisition which would have confiscated the family property, he set on me, in my father's own house, with hired assassins. I killed him, and fled to Seville. His family swore revenge. Even in Seville there is no hair as red as mine. I am marked for death, if not from my family, then from the Dominicans. It is not a pleasant prospect."

"Then by all means go back to Peru," Orellana urged him. "I would not twice put your life in jeopardy."

"No," Robles said, "I have thought about it. You forget the promise I made to my little cousin, that I would bring her a governor or a dowry. We are going back to Spain, Francisco, and when you are safely wed to Ana, there will be enough time left to think of flight. First things first. It is our family legend, and I would not be false to it through fear."

"Well, then," Orellana said, fighting to keep the excitement from his eye, "but you are free at any time to change your mind. I know by heart now the way to Ana de Ayala's gate, and I can go there without a matchmaker prodding my behind."

"Just the same," said Robles, "I am going."

"And I," said Gutiérrez.

"I, too," Hernández said. "Before this is ended, you will need all your friends, if I know Spaniards. I would not desert you now, when the hardest trial is yet to come."

"You forget the forest easily," Orellana commented.

"No, no," Hernández said quickly, "I forget nothing. Particularly I do not forget Spaniards and their ways. I tell you, General, the worst is yet to come."

Robles took the little man by the shoulders, like an older brother affectionately addressing a younger. "He likes Spaniards," he laughed.

"I hate Spaniards," Hernández said evenly.

"You are in good company, then," Orellana said. He was light-hearted, intoxicated by the prospects before him, his blood heated by the wine of friendship and loyalty. For the first time in all his life he wanted to sing a song, and the only song he could think of was Carranza's plaintive dirge on the great river. *"Los mis cabellicos, maire. Uno a uno se los llevó en el aire. ¡ Ay, pobrecitos, los mis cabellicos!"*

A shout from the doorway saluted the end of the song. Half the company crowded the entry, astounded at this aspect of their stern leader lifting a scratchy voice in the gambling song of Peru.

"By my grandmother's virtue," Juan de Illanes cried, carrying heavily through the door his load of wine, "this is a day to remember. The day our captain sang."

Orellana grinned. His expression, too, was new to the men.

"Something has happened to you, Captain," Illanes said. "Something of great fortune has happened to you. You have met a beautiful woman."

The men laughed, crowding into the room: Blas de Medina, Mexía, Contreros, Miradero, Father Carvajal, the Negro Nogal. Half the company at least, but not, Orellana observed, Friar de Vera or Maldonado.

"You are in a good mood, then, for what we come to ask," Medina said. They had chosen the knight for their spokesman, now that they were among civilized people.

"I know what you want," Orellana said. "You are going to Peru."

A great shout arose.

"If—you can get there."

A great silence.

"The ship is here, and its master will carry you to Panama—it is now merely a matter of castellanos. No?"

"The General is always ahead of us," the helmsman Miradero said. He, too, was a little drunk.

"I have made inquiry," Orellana said. "Our brigantines have some value to the pearl fishery here. The Casa Gómez has bought the ships. Divided forty-three ways, each man's portion should see him to Peru."

Mexía laughed.

"Forty-three portions, General? That is very good. No portion for the black slaves, Maldonado, and de Vera."

"The portions include Maldonado and de Vera, and the blacks. The Casa Gómez will give each man his due. You have only to go and ask."

"But what four are not included?"

The silence was weighted now with anxiety.

"Robles, Hernández, Gutiérrez, and myself. Our way lies east, to Spain. Besides—if there are too many portions, there will not be enough money to go around."

"And you?" The question was from Father Carvajal.

"We have made certain arrangements with the Welsers to see us home."

A cheer then, and boisterous goodbys. Men who in two years had been no closer to Orellana than the thickness of a hard fight came forward to embrace him. A few fought tears.

Miradero, wiping his eyes, said, "But for you, Captain, we should all be dead. Each day I live henceforth I shall thank you for."

Contreros, the fisherman, muttered humbly, "Mother of God, General, you are a man of whom my children shall be told. If one of them should be half the man you are—just half—" He got no further, but hurried out the door.

"By God, sir," said Illanes, "I shall never again go to the wars unless it be with you; you have spoiled me for other captains."

"You are still looking for a rich widow?" Orellana asked.

"I am. And when you come again to Peru you shall find something running about my garden besides a fence, Señor. I plan to propagate many children."

Finally only Nogal and Father Carvajal remained. The black came forward slowly.

"What is required of me?" he asked.

Orellana reached to the table and picked up a scroll. "This is your freedom, Nogal. The audiencia approved it this morning, in view of your great services to His Majesty. At the Casa Gómez there is a share for you. But I would not advise you to return to Peru."

Nogal's face was studiously blank. He did not reach out his hand for the scroll.

"To be with you is all the freedom I require," he said. "I will go back with you to Spain, and then to the river."

Orellana put an arm about his shoulder. "No, Nogal," he said. "When I go back to the river, I will be going there for you. For you, and for Carranza, and for myself, but you may not go."

"I would go gladly."

"It is not possible. If you return with me to Spain, it must be as a slave. Men do not understand that a black and a white man can be friends. To be friends now would only hurt us both. As Carranza might say, 'It is not yet written in the stars.' A whole new world must first be born."

"Then let me go as a slave."

"No, Nogal. I have thought of that, too. It is quite necessary that you be free. Freedom for your people is the drop of water that wears away stones. Many drops will be required to erode the prejudice, for the stone is hard. But there must be the first drop if others are to follow. You are the first. Just the first. Remember that, and do not expect too much from one drop of water. Erosion takes many generations. Your children, Nogal, will inherit the land where Carranza lies, not you. But you will make it possible for them."

"You are Moses," said Father Carvajal.

"Yes," Orellana agreed, "you are Moses."

"Thank you, Señor," Nogal said. "I would still like to go."

Father Carvajal stepped forward, and held a letter in his hand toward Orellana.

"The ship from Panama, my son, brings this for you."

"For me? Impossible."

"Impossible, General, but true. After such miracles as we have seen, why doubt one more?"

Orellana put down the letter, unopened. "And you, Father?"

"I return to Peru."

"Yes, of course."

"I vowed when de Vera was lost for two days, that if he returned, I should devote the remainder of my life to missionary work. That would best be done in Peru."

"Godspeed, Father."

The priest did not leave. He looked about the bare room, to Robles, to Gutiérrez, to Hernández, and back to Orellana.

"I used to pray," he said, "that with your great gift of languages God would speak to your heart, my son, and persuade you to come back with me as a missionary to the Indians."

Orellana would have spoken, but Carvajal held up his hand.

"I know that cannot be. I have not mentioned it until now, but I know it cannot be. It was revealed to me on Good Friday, while I was preparing my Easter sermon."

Robles stirred, and the priest felt it. He had never inquired, but he knew that Robles was under the witch spell of dangerous doctrine, and he could not understand why God had chosen Robles as a companion in Orellana's new enterprise. It was not, however, his purpose to understand, merely to believe.

"I know now," he said, "that you are going back to the river. I know God intends you to go."

"So I believe," said Orellana.

"But do not expect to accomplish too much," the priest went on, fearing that he might be struck dead for revealing this much of what he knew, yet daring even God's wrath for this one-eyed man to whom God had shown such incredible favors. "As you said to Nogal, my son, many drops of water will be required to accomplish what you dream. Like Nogal, you also are the first drop. Do not expect to erode too much."

"Thank you, Father. I understand."

"You shall be henceforth daily in my prayers."

"I shall need them, Father, thank you."

"I—I—" the priest faltered.

"Yes, Father?"

"Not once on our long and bitter journey did you ask me for my blessing. May I give it to you now?"

Orellana pondered this, and finally shook his head.

"No, Father," he said. "Your prayers I gratefully accept, but your blessing I cannot—God blesses man, not priests."

Sadly Father Carvajal turned toward the door.

"I do not understand," he said. "God's hand is upon you, that I know. Yet you will not receive my blessing. What do you believe?"

Orellana smiled.

"I believe as do you, in God, but He reveals Himself to us differently. Be content with that."

"It does not ease my soul."

"Nor mine," Orellana replied. "I would wish He had revealed Himself more compassionately to you. Go with God."

"And with thy spirit," said the departing priest.

Hurriedly Orellana tore open the letter, and handed it to Robles.

"From now on," he said, trying to be casual, "you must be an eye to me—the eye that can read. Who is it from, and what does it say?"

"It is from Quito, and it is signed García Tapia."

"Aha! Read it then."

Gutiérrez and Hernández also listened closely to the first news they had had of Peru in two years.

"Most Gracious and Worshipful Companion," Robles read. "I write these lines in darkness and can only hope that by sending them to the Council of the Indies, addressed to you, they will one day reach your Eminent and Virtuous hand. . . ."

"You may dispense with the sauce," Orellana broke in. "Just give us the meat. We are hungry men."

Robles nodded.

"His Excellency," he read on, "Don Gonzalo has returned . . ."

"Aha!"

". . . and it is rumored that if you have not been devoured by loathsome beasts, as His Excellency hopes, then you have reached Spain by another route."

"Quickly, quickly," Orellana cut in.

Robles read faster. "I can only hope that this latter fortune is truth and that you are even now presenting to the Council of the Indies that Memorial of your past services of which you told me in Quito just before you set out across the mountains . . ."

"I will explain later about the Memorial," Orellana injected.

". . . You will need such a Memorial, for your character is black in Peru. Don Gonzalo says that you abandoned him, took all his stores, left him to die in the wilderness and came out by some passage known only to yourself . . ."

Gutiérrez gasped. "Read on," said Orellana.

". . . displaying toward his expeditionary force the greatest cruelty that ever faithless men have shown . . ."

"Dog!" exclaimed Robles. "Read on," said Orellana.

". . . His Excellency has written the king of your infamy, and has set it all down. That is why I write these hurried lines, together with such information as may be useful to you. He has told the king that he went to a junction of two rivers to which you were to return in twelve days' time, and found there only starvation, and that after living for months on palm shoots, dogs, and horses, he finally traversed four hundred leagues and arrived in Quito with only eighty men and these like himself clad in animal skins and with rusty swords in hand . . ."

"Only eighty," Orellana said. "May God have mercy on the rest."

". . . Don Gonzalo tells everyone who will listen that only desire for revenge against you kept him alive, else he had died of his hardships, and the men who returned with him bear out his accusations."

"He should thank you, then, for saving his life," Hernández said.

". . . So I pray you to be on your guard against such accusations as may already be made concerning you in Castile, and particularly before the Council of the Indies, where your character has been darkened beyond that of any man who ever set foot in the New World."

"An auspicious beginning for your own enterprise," Robles commented.

"Is that all the letter says? No? Read on."

"You should also know," Robles read, "that His Excellency's opinion may now no longer bear more weight anywhere than in Peru, where it has none . . ."

"What's this?" Orellana exclaimed.

". . . Don Gonzalo returned to learn that his brother the Marquis was assassinated in Lima a year ago, and the whole country is in chaos."

"Madre de Dios!" said Orellana. "The Marquis slain?"

". . . The new governor, Vaco de Castro . . ."

"Vaco de Castro, who is he?" None knew.

". . . has not yet been to Lima, such is the civil war. He was here in Quito when the Marquis died, and promptly repudiated the governorship of Don Gonzalo."

"Good comes from every evil," said Gutiérrez.

". . . Don Gonzalo has been banished to his lands at Potosí, to work his silver mines, but I suspect that he is waiting for a chance to pounce on the new governor later."

"There is more news?"

"No, Francisco, nothing but flourishes."

"Well! We must hurry. Hernández, take our common clothes and go out to the *Colón*. Our compliments to Senhor Martins. The condition of his rigging convinces me his trade is not too good and he may welcome a charter. Offer him a thousand ducats to take us at once to Palos."

The sailing ball was up when, next day, Orellana and his three companions went aboard. The rattle of anchor chain piped them up the side. The wind was fair.

Orellana exulted to feel sturdy decking under his feet, and looked about the caravel, a smile crimping his lips. Of a sudden his humor disappeared. Standing on the forecastle, their backs to him, were Friar de Vera and Maldonado. They, too, were bound for Spain.

33

ORELLANA hoped to reach Spain by the first of March, but he was disappointed. For four months the vacillating Captain Martins nosed his ship about the Caribbean searching for passengers and cargo, before finally turning his prow eastward for the long run to Tenerife, the Grand Canary, and home.

After six months he bore down upon Cape St. Vincent at last and Orellana jubilantly asked Martins to take him at once to the Spanish port of Palos. Martins, however, was unobliging.

"I must put in at Lagos," he said. "It is not fitting that I take you to Spain before my own king has heard your story of discovery."

Orellana pleaded, but to no purpose. Martins was obstinate. "My king must be informed," he said.

"He will never know," Orellana replied. "I swear I will tell no one what ship transported me, if only you will hurry."

"Unfortunately, Señor," Martins said, "we are not alone upon this ship. One of your companions, who is going to Portugal rather than to Spain, assures me that if I do not do my duty to my king, he will do it for me. I cannot run that risk."

"Maldonado!" Orellana exclaimed.

"The same, Señor," the captain said.

Safe in the Portuguese roadstead of Lagos, Maldonado sought out his old commander. They had exchanged few words during the voyage. The former equerry, strong again after the sea trip, had resumed his old swagger and he wore his sword close to his hand.

"Well, Captain," Maldonado said, "here at last we part."

"I am grateful," Orellana answered coldly, "to your fear of the Inquisition that prevents your return to Spain. So far as I know, it is the only good thing the Inquisition has ever done."

"You are not rid of me," Maldonado said. "I doubt King John of Portugal will be willing to let you take your discovery to Spain. I think I can convince him that what you have found is his, by treaty and the Pope's law."

"You are a scoundrel," Orellana said. "I can understand a man's being disloyal to other men, but not to his native land."

"Patriotism is a sentiment I cannot afford," Maldonado replied. "Adiós. You will hear from me."

King John kept Orellana waiting many days. The king's agents put him up in such sumptuous quarters as he had not known since Guayaquil, his three friends with him. They asked many questions and went away, and in a few days returned with many questions more. A king's counsellor came from Lisbon to hear the tale again and to scan minutely Orellana's chart of the great river. From him Orellana withheld little, hoping that the truth would speed him on to Spain. The counsellor departed and was gone a week, returning with high ceremony and a proposition.

King John, he said, was convinced that this river of the Amazons, for so everyone who heard Orellana's story called it, lay within his own realms. Would Orellana therefore undertake, on Portugal's behalf, a colonial mission to those regions, with the title of governor and adequate honors, and a fleet of four ships, three hundred men, complete provision and supply?

"And what guarantees," Orellana asked, "that the Indians shall be free men, that there shall be no slavery, that as governor I shall have the right to establish such laws and customs as I believe are necessary to colonize a new land, even if some of such laws are contrary to the existing codes of Portugal?"

The emissary departed and did not return. Four days later Orellana was free to sail to Spain. Robles, Gutiérrez, and Hernández accompanied him. Maldonado and de Vera had disappeared.

Orellana was boisterous with hope.

"The Emperor Charles cannot possibly refuse us now, amigos," he said as they sailed aboard a coastal galleon. "We have only to tell him what Portugal proposes. Our delay was not for nothing, after all."

That evening Hernández approached Orellana, who stood alone on the high poop of the galleon looking off into the distance at what was now the coast of Spain.

"It is a beautiful shore, Don Francisco," he said. "What a pity that its people are not as beautiful."

"Men are what you believe them to be," Orellana said. "Good, evil, beautiful, ugly. I did not notice, during our three weeks at Lagos, that your Portuguese were so handsome, Antonio; and I did not find a woman as fair as the one I hope soon to see."

"Ana de Ayala," said Antonio Hernández.

"Ana de Ayala," said Orellana.

Hernández writhed uncomfortably.

"Is it wise, Don Francisco, to place so much hope in a woman you have never seen?"

"Robles is my friend. He vouches for her."

"He is not an impartial judge."

"But he has a fine eye, and a soul, Antonio. If she turns out to be a crone, but is beautiful of heart, I shall be content."

"And if she is beautiful of body, and a crone at heart?"

"I shall know it at once."

"You have been away from women a long time, my friend, and they are most dangerous when they are being subtle."

Orellana smiled into the face of the sunset.

"I believe you are afraid for me, Antonio," he said.

"On this vision of perfection you have feasted for a long time," Hernández replied. "No woman is so perfect, save the Madonna, and she is unattainable—if she were attainable she would be found to have faults, like other women."

"Well, I have faults, too."

"The more reason you should not go out of your way to accumulate others. The task ahead of you will demand your whole strength. So, too, will a woman. How will you temporize between them?"

"In Ana I hope to find strength."

Hernández shook his head.

"I am very much afraid for you," he said. "You are ripe to be plucked, and women feel such things."

"I shall be careful."

"Ah, but you won't, amigo. You have set up a pedestal in your mind, and on it you have placed a perfect figure——not the perfection that a woman herself would call ideal, but a standard of your own dreams. For a year you have cultivated this model, shaping it, changing it, enhancing it, adoring it, endowing it with virtues and delights such as only poets have ever created. You are convinced that this Ana de Ayala will fuse into your vision and become one with it, and if you believe it, then she will appear so, until it is too late. Women have genius for appearing to be what they are not, and like chameleons changing color to match the reflection in a man's eyes."

"Por Dios," Orellana exclaimed, "you hate women."

"Not at all, Don Francisco. I respect them. There never was a man born but there was born a woman cleverer, and it is God's whim to throw them together at mating time."

"You are a cynic."

"True. And if you were one, I should have no fear for you. Only a cynic can get the better of a woman, for he knows that she is capable only of such love as will enhance herself, and therefore he enhances her and leaves her. An idealist, you see what you wish to see rather than what is there."

"Surely I am not that bad," Orellana laughed.

"If you were not, I should hold my tongue. See how your mind already visualizes the river of the Amazons as an established land. So your heart fancies this woman as a materialized delight. You forget that both the river and the woman are only dreams——and when did an entire dream ever come true?"

"This one will."

"How can it, my friend? Reality is the compromise of many men's dreams, not yours alone. Dreams are too soft for use; like gold coins

303

they rub thin in circulation. I should not want that to happen to yours, Francisco."

"Do you doubt," Orellana challenged him, "that I can establish a colony along the river that will be a credit to the dignity of man?"

"No, I do not doubt it, if men will allow themselves to be dignified."

"Then why doubt that I can take this Ana de Ayala and make of her a credit to my heart?"

"You may be asking too much of her."

"In what way?"

"You will expect her to be a dream—she who is a human being. You will expect her to help you become a governor, but what if she wants slaves? You expect her to be self-effacing; what if she is bold? If she returns to the Amazon, a frail woman among a fierce company of men, and you are busy with the work of empire, she may even become too human."

Orellana's eye flashed.

"Forgive me, Francisco," Hernández said. "I speak bluntly only because human beings are unpredictable. In that fact alone has perished many a dream. Dreams are easy; humanity is very difficult. If you are content to realize just half your dreams—both of the woman and the colony—then you have a chance. But if you demand too much of either, you will attain neither."

"Why are you so sure I will expect too much?"

"Your attitude in Portugal prophesies the danger. You might have returned to the river for King John. But you chose to bring up such chimerical questions as made him run from you."

"Those questions must be settled. Otherwise why go? I am not Pizarro. If I return, it must be with guarantees."

"The river is a long way off. Might it not be better to accept what you can get for now, then establish the colony as you see fit once you are there?"

"With fifty priests in attendance, what chance has the common Castilian, let alone the Indian savage? No, there must be certain guarantees, clearly understood."

"And with the woman—here also there must be certain guarantees clearly understood? I fear, Francisco, that you know very little of either kings or women."

"It is a risk I run," Orellana said.

"Not a risk you run, Francisco—rather it is a gauntlet."

Orellana turned his eye back to the shoreline, azure in the evening light.

"Well," he said, "at least you have put me on my guard. With you beside me to keep me from folly, Robles to counsel me upon affairs at court, and Gutiérrez to organize an expedition, I cannot fail."

"You do not fear that Robles' family may turn its wrath from him to you?"

"Family feuds are not often distracted by outsiders. No, I have no fear there."

"And Gutiérrez—what of him?"

"I do not know. I have not inquired, and he has not spoken. Whatever it is he fled in leaving Spain, I think he is sure it will not involve us all."

"I feel the same about myself, but one never knows."

Orellana said nothing.

"I was married once," the wizened little Portuguese said, "to a Spanish woman."

"That is why you hate Spaniards, then."

"Yes. I was young, and had a little wine business. Trade with England was permitted at the time, but the English preferred Spanish wines. I thought an alliance with some Spanish woman might provide me at once with dowry capital and wine-growing relatives, and greatly enhance my trade."

"A clever idea," Orellana said.

"So I thought. The matter was arranged through a broker. I came to Spain. My bride was a nice looking woman, tender and meaty. Her dowry was in the hands of a merchant, put there by her late father against her wedding day, but when we went to get it, the merchant said he had lost it in a venture overseas. He would not pay. Being rich, the law was on his side. The humiliation was more than my wife could stand. Spanish women are too frail; she died."

The story began to stir echoes in Orellana's mind. Somewhere he had heard it before.

"My pride was like a two-edged sword, doubly blunted. One expects to be swindled, perhaps, but not like this. Love, family, business, future, gone all at once. I buried my wife and at her bier vowed I would make the merchant pay, since loss of gold was the only hurt he could not bear. I could imagine his pain if money that was his was taken onto the streets and scattered among the poor, and this I vowed, by my wife's memory, to do."

Orellana nodded. He listened as though for the second time to all this. He knew what was coming.

"I was alone in a very bad land, and needed help. I found it finally among my wife's relations whose grapes I had planned to buy. A gentleman, a real knight of the days when knighthood meant something, succored me. We broke into the merchant's house and took his gold. There was a great deal of it, since he trusted no one but himself, and for good reason. We were set on and forced to flee, taking the gold with us in sacks so heavy that the horses stumbled under the weight. The merchant sent men, dogs, everything against us. We hid, but he would not give up the chase. In the end we could not return to give away the gold. So the knight and I split the money and separated, and I understand that he, too, went to the New World."

Again Orellana nodded. He knew now, where he had heard the tale before, and laughed aloud.

"And you still fear this merchant?"

"I do. He is a dog and has the nose of a dog. If he is living, he will smell me out. That I know."

"Well, my friend, you needn't worry. Your merchant is well known to me, too. He is Carlos Sánchez of Truxillo."

"Name of a name!" Hernández gasped. "You are related to him!"

"Far from it. I am related to you. The knight who helped you was my Uncle Sebastian. It was with him that I went to the New World."

"Holy Virgin!"

"I have heard your story from my uncle, but I did not dream that his Portuguese partner was yourself."

"Well, now you know."

"It is a good thing you told me, Antonio. The merchant may make some claim on me, too. He must know that I was Sebastian's heir. We must be careful to avoid him."

"Doubly so, now," Hernández replied. "He is a locust and would strip us like an orchard."

"He would that," Orellana said.

34

THE COURT was sitting at Valladolid, Orellana discovered when he reached Seville. Charles V had come home to Spain for his first long stay in many years. His vast affairs of empire, embracing as they did nearly half of Europe, were under control. The Turks had annexed Hungary, and France again courted the Ottoman emperor, but the situation was not yet acute. Prince Philip, now seventeen, had relieved his father of the petty details of statecraft so that, this spring of 1543, Charles for the first time in his adult life had a little leisure. The time appeared auspicious for Orellana's petition.

Important as was this matter, it yielded first place in Orellana's attention to another. The news of his discovery already had reached Seville. Orellana's name was well known. He made immediate use of the precious capital of public esteem. He bought the finest suit of courtly clothing to be found in all Andalusia, of black satin edged in Flemish lace and adorned with gold braid. It was a costume fit to impress a woman, and that was the reason for its purchase.

The evening was as rich as a mellow wine, overcast with a bouquet from Seville's thousands of gardens, enlivened by the promenade of Seville's citizens through gay streets. The Andalusian understands the subtleties of springtime, the season that expands the throbbing vulva of nature. He understands, and knows that God is with him, else why does God give to Andalusia, in May, the quickening delight of velvet sunsets and the lightest of Mediterranean breezes that fleets ahead of lovers into the harbor of night?

Flowers, great luscious blooms of camellia, appropriate to the conqueror of tropical jungle, Orellana carried with him as he and Robles, also dashingly clad, ascended the hill from the old city to the grape-cluster of houses that looked from below as though they were pendant from the wall of the Moorish Alcázar. The people of Seville, clad in wooing finery, promenaded in the park along the Guadilquivir and the cathedral plaza, nodding appreciatively at the sight of these two caballeros so obviously intent on courtship, and uttering loud asides upon their chance of conquest, after the Sevillian manner. Here and there a priest gave the passing pair a benedictory smile, knowing, as only they know in Seville, that the surest propagation of the faith lies not in missions but in courtship. Girls revealed, with pirouettes that uncovered high, dainty heels, a modest sample of the Andalusian woman's ability to make even a dour man smile.

Orellana smiled. He knew now what Robles had meant, that night in the jungle. Seville was gay, and it was also wise, for none turned upon his ugly eye that quick shocked gaze to which he was accustomed. As he walked up the crooked street there was no difference, he observed carefully, between the coquetry that flashed to him and to his red-bearded companion.

They turned into the Avenida Teresa and from a distance Orellana knew the gate, knew it as well as though out of it he had stepped en route to the New World. It was as Robles had said it would be: the knotted olive tree on guard, the silver bell the blessed lady of God had rung with her own hand. They crossed a little plaza. No one lingered about the common well. A breeze that had accompanied them up the hill now sped ahead and whorled the white dust into tinsel before Ana de Ayala's gate.

"It is here," Robles said.

"Yes," Orellana did not dare say more. An arcade, blocked by a metal grill, opened from the gate, framing a gentle passageway beyond which was a paved patio. Robles rang the bell at the grill, opened it and walked confidently inside.

A girl stood across the court, in her hands a jar from which she had been watering poppies in a deep window box. One of the flowers, reaching higher than the rest, stretched out as though it could not resist an impulse to touch her ripe young breast. Another poppy, freshly picked, was tucked in her braided hair, jauntily over the right ear. Her hair was the color of Jerez sherry long in cask, deeply mellow yellow, comfortable in the company of poppy red. Her bodice was tight, a white blouse throated with narrow blue lace, her skirt full and long. The hands that held the water jar were pale as honey, the fingers long and slim; the arms, uncovered to above the elbow, were gentle, companionable.

She looked across the little patio, saw Robles and ran to him, setting down the water jar as she passed a small fountain in the middle of the court. She greeted him as though he were a lover, arms and lips open. He met her and enveloped her. Her arms caressed his red beard, her body clung to him. She was poetry, lyric and light and fragile. Robles set her down on her feet, and turned to Orellana.

"This is Ana," he said. "Ana, Don Francisco Orellana."

She turned her brown eyes full upon Orellana, and his knees shook. Everything, everything, depended on what she would do next. She had seen his face, with its cruel eye socket. The camellias were awkward in his hand.

She looked at him, her eyes upon his good eye.

"He is my friend," Robles said.

Now the cocoa eyes took on new depth. She did not look away. She looked at him as though she had rolled the shutters from her eyes that he might see inside, and he was dizzy and breathless from what he saw.

She smiled, unlatching the window of her heart, and held out both her hands. He took them, crushing the camellias in her clasp. She leaned forward quickly, on tiptoes, and kissed him richly in the corner of his mouth.

Orellana closed his eyelids. The fruitful smell of her was like the bouquet of peach brandy in his nostrils, exciting alike the brain and the tongue. He wanted to crush her, as he was crushing the camellias in her hand; he wanted to drench her with a cascade of long-dammed words; and he wanted to cry. All this at once, while the corner of his lips burned wet from her kiss, and a truant hair from her braid rubbed like a gentle finger across his brow. All down his body he could feel the presence of her.

She relaxed. He opened his eye and clutched for another glimpse of her. Her eyes were waiting. She released his grip upon her left hand and touched his cheek with her fingertips. The camellias, and Orellana's right hand, remained with her.

"I thank you," she said, "for bringing my cousin home."

He had wondered what her voice would be. It was throaty, soft, mellowed by lazy Andalusian accents that made voluptuous the syllables that Estremadurans were inclined to harden.

"He brought me home," Orellana said, "to see you."

"To see me?" The brown eyes widened and she stepped back. A petal from one of the camellias fell to the flagstone.

"Ten thousand leagues, Ana, to see you." Orellana was husky of voice, and he realized it; more, he knew that she knew it, for there was a quick dart of impishness from her.

"Then I am doubly grateful," she said. "To you for bringing him—to him for bringing you."

She said the words as though she had been waiting for him, as he had been for her, these long two years.

"I told my little Ana that I would bring her a great gentleman," Robles said. "Have I kept my word, mi Anita?"

The lovers' breeze of Andalusian Maytime caught at her skirt and pushed it against her fleetingly, outlining a body that would glorify any woman.

She turned quickly back to Orellana, as though the question freighted a heavy cargo of challenges that must be met. She looked him up and down, not at all coquettishly but as a man might balance the points of a horse he contemplated buying, frankly and appreciatively.

"He is from Truxillo. He has discovered a land in the New World many times larger than all of Spain, and he is going back to be its governor."

Her eyes quickened again, and she flipped her head, as though she had decided to buy the horse but was too clever to say so.

"You must go in the house and see my mother and stepfather, Cousin," she said swiftly to Robles. "Meanwhile I will get our guest a glass of wine, and when you come back, you must tell me all about yourself."

Robles took the hint; he was a gentleman as well as an Andalusian. The sun was setting over the old town, underscoring the tall minaret of the giralda and the strangely contrasting Gothic splendors of the new cathedral; shadows played with the spring breeze among the flowers in the patio. Over the wall from the street eddied drifts of love songs from a passing minstrel.

"Very well," Robles said. "I should not leave you alone with a stranger, Cousin, except that the adelantado and I are brothers."

"The adelantado?" Ana de Ayala's voice caught on the word, stumbling.

"Well, perhaps not yet," Robles said, "but soon. The emperor himself will decree it."

"You are going to see the emperor?" Ana's voice bore the quick timbre of a woman who is thinking fast and clearly.

"As soon as I can reach Valladolid," Orellana answered.

She gave him another smile, touched his sleeve and then, as though she regretted the unladylike impulse, she directed Orellana to a tiled bench beside the fountain.

"I shall return immediately with some wine," she said quickly. "If you will excuse me."

Orellana watched her go, lightly on little feet, hand in hand with Robles. He threw the camellias exuberantly into the air and let them fall to the flagstones. She was young, she was beautiful, and she had kissed him. Not for a second had she recoiled from his gruesome eye or even evidenced notice of it. It was as he had known it would be. It was as he had dreamed it in the deep jungle, and on the green sea water. He had dreamed it, and the dream had stepped out of his mind and touched him; it had touched him with the fragrant bouquet of soft flesh and hot blood.

What was it Hernández had said? "When did an entire dream ever come true?" When, indeed! She was as he had pictured her—young enough to be molded, quick to understand. She had kissed him; she, too, was an idealist, then—the complement to his own soul, the strength to add to his strength, the body to unite with his body. There was no doubt. There could be no doubt, for she had looked at him, and had not turned away.

She returned. The shadows ran lovingly over her tight bodice as she came toward him, smiling. She poured sherry for him, and watched him drink it, delighted when he nodded approval. Again Orellana was happy. She wanted to please him.

She sat beside him on the tiled bench, and inquired about himself, not as a man asks questions challengingly, but ebulliently and sharingly, wonder-eyed at his description of the great river, intently as he passed on to the hopes that would take him to Valladolid, to the king.

"You leave me so soon, then?"

Orellana smiled, remembered the prediction that in Andalusia he would smile, and blessed Robles for leaving him so long alone with Ana.

"I shall be back," he said.

"But you have not even consulted the Council of the Indies!" Ana exclaimed, her manner making swift transition from excitement to anxiety. "How do you expect the king to consider something his ministers have not seen?"

"He will see me."

"But you don't understand! The approval of the Council is everything. It is very powerful. Even I, a poor little girl, know that! You must have the Council with you before you see the king."

"That would take many days."

"Then take many days." Her tone was didactic.

"I think it would be better to go directly to the king."

"You are a fool," Ana snapped. Then quickly, as Orellana stiffened, "Or is it just that you have been so long from Spain, my friend, that you forget our Spanish ways?"

Orellana drew a quick breath. She had used the familiar pronoun "you."

She touched his sleeve again.

"Forgive me," she said. "I feel as though I have been sailing with you all down the river. I would not have you fail now in your desire to become a great general and an adelantado. I should be disappointed, too." Her eyes, in the twilight, were wistfully soft. "I do not mean that you are really a fool."

Orellana felt the touch on his arm, and lifted his hand to her finger-tips. She did not withdraw. Soon his big hand completely covered her little one upon his sleeve.

"I like a little spirit in a woman," he said. "Perhaps you are right about the Council. I will think about it."

"Do," she said. "Whatever you decide, I know it will be right. Now tell me about my cousin. Did he have many lovers in the New World?"

Robles returned after it was quite dark. He was alone. Orellana still sat beside Ana on the tiled bench.

"We must go," Robles said. "I cannot leave you two alone in the dark. It is not done, even in Andalusia."

Ana went with them as far as the grilled door in the arcade. She turned to Robles and lifted her face for his kiss.

"You will come again tomorrow?"

"Yes, mi florecita."

She turned to Orellana.

"And you will come with him?"

"May I?"

"I shall be very unhappy if you do not."

Orellana smiled.

She went to him, stood on tiptoe and turned up her face.

He fumbled clumsily, looking at Robles. She waited. He bent down

314

carefully to kiss her cheek, but she turned his chin with her fingers until his lips could feel the moisture of her own. She kissed him.

"God in heaven!" he said.

She smiled and closed the grill.

35

ORELLANA returned to the little house in the Avenida Teresa alone, while the morning was still dark. He wanted to tell Ana that he had adopted her suggestion to present his case first to the Council of the Indies.

He had been too disturbed the previous evening to think of anything but her for a long time after he had left her. Drugged by her reception of him, he had walked in a stupor through the lower town, loitering with the rising tide in the Guadalquivir, crossing by the old Roman bridge into the suburb of Barrío, returning by the new bridge, dimly conscious of the nocturnal toll of many church bells, vaguely aware that he was back in Spain and in the part of Spain that traditionally had blessed learning and happiness. Robles was with him but they talked little, and Orellana had not noticed that until the night was quite dark his blaze-thatched companion had walked with averted face through the populous streets.

Orellana was full of Ana, and the implications of his meeting with her. She was a gem fairer than all the emeralds in the vicuña sack about his neck. He saw her again and again, her stances, her gestures, her smiles, as though he gazed at pictures in a grandee's gallery and could linger over them, studying and weighing them and returning again and again to his favorites. He liked best that picture of her, seated beside him on the tiled bench, listening with almost naive attention to his dream of empire along the great river. Her hand had been cradled in his, then, as naturally as though he had known her since boyhood and had carried her ribbon over his heart in the New World. She had seemed rapt in the humanity of his enterprise; he had felt it in the tingle of his fingers upon her hand. She seemed at once to have understood and to have approved. Two pictures only disturbed him, and to them he returned again and again, searching them for implications.

The first was the dark flash of her eyes when she had called him a fool; but he was inclined to believe that this was favorable rather than the contrary, an evidence of eagerness on her part that he should not fail. Her argument, that he start with the Council, was wise. He knew it was wise; Hernández had heavily advocated the same course. Short cuts in bold ventures usually lead only into a morass. Charles was indeed a great lord, Orellana an unknown begging favors. She had not put it quite so bluntly, he thought, a score for her quickness of mind.

The second picture was more disturbing. The kiss at the grill, her lovely body poised as though to receive all of him rather than just his lips, her breath hot and plunging, her lips—Madre de Dios!—the lips of a searing iron. Robles had said she was a ripe fruit. But should she drop from the tree at the first touch? This picture he could not understand, and with this picture before his eye he had walked away the night, until the new moon had set and the sky was a purple canopy held overhead by a million stars.

The first kiss he could understand—a young girl's enthusiasm bubbling over at the sudden appearance of her beloved cousin. But the second, beside the grill? His body argued that the thing was natural, but his mind was not so sure. He had wanted her so desperately to love him; had this urgency of his own communicated itself to her? Had she, with that canny instinct of women, felt the turmoil that was in him, the turbulence in her heart, and responded to it, swept away by it even as he was? That was what his body said, and that was what he wanted to believe. Even in uninhibited Andalusia, however, women were reared to some restraint. Robles himself had said so—he could not leave them together in the dark, even in Andalusia. Perhaps Robles had said this because he saw his cousin opening like purslane under warm sunshine, and was bringing her back to her senses with a subtle reproof. Then why, under reproof, the kiss at the grill? Defiance of her cousin? Or an admission that she had been drawn to Orellana beyond modesty, beyond herself?

That was what his body wanted him to believe, and his mind finally conceded the argument. She was too young, too fresh, to be brazen. Enthusiasm had carried her away, as it had carried him away. He could understand the intoxication, since it was so much on him.

This finally had satisfied him, and he could not wait to see her again. Everything else—the Council, the king, even the river—might wait; but he could not. With an excuse he bade goodnight to Robles shortly before dawn, and went again to Ana's house. He stood by the common well and searched the windows for her. He almost expected to see her standing, in a white nightgown, looking out sleeplessly at the purple night sky, waiting for him to come. He was disappointed that the house was quiet and shuttered. He stood before her house until dawn came, and the curious neighborhood housewives began to gather at the well. Then he went to his lodgings, sheepishly praying that his three companions would not awake, and lay down without undressing to await the time of day when he might pass her house again.

He left the house before Gutiérrez and Hernández were awake, nudging Robles carefully in passing the red-beard's bed. Robles leaped up, his hand on his dagger. Orellana signaled silently, and met him outside.

"Look, my friend," Robles said testily, still half asleep, "I have introduced you to her. I have walked the streets one night with you. That is all friendship requires of me. If you want to lose sleep over her that is your affair, but I do not propose to lose mine."

Orellana laughed. "Just once more, amigo," he said. "You promised that we should come together. Besides—I have not met her stepfather. I cannot go to the house alone."

"In good time then, at five o'clock, like gentlemen."

"No, now."

"She will be working. A girl does not like to be caught working."

"She will be waiting. I know she will be waiting."

"I was right about her, then."

"Yes, Alonso, you were right. She is perfect."

"And ripe, no?"

"Yes. I must hurry before someone else gets the harvest." He paused in his rapid strides. "Alonso—you do not think—you do not suppose—"

"That she already has a lover? What difference? You are an adelantado."

"No. I could not bear the thought of—"

"Then don't think about it. She is too wise to give herself away. The man who buys her must pay."

"Yes, she is wise. Much wiser than her years."

"A girl who has no dowry must have other capital," Robles said laughing. "Money cannot buy what she has."

They had ascended the hill. The town below lay lazy in the rich sun, but the Avenida Teresa was still shaded by the wall of the Alcázar, and a breeze as clean as orange juice freshened the common. The gate, bursting with red roses, was open, but the grill was closed. Robles put out his hand to pull the bell.

"No," Orellana said. "Let us just go in, as we did last night."

Robles shrugged. They entered. Immediately Robles went through a closed door to the right and Orellana was alone. He stepped hesitantly to the patio.

She was there, upon the tiled trysting bench, picking beans into a pot that was cradled in her thighs. Her skirt was shorter this morning and pulled back over a white knee. Her blouse was low-cut and loose, freeing her breasts from confinement. Red Moroccan sandals were on her feet. Her fingers were nimble at her work.

She rose quickly at the sound of his heels.

"But—"

"Forgive me," Orellana said. He longed to take hold of her.

"But I am not dressed, I am not—"

"I wanted to see you as you really are, Ana. I wanted to see whether the dream I have had of you—"

"You have dreamed—of me?" She held the basket of beans in her hands.

"For two years, Ana. I have dreamed of you."

She became all tenderness, looking intently at him, meeting his eye.

319

Slowly she put down the basket and touched her fingers to her golden braids. She stood erect, then, lithe as a pageboy, inviting his attention.

"So," she said, relaxing. "And how do I compare with the dream?"

He stepped forward to seize her shoulders, but she retreated before his fierceness and the flood of his words.

"You are perfect," he said rapidly. "You are the dream. I was afraid you might be ugly; but you are beautiful. I was afraid you might be cold; but you are warm. I was afraid you might be proud; but you are lovely. I could wait no longer, Ana, to tell you."

He stood helplessly before her. She did not move or speak.

"I love you, Ana," he said.

She pushed him away gently, her face averted. "You are in love with a dream, Don Francisco," she said. "Do not say anything you will regret."

Again he stepped forward, and this time she did not withdraw. He touched her shoulders, then clenched them.

"How can a man regret loving perfection?" he said. "How can I say half the words my heart dictates? Let me speak, and you will know."

"No," she said quickly, freeing herself from him. "You have been away from women a long time, so that even I look good to you—but that will pass."

"No, I swear it. I have not dreamed of women, but of you."

"It will pass, then. An adelantado does not dream long about a peasant girl."

"It was of you, though, that I dreamed. As Alonso described you—standing by the common well, a jar on your shoulders, barefooted and bare-legged in the sunshine. That is how I hoped to find you this morning."

"An adelantado's lady does not go barefooted, my friend," she said. "She wears jewels, and thumb rings, dresses of blue silk and a manta of the finest lace."

"I shall give you all those things."

"No. You will think of me barefooted by the well—but it is a great lady who will capture your heart."

"You are a great lady and you have captured my heart. After the vision I have held of you, a vision now fulfilled, no one else would do. It is you, Ana, or nobody."

She smiled and walked past him, patting his arm, and sat on the bench.

"You are a little boy," she said.

"No. A boy does not know what he wants, so he tries everything. I know what I want—it is you."

"But you do not know me."

"Well enough. The rest I can learn."

"You are very sure of yourself."

He threw himself to one knee, his cloak spreading upon the flagstones about him, and clutched at her hands which were folded on her lap.

"Ana," he begged her. "Listen to me. I have never been so sure of anything as of this moment. All my life I have been waiting for you. All my life I have needed you. Now I have seen you and I will not let you go. What does it matter if until yesterday you were only a dream? I have known the dream a long time. What does it matter that until last night you did not know me? Today I am here. I worship you. That is enough. I am sure of you; you may be equally sure of me. A love that has been waiting years for fulfillment does not cool off like a summer evening with the first shadow. It grows like a strong tree, putting down its roots more firmly year after year, and no wind can shake it. And I need you, Ana. Need you in the work that lies ahead of me. It will be difficult. With you I can accomplish anything. I know it. And you shall be a great lady in the New World, with a marble palace and eight horses to draw your coach, and clothes that will be the envy of every woman. What more can you ask than this—that I love you, and need you, and can make you rich?"

He felt the vibrant warmth of her rising in him.

"You are going to marry me, Ana," he said.

She withdrew her hands, forcing him to rise, for he could not very well kneel before her, clutching at her knees.

"You must give me time," she said.

"All the time you like, Ana, but hurry."

"It is you who should hurry. Why are you not even now pressing your case before the Council of the Indies, instead of wooing me? First things should come first."

"You are first," he said.

"No," she replied, rising, "I am last. When you are an adelantado, with the king's commission in your pocket, when you are sure of your other dream, then come to me, and I will answer."

"That is impossible. I must have you, first. Then together we—"

She cut him off with an impetuous shake of the head.

"You waste time speaking of love when you have so much to do," she said. "Your eloquence should be pleading your cause downtown, not here in a garden. Come to me an adelantado, and you will need no eloquence."

"Is that a promise?"

"In love, nothing is ever promised. It is given, or withheld. But you do your cause with me no good by loitering here. It does not speak well for your sense of balance. Go to the Council, then come to me."

"Ana!"

Her lip curled faintly.

"The one I marry must be a man," she said firmly, "not a beggar. Go. You are wasting your time."

He left. He did not wait for Robles, who remained inside the house.

36

HE FOUND Gutiérrez and Hernández waiting in their lodgings. Obviously they had been speaking of him, for they became silent when he entered the room. Hernández, his wiry frame protected by a breastplate that he did not doff even at night, was plainly depressed. Gutiérrez looked guilty.

"So," Orellana said, flinging off his cape. "You are weary of idleness."

"Yes, General," Gutiérrez said. "We are wasting time, and are beginning to wonder what brought us here."

Orellana patted his arm. "Always direct and blunt, my friend," he said cheerlessly. "Well—you need wonder no longer. Today we act."

Hernández jumped to his feet. "That is more like," he said. "Work I can take. Idleness, no. You have seen Ana?"

"Yes, I have seen her."

"She was ugly. I can tell by your manner. Ugly and bow-legged and a mole with three hairs on her upper lip."

"No. She was beautiful. Too beautiful."

Hernández' banter disappeared.

"God in heaven!" he said. "You have not been turned down already?"

"Yes."

"But how can this be? You have just now seen her."

"I crowded her too hard."

"Oh, that. Women always say no at first. It is not proper otherwise; they must not be caught jumping at their great chance."

"No. This is something else. She told me I should be pressing my suit before the Council instead of before her."

"By God, then, I like her better," Hernández said. "And you are going to take her advice, where you would not take mine."

"I cannot go against the judgment of you both, when I regard you both so highly."

"Good. I must meet this woman. But not today. First things should come first."

"What did you say?"

"I said first things should come first. Why?" He looked up questioningly. Orellana did not reply; he was thinking that Ana had told him the same thing, in the same words. Hernández went to him and patted him on the back.

"Old friend, don't take it so hard. This is Andalusia, not Peru. Give her time. The smarter she is, the more time she will require. For now, put your mind to work; it will help you forget the lady."

"Yes, let's get to work," Orellana said. "Gutiérrez, you are going to Valladolid, at once."

"Good. That is good."

"Make friends with whom you can of the court, and tell them about me. Do not say I am coming, but talk. Talk to the king's barber, and his confessor, and his fool. Get them excited if you can, over the river. Then when we arrive, our work will be half done."

"Good. And for money?"

Orellana hesitated. "I will have money for you this evening. You shall leave tomorrow."

"I am ready."

Orellana hesitated a moment, then said, "There is no reason why you should not go to Valladolid?"

"No," Gutiérrez said curtly. "There I am all right."

"Then get together your things. Antonio and I are going to the House of Trade to open our suit."

He went out swiftly, as though the thing must be accomplished before noon. Hernández trotted beside him, unable to match his great strides. Already Hernández had been to the Casa and had ascertained that Orellana's Memorial, executed in Guayaquil, was on file, together

324

with a letter from the chronicler Oviedo to Juan de Samano, the king's secretary on the Council of the Indies.

Samano was no fool. Charles V had not surrounded himself with mediocrity. The secretary was an Asturian of proud blood and ancient line, quick of thought but slow of speech, a devotee of epigram and the neat orderliness of mind that produced economical expression. His grasp of New World affairs was acute for one who had never been there, and his enormous capacity for work belied his Castilian origins. He was gaunt of frame, burdened at the shoulders with a spinal impediment that made him always appear on the verge of genuflexion. This made him a great favorite with churchmen though unrightly so, for he was contemptuous of the sacraments and all other forms and symbols that were subject to many interpretations. He was a stylist with the newly invented French fencing foil, admiring the singleness of purpose to which the lithe blade was put.

In mind he was a stylist also, preferring the rapier to the mace in all affairs, and the clear phrase to the obtuse. He wrote in a meticulous hand unadorned by embellishments and spoke as he wrote, directly and to the point. He was as honest as an Asturian could be, which is to say that he would not be bribed with money though he would accept the gift of a vineyard, and if opportunity came gratuitously beneath his hand to rob the king's treasury he did not do so himself, but pointed out the method to his father from whom one day he stood to inherit. He was loyal to the king, but his first loyalty was to Spain, and he worked zealously to surround the monarch with gentlemen of Spain rather than of the Flemish or German courts. His dominance of the Council of the Indies was the result of hard work; he alone knowing the facts often made the decisions, and his decisions were enlightened for his generation. Having listened to Las Casas, he sympathized with the Indians, particularly after having met Pizarro face to face; and he was a foe of the blatant cupidity of conquering heroes which, he saw with unusual clarity, heaped up riches at the expense of future kings.

Juan de Samano received Francisco Orellana in a fine room that once had been a Moorish banking house. A balcony opened on the river side, its roof supported by byzantine columns deeply inlaid and on this balcony, in fine weather, Samano placed his desk. He liked to walk up and down, scanning the river, as he talked.

He wasted no words with Orellana.

"I am in receipt," he said, "of a letter from the chronicler Oviedo, describing your remarkable voyage, together with a copy of a journal written on the expedition by one Friar Carvajal. Your fine leadership speaks for itself."

"Thank you," said Orellana.

"A return expedition to the territory is, however, an entirely different matter. I have studied the case and have written the king that I believe your discovery is more prejudicial than advantageous. I fear that you have given the king of Portugal rich new possessions."

"The land lies south of Brazil," Orellana said.

"But how far south?"

"That I do not know."

"Nor I. One claim is as good as another. I do not think His Majesty should countenance the settlement of lands that can lead only to friction. Spain at this time has friction enough in other directions."

"Certainly the Portuguese claims cannot extend to the south bank of the river. The river itself would make a good common boundary between us. You must meet the issue one day anyway, with the northward growth of Buenos Aires."

Samano's tortured spine appeared to bow.

"I had not considered that," he said.

"It is better that we should have a foothold on the south bank to protect the interests of the settlement on the River Plate. Then at the proper time, a treaty can be arranged, demarking the Amazon river itself as a boundary. I doubt King John desires war in the New World any more than yourself."

Samano nodded gravely. "It is possible," he said. "It is possible."

"Then let me establish a settlement on the south bank. Let me arm it with three strong forts. The river there is as wide as a sea."

"You surrender the north shore easily," Samano said.

Orellana held out his hand to Hernández, who produced a sack containing two magnificent specimens of glazed porcelain, jars filled with oats, yucca, wood samples, dried spices and other curiosities, including a corona of yellow and blue feathers.

Orellana arranged the articles, except for the corona, upon Juan de Samano's desktop.

"All these," he said, "I picked up along the south shore. On the north shore lie only swamps, savages and death. I had in mind a colony in the town whence comes this porcelain. The chips are of hardwood trees half the height of yonder Giralda."

"And the feathers?" Samano said. He did not like to be excluded from anything.

Orellana fingered the bauble gently. "This was given to me by the son of a native chief. It is the symbol of his rank. Upon my ship he met the native girl he married. The feathers are a pledge of friendship against my return."

Samano was impressed. The conquistadores of his acquaintance had shown him no such favors from the Indians.

"And gold?" he asked. "What of gold?"

"We heard tales of it, but did not seek it out," Orellana replied. "I do not seek gold on the river of the Amazons, Excellency, but a colony in which men may live and grow and enrich their lives. Such a land would be of great value to His Majesty in generations to come, long after the gold of Peru is spent."

Samano turned over in his hands the larger piece of porcelain, ran the grain through his slender fingers, scuffed the wood chips with his thumb nail.

"You must prove to my satisfaction," he said, "that a Spanish colony would not encroach upon the sovereignty of Portugal."

"That I can do."

"You must give me a written report outlining the advantages to His Majesty of a permanent settlement, the opportunities for lucrative export, and what you, as governor, propose to do, and likewise what

327

you hope to gain for yourself, since I assume your palm is as large as every other."

"For myself I ask only sufficient authority and perquisites as will assure the success of the enterprise."

"Spoken like a Cortez, or a Pizarro," Samano said. "Outline it all, that I may see."

"Yes, Your Excellency."

"If this report is in my hands within the week, I shall take it with me to Valladolid in a fortnight. Otherwise the matter must wait at least six months, perhaps longer."

"You shall have it."

"Then go with God, and start on it," Samano said, and bowed him out. He rubbed the porcelain meditatively in his hands as Orellana withdrew.

For two days the miserable lodgings of Orellana were a babel of harangue and a shambles of confusion. Orellana's carefully annotated charts were spread about everywhere, on the beds, on the ugly Italian clothes chest, on the rugless floor. At a table by the window Robles sat, scratching with his pen until his muscles collapsed, yielding his wrist to Hernández for massage, then returning again to his scratchings. Orellana walked up and down, dictating, arguing with his companions over words and phrases, descriptions, forecasts. The pressure of urgency shortened the tempers of all three, and by the second midnight they were clashing violently. But the frantic work emerged, page by page, and as each parchment was sanded and fell to the floor finished, the men would smile grimly, as a fighting man smiles when he pulls his blade from the ribs of a foe in battle. Occasionally Hernández descended to the street to buy dates or buns from a passing huckster. In the main, however, the work went on uninterrupted by either repast or sleep. Time was too short.

The labor would have been much easier had not Orellana insisted on inserting a detailed account of his own demands upon the king. Robles was impatient at the length of these appeals, Hernández fretful at their indiscretion, but Orellana was firm. Upon his demands rested his fulfillment, and he would not compromise.

As he dictated he recalled, again and again, the many evidences that God had worked with him in this enterprise: the incredible escapes from death, the miraculous appearance of food when they were starving, the bird that had five times saved them from destruction, the calm waters over which the brigantines had sailed the open sea, the rescue from the Gulf of Paria. These were not the produce of mere chance. Two years ago he might have believed them so to be, but now such cynicism was impossible. And what luck that Juan de Samano was at that very moment preparing a trip to Valladolid, saving months of time! Luck was not so faithful to any man that it followed him for two years! No, there was more than that. A trust was upon him, to which he must be faithful. His demands might appear impudent to Hernández, but the king would, under God's grace, understand. This colony along the Amazon was ordained. The king would consent.

Orellana could not know what would not be apparent for another hundred years, that his firm eloquence of petition would turn the concept of colonial expansion. He could not see that here, in a shabby lodging, was being written a creed for the future colonial enterprises of all Europe, that was to turn men and monarchs forever away from slave empires and the foulest exploitation of conquered peoples, and set in motion the enlightened concept that all men are created equal in dignity under God and entitled to the opportunity to use the talents with which they were born.

Orellana had no illusion that all men have equal talent; but he did understand that privilege is no index of worth, nor a standard of opportunity. He saw quite clearly the kind of society most likely to enhance the development of useful, dignified man, at no cost to the sovereignty of his monarch or his God, and how such a society might be ordained and administered. He also saw as clearly the difficulty of fulfillment of his dream in a civilization as debauched and greedy as that of his own time, and anticipated the human weaknesses of mankind that have, even to this day, prevented all of his dream from com-

329

ing true. He did, however, know his fellowmen well enough to insist upon a clear directive from the king upon the concepts revolutionary for his time, and insisted that Robles write it all down.

He wrote that his purpose was to colonize, not to exploit. That "neither now nor at any time is it just that there be in the said land any slaves of one form or another." That only priests who had proven themselves worthy sons of God be allowed in the colony. That the personal property of the Indians be respected in law, and no man be coerced into any form of labor other than of his own choosing. That military force was not to be used; rather by Christian example was the Spaniard to win the devotion of the native peoples.

Strange concepts for his age and day! To these he added another, not knowing that for twenty years a priest named Bartolomé de Las Casas had fought the same fight. He insisted that the natives of the Amazon, when incorporated into the colony, must be dignified with all the freedoms and privileges of the proud Castilian himself; freedom of property, freedom of person, freedom of mind.

The Indian, Orellana said, was human and thus divine, and upon him was the right to receive the sacraments, to educate his children, to intermarry with Spaniards, acquire estate, hold public office, and attain to such social levels as his talents might determine. Once he had sworn fealty to God and Spain, Orellana said, the savage was Christian and Spanish, be he black, white, or red. Under such auspices, Orellana argued, the Spanish domain upon the south bank of the Amazon would grow great and rich, profiting equally from civilized knowledge and the simple honest dignity of the aborigine. There was no accident in Orellana's determination to call his world New Andalusia, after the one province in Spain in which learned men flourished and humble men wrote and read, where the Inquisition least prospered, where Moors and Jews and African blackamoors traditionally had benefited from the cultures and religions of each other, and where even the poorest child knew how to smile.

Robles shook his head when the petition finally was finished. It would never do, he said. The priests who surrounded the king would see to that. They and the bankers. Better, he urged, to be prudent and humble, in petitioning a king.

"I have seen Spain," Orellana replied, "and I have seen Peru. I could not go back and explain to Chief Aparia, or your little friend Lalah, or any other of our friends along the river, that what we brought them was Spanish misery or Peruvian death. No, sooner I would let the Amazon live on undisturbed—peaceful and honest."

Juan de Samano said little when Orellana took to him the completed document. He thumbed it quickly, while Orellana stood before him anxiously. Then he tossed it on his massive table.

"All right," he said, "but you have not yet convinced me that the land does not lie within the territory of Portugal. That I expressly asked you to clear up."

"No man knows," Orellana said. "I have done my best. I do know that if we do not colonize this land, others will."

"How do you know that?"

Orellana told him of his experience in Portugal, and of King John's offer to outfit, at his own expense, a handsome expedition to colonize the river.

"Greedy John!" Samano exclaimed. "It is not like him. You mean he offered to bear the expense!"

"Yes, Excellency."

Samano tapped with his slender fingers upon the desk top. "It is contradictory to his nature," he said. "There is more here than appears."

"Is it, perhaps," Orellana suggested, "that he knows the river is not his, and therefore is the more anxious to plant his flag securely upon it?"

Samano looked up sharply.

"It is quite possible. Quite possible. Otherwise— But there is no use bothering ourselves with possibilities. I leave next week for Valladolid. You had better be there, in case your person is required. One never knows."

"Yes, Excellency. I shall be there as soon as you."

37

Encouraged by his success with Juan de Samano, Orellana decided the time had come to press formal suit for the hand of Ana de Ayala.

Fresh from a long sleep and a brisk drenching in a barrel of cold water, he appeared at the house of Cosme de Chavez. The hour was proper for calling; Robles this time had insisted upon it.

He did not immediately see Ana. The gate was latched. Robles rang the bell, and Chavez himself answered, ushering Orellana and Robles almost silently into a reception room that obviously was little used. Lace curtains, aged enough to have been a wedding gift to Ana's mother, tightly covered the room's one window, and a gloomy trio of heavy carved chairs ranged like stiff-backed pages along the wall. A Moorish carpet with two patched rips at one end, and a small oil painting of the Madonna on the wall, only made the shabby room appear more bare. Chavez seated them with a wave of his hand, and himself sat in the largest of the three chairs, nearest to an inner door.

The conversation was anticipatory, that of a secretary dallying with early guests until the hour of their appointment. Staring formally at him across the room, Orellana had the feeling that Cosme de Chavez was not the master of his own house.

Chavez was a little man, thin as a twig, baldish, self-conscious. His voice was nasal and two upper teeth protruded from his mouth when he talked, thrusting his upper lip against the tip of his nose. The nose itself was constantly in motion, like that of a rabbit, due to some nervous condition, and this made Chavez' eyes appear small and greedy. He was not much of a man, Orellana thought, and therefore must have some kind of income, else no woman capable of being Ana's mother would look at him. That the income was not much was apparent from the house. Therefore Orellana concluded that this little man had been a bachelor until his middle years and then had been enticed into matrimony by a calculating woman whose husband had died impoverished and left her with a child to support. Orellana also decided that there were times when Chavez regretted that he had been trapped, and that on such occasions his wife exhausted him into an illusion of spiritual well-being while at the same time leaving him too weak to oppose her.

Orellana smiled at the thought of this endless round of belligerence ending in exhaustion, and tried to estimate Chavez' present point in the cycle. The man looked as though he had had one good night's sleep, but not two. He was, therefore, in the recuperatively submissive stage.

Robles attended to the conversation, a description of his occupation the past three days. Chavez twitched a polite interest but did not ask the sort of questions that might have kept the talk moving. He seemed to have one ear on the door at his back, fearing lest any involved discussion might break off awkwardly if the door opened. He therefore kept the talk upon easily interrupted pleasantries.

Orellana appreciated what was behind the door. Ana's mother would be a forceful woman, robust, with the red hair of the Sidonias and the shrewdness of the peasant. She would be an aboriginal version of her more refined daughter, for Orellana had no doubt, after seeing Chavez, that the sharp spirit of Ana came from her mother's side of the family. A woman who marries more than once usually selects as her second spouse a close replica of her first.

At last Cosme de Chavez rose on his spindly legs and opened the door. A large, confident, red-crowned tower passed the portal and settled massively into a curtsy before Orellana. Gallantly he kissed a fat, working-woman's hand adorned only by a bad amethyst, and looked into the eyes of Ana de Ayala's mother. He saw indeed a calculating woman with hazel eyes and absurdly large eyebrows. The woman looked at him as though she had just caught him violating her daughter in the patio—although with the daughter's consent so that she could only be stern and not angry.

She was not trying to put him at a disadvantage, Orellana discovered. In fact, she fawned on him, as a woman will whose daughter has no dowry. She pressed herself alongside him in a chair vacated by Robles, and signaled the other two men to retire. They went without question, and Orellana was alone with this monument of a woman.

Both waited for the other to speak, Mama Ayala scratching at a bit of refuse that clung to her skirt, Orellana stiffly formal in his fine clothes. Finally Mama Ayala caught sight of Orellana's silk-clad leg and Genoese slippers, and appeared to approve. Her head perked a little, and Orellana could see that her eyes rested sharp and birdlike for a moment on the pearl-encrusted hilt of his dagger, as though she was appraising its worth. Then she slumped, turned suddenly, placed her moist hands over those of Orellana, and said,

"My daughter has told me of you."

"Thank you," Orellana said.

The bird head darted quickly from his hands to his head.

"But I was expecting a more—more handsome man," she said.

"Every man cannot be the equal of your distinguished husband," Orellana replied.

She laughed, appreciating the joke, and, releasing his hands, ran her eyes again down his silken leg.

"You have beautiful calves," she said. "They were born for the life of a courtier."

Orellana nodded bewilderedly.

"I am told that you are a great adelantado and a captain general."

There was challenge now in her tone. She did not quite believe that such honors were his, but the jeweled dagger hilt was convincing.

"I am a captain general, madam," Orellana replied, "and I expect in a few months to return to the New World as a governor."

"You will rule a large territory?"

"Many times the size of Spain, madam."

Mama Ayala nodded emphatically.

334

"You are sure of all this?"

"I am sure, madam."

"Well, then—" The enormous block of woman arose. Orellana too stood. Only the reality that this woman barred the threshold over which he hoped to carry Ana prevented him from bowing curtly and fleeing the house.

"My daughter," she said, "has a mind of her own."

"I have discovered that, Señora."

"Since God has seen fit to bring her poor into the world, her family cannot choose a husband for her. That she will do for herself. Before I give you permission to call on my daughter, however, it must be understood between us that there is no dowry. She has the blood of the Sidonias, but not a single penny, so do not get ideas that she is a rich prize."

"She would be a very rich prize for any man," Orellana said.

Mama Ayala cackled.

"Mother of God, yes! You have a good eye, Señor. Ana's father, God rest his soul, once told me—but enough of that. Ana is waiting for you, and she does not like to be kept waiting. Mind your manners, young man. I am told that you hidalgos from the New World are rough. If you want my daughter, publish the banns first. That's all I have to say about it."

Orellana bowed. Mama Ayala retired ponderously. Orellana closed his eye a moment and was about to withdraw to the patio when the door opened again and Mama Ayala's head jutted out.

"If you take my daughter to the New World, Señor Orellana," she said, "I expect to go with you. Do not forget it." The door closed again.

"Madre de Dios," Orellana muttered. "Madre de Dios!"

Ana was waiting in the patio. As though she appreciated Orellana's ordeal with her mother and desired to counteract its effect, she came to him as he emerged from the hall, with a lithe skipping motion that pressed her cotton dress tightly about her. Through it he could see the entire rich mold of her young body. She took his right arm in both of hers, touching his wrist to her bosom as though by accident, tugging him playfully to the fountain seat. She seated him and stood before him, her body firm on wide-apart legs, her unbraided hair falling over her shoulder. Her blouse was cut to leave both shoulders exposed. Her stance, her eyes, her dress, all seemed to invite him. He leaped to his feet and pressed his body hard against her. She stood to him a fleet moment and backed away laughing.

"You are an impetuous lover," she said, throwing her hair from her eyes and sitting on the bench.

"I have not seen you for three days," he said. "They are three centuries gone from my life. In all the miserable details of writing my petition to the king your face was a lamp illuminating the pages, and the thought of your body was food and drink."

"Poor man," she said. "You must be starved, then."

"Yes," he said, drawing close, "I have starved for the sight of you, for the—touch of you—" his hand reached out but she withdrew from it—"for the sound of your voice. God, Ana—" he clutched her bare shoulders and buried his face in her neck, "what you do to me. . . . What you do to me!"

She was tense. Her head was thrown back before the fierceness of his attack.

"Ana," he whispered, "Ana tesorita, come with me to Valladolid. I cannot go without you." His lips swept up her bare neck and sought her lips.

"Francisco!" she whispered, breaking his hold by rising. "You forget yourself!"

"No," he said, pursuing her, enflamed by the softness of her shoulders, "I do not forget. I remember how I have wanted you, how I have waited for you. You cannot pretend any longer that you do not love me."

"Francisco!"

"No! Your shoulders! Ana! You know how I feel about you.

336

You know I have never felt this way about any woman. You are the first woman I have ever loved—I swear it. Now I have you and I am not—"

"Francisco, you are hurting me!" Her voice was sharp.

He released her.

"Forgive me," he said, penitent. "I cannot help myself. I see you, and my mind races ahead of my clumsy hands. Oh, Ana, I love you. You do not know how much."

"I don't wish to be killed finding out," she said tartly. "Francisco, you must control yourself. I am no baggage that you may maul me at your pleasure."

"Forgive me."

"I am not a slut, whose body may be pawed in my own house."

"Forgive me, Ana, my treasure."

"You think that because I am poor, I have no value, and may be taken without the asking."

"No, Ana—you are precious. You are my whole world. Without you everything is nothing and I the least of men. With you I am everything."

"With me you are a clumsy fool, Don Francisco." She composed her disordered blouse. "Now sit beside me and prove to me that you are really a gentleman."

Chastened, he sat down, trembling. The comment of Hernández, that he understood nothing of women, recurred to him, and ruefully he admitted it. But he knew that she was not too displeased. In fact, she had responded to the curl of his beard and the heat of his lips on her shoulder. He had felt it in the way she had clung to him while he was holding her close. Her body had tensed, as though listening. His own face was hot and his temples pounded. He raised one finger and turned her chin until her eyes looked straight into his own.

"You must not blame me if you are a hot fire that crazes me," he said. "You would not like a lover who was cold."

"I am not interested in a lover," she replied, looking frankly at

337

him, "—although, if I had one, I wonld not want him to be cold."

She smiled, and abruptly flung at him, "You have sent your petition to the council?"

"I took it to Juan de Samano myself."

"Good. It convinced him?"

"He did not say so."

"What did he say?"

"That he would take it to the king, and I must go to Valladolid."

"Good. Tell me about it."

"It was very long."

"Tell anyway."

He described, falteringly and groping for words that would make her appreciate the importance of his many supplications, the demands he had made upon the king. She listened a long time without interruption, grasping his meanings quickly, her facial expression implying that she was a little ahead of his words. Finally she stirred restlessly.

"That is all very well," she said. "But what of you? What have you asked for yourself?"

"It is not I who am important."

"Of course you are important! How do you expect to accomplish all these grand things without authority?"

"I asked for authority."

"What kind?" She pressed him hard. "A governorship?"

"Yes."

"Military commander?"

"Yes."

"A palace for your prestige?"

"Well, no—"

"Why not? How will men respect you unless you live in a manner all men may live up to? Money?"

"Enough."

"How much?"

"Twelve hundred ducats a year, as governor."

"Such a trifle?"

"It will be enough. There will be more when fortresses are built. You can be a queen on twelve hundred ducats, sweetheart."

"Lands?"

"A grant that I will pick out at the proper time."

"How large?"

Orellana stirred.

"Is all this important?" he asked irritably. "Is all this important to you and me?"

"It is important to you, not to me," Ana answered evenly. "Spaniards do not recognize authority unless it is clothed in marble and damask and great estates. You know that."

"In the New World it will be different."

"Fah! New World or Old, men are men."

"I think perhaps under the right leadership, some of man's values may change."

"A dream. A wild dream. Men do not change, only climates and styles. You—for all your great dreams—come to my house and maul me like a beast. Dreamers cannot understand men—only women can do that, because women see the rotten side of every man, and know that every man is rotten."

"Please, Ana."

"I tell you you must be practical. You must go to Valladolid and ask more for yourself."

"Ana, please. There will be plenty for everyone."

"You asked for money to outfit your expedition?"

"Of course. I cannot do it alone."

"You mean you have no money?"

"I have some—but not enough. It costs a great fortune to outfit a fleet and supply a colony."

"How much?"

"I don't know. I guess—" he laughed—"I guess you would say it will cost as much as the king will give. No more, no less."

"Then ask for plenty, so you do not have to spend your own."

"The King of Portugal offered to bear the entire expense. Charles will scarcely offer less."

"All right. But do not forget yourself. One day you may have children, and you will want to provide for them. It is a very terrible thing for a girl not to have a dowry. Think of your own daughters."

Orellana reached out and took her hand.

"I must first have the daughters, Ana. . . ."

She melted.

"Now it is your turn to forgive me," she said. "I did not mean to question you like a shrew. It is just that I want so much for you to succeed—you are not a practical man, Francisco."

"That's where I need you, darling. You are the practical half of me. I can wait a little before going to Valladolid. Your mother says the decision is your own. Let me publish the banns. Marry me, and come with me."

She brushed her cheek against his beard.

"What would the court say if you turned up in Valladolid with a wife who had come to you without a dowry? You see how impractical you are? No, no. You must do this yourself."

"But I would do it so much better if you were with me. Then I could keep my mind on my work, for my heart would be with you in Valladolid, not back here in Seville."

She shook her head.

"I will not be humbled by the gossip of a court, Francisco," she said. "Do your work and return. I am not going anywhere in your absence."

"You will wait for me, then? It is a promise?"

She rumpled his beard with her hand and playfully tugged his chin whiskers as she said, "I make no promises. The king may not even listen to you—and then you will be glad that you do not have a girl about your neck, keeping you from returning to your Indian women in Guayaquil."

"The king will hear me."

She arose.

"Then go to Valladolid," she said, "and come quickly and tell me what the king says."

"You will give me your answer then?"

"Yes, I will give you my answer then."

Impulsively he reached for her, but she turned away, and he had to be content with kissing her bare shoulder.

"I won't be long," he said.

"And don't forget what I said," she answered. "Ask more for yourself."

38

LIKE a hound on a deer's trail Hernán Gutiérrez sniffed his way cautiously through Valladolid. The scent was confused. All men smelled, and all the scent was bad.

The human aroma that surrounds kings is mildew overlaid with decay. Royal favor hastens putrefaction. The body, fed too well, and the mind, fed too little, both degenerate. However much the nobles covered themselves with perfume, the priests with veneer, and the servants and pensioners with importance, the rot welled up from underneath, and the flat musk that suffocated the old palace of the kings of Castile and León clung to everyone who was exposed to it.

The hound that was in Gutiérrez learned to isolate this smell from afar off, separating it from the work smell of the townspeople and the scholar smell of the university students. He could distinguish, without looking up, every passerby who lived off royal favor, for on them was the palace musk and the aroma of degeneration. Those upon whom the musk smell was strongest but not the noble scent or the priest smell, Hernán Gutiérrez turned and followed.

He followed many before he met one. Men who live on royal cream have no taste for the skim milk of companionship with ordinary folk. The lackey courts the cook, who courts the housekeeper, who courts the barber, who courts the physician, who courts the confessor, who courts the nobles who counsel the king. No one looks down from the loftiness of his own position lest he tumble dizzily from his precarious pedestal before the throne. To look down is to be cast down; everyone aspires higher. Even the royal hostler is great in his nearness to the king.

To Gutiérrez this importance assumed by those who served the king was bewildering. Of course he appreciated that Charles V, the mightiest man in all Europe, a man so great that in his lifetime he had held the Pope captive for seven months, and the King of France for a year, was worthy of great veneration. Every man being selfish, power breeds respect; but he could not see how the halo of pomp aurated from the head of the king's barber who merely trimmed the square beard on the jutting Hapsburg jaw. Every man who knelt in the great Presence expected in turn to be knelt to, a sop to compensate for his own groveling. Gutiérrez knelt before the hostler and the barber. He did not like it, but he had a job to do.

His first contact was with the butcher's boy who early each morning delivered meat at the palace. Feigning an interest in the palace courtyard, he accompanied the boy, with elaborate compliments, and helped him unload his wagon. In this way he met a guard. The guard led him to an inn where many bottles of wine later he met the man he had come to Valladolid to convert: Pietro Semplono, His Majesty's barber. This dignitary was a Neapolitan; he had been with the king for many years. He knew the gossip and rancors of the court as well as any man, and appreciated his own importance. Even kings relax under a hot towel, and speak before ignorant barbers of matters they would not dare to mention in the presence of more alert minds.

Men courted Pietro Semplono for what he knew, and for what he might say to the royal ear in the privacy of the chamber. His gossip was legal tender in the court, and he knew from long experience its exchange value: the mood of the queen was worth ten ducats, the attitude of the king toward the backstairs seduction of his chambermaid was worth twenty-five, while the king's next move in the war with France was of great price, and readily marketed.

Semplono, dealer in advice and gossip, would not, however, sell the king's ear. He had never been known to take money for advising the king. That he did advise the monarch was well known—he said so— but with a peculiar integrity that stemmed from the honorable tradition of his profession. Semplono believed, in his simple gossipy heart, that the course of empire revolved about himself. He advised the king; therefore he was in effect king, and his advice must be sound, to the greater luster of Charles and the throne. When men came to him, as did many men, with seeds for him to plant in the royal ear, he selected from them carefully, culling the weeds, planting only such as would be a credit to him, enhance him in the monarch's eyes, and enrich Charles' dominions.

Trained in the New World where an accurate estimate of a man was often the margin between life and death, Gutiérrez bought wine for Semplono, flattered him, and studied him. He did so doggedly, directly, and his earnestness and naïveté charmed the Italian accustomed to perpetual guile. Seemingly Gutiérrez had nothing on his mind, but merely sought illustrious companionship during the monotonous hours during which he awaited the arrival of his illustrious master, Francisco Orellana. The barber was flattered. He had never before been courted by a warrior from the New World. He was vastly impressed with tales of swordplay, murder and gold, and rough details of rapine. Gutiérrez allowed himself to be drawn out, and in exchange permitted himself to be enlightened concerning the refinements of the polished life that went on in the palace, so different from that of Peru: fortunes amassed by contrivance rather than seizure; seduction rather than rape; poison rather than the sword.

Amid all this, little by little, Gutiérrez discovered what he had to know, and in turn was looted of Francisco Orellana's dream. Semplono was exceedingly pleased with himself. From this simple fellow he had extracted the rich secrets of the fabulous Amazon, and the key to the character of their discoverer. Now if Charles should ask him what he thought of a new expedition to Brazil, Semplono could advise him well. He even began to buy drinks for Gutiérrez.

He knew, of course, the day that Francisco Orellana arrived in Valladolid. Gutiérrez had excused himself that morning from their daily conversation. He knew where Orellana had lodged, in a little street off the Plaza del Campanilla near the church of the Magdalen, within sight of the house where Christopher Columbus had died. He knew a great deal, and he was proud of himself.

Gutiérrez likewise knew a great deal, but he was not pleased. He saw Orellana and Robles safe in their lodgings, and let them sleep off the fatigues of the four-hundred mile journey from Seville. Orellana appeared downcast, Robles gloomy. The girl had not accompanied them, although Gutiérrez had selected lodgings large enough to accommodate her and had expected her. Hernández likewise was absent, and this troubled Gutiérrez. He did not like Hernández to be absent at a time when so much clarity was needed. Orellana, the visionary, worked best in team with a practical man, and the Portuguese was the pendulum to Orellana's clock, keeping him on the hour.

"Where's Hernández?" he asked the morning after Orellana's arrival. "Will he come later?"

"No," Orellana said. "He remained in Seville. He did not choose to pass through Estremadura."

Orellana was weary. He looked older, his eye sockets black-bordered with fatigue, his shoulders withered.

"Well," Gutiérrez said. He accepted Hernández' avoidance of Estremadura without question. He himself, now, would not like to go back to the mountains.

"Tell us how the land lies, and what you have done," Orellana said. "Has Juan de Samano arrived?"

"He has," Gutiérrez said, and proceeded to detail the estate of the court. He saved until the end his two pieces of anxious news.

"The time may not be as propitious as we anticipated," he said at last. "The king is returning shortly to Italy."

Unconsciously Orellana arose to his feet.

"We must make haste then."

"Affairs here are being given over to the prince. He will make the decisions affecting Spain henceforth."

"The prince!" Robles said. "God in heaven, why the prince? He is a nobody, a fool, a priest-raised idolater—"

"He is also in fact King of Spain," Gutiérrez said. "Your petition will be reviewed by him, not by Charles."

Orellana sat down again, meditatively. "What kind of man is this prince?"

"Young, not yet eighteen, stubborn like his father, idealistic like his great grandmother Isabella; morose, visionary, they say."

"He was raised entirely by priests," Robles injected. "He is bigoted, anemic, and has the Hapsburg temper and asthma. If he rules Spain, the Inquisition will tighten, man's freedom will wither away, and may God have mercy on us all."

"You say," Orellana said to Gutiérrez, "that he is a visionary?"

"That's what I am told."

"Then we are on good ground."

"Except—" Gutiérrez said this sadly—"that an alliance is now being contracted between the prince and María of Portugal. He may not wish to undertake an expedition into his father-in-law's dominions."

"We are not going to Portuguese dominions," Orellana said. "If Spain and Portugal unite, so will their colonies. We have nothing to fear there. You are too gloomy."

"Gloom is a good thing," Gutiérrez said. "It makes men cautious. I fear the prince will be so engrossed in his wedding that he will not have time for expeditions or anything else that takes time and money."

"He is young," Orellana said. "He will follow his advisers."

"His advisers are all priests!" Robles said.

"You forget that Juan de Samano is on our side."

"He is the king's secretary. Sons usually do not take advice from their father's counselors, just on general principles. How do you know Samano will not go to Italy with the king?"

"He may," Orellana said. "That's why we must move fast. We are wasting time sitting here." He arose. "I am going to the palace to see Samano. I will be back soon."

He was gone a long time. When he returned, he was silent. Finally Robles said, "Well—you saw Samano?"

"He would not see me."

"Would not see you?"

"No. He sent word to leave my address with his servant, and if he wanted me, he would summon me. He said in any event he would get in touch with me within three months."

"Three months?" Robles exclaimed. "Does he expect us to sit in these rooms for three months, just waiting for him?"

"I guess so," Orellana said. He unbuckled his sword, threw off his cape and gloves, and sank back full length on the bed.

"What, then?"

"Let me think," Orellana said. He closed his eye. The men waited. He needs Hernández now, Gutiérrez thought. And Robles was thinking, curse the day I ever introduced him to my cousin; he can think of nothing but her, and she, little bitch, thinks only of herself.

"This war with France—" Orellana said. "The barber thinks it is serious?"

"Very serious," said Gutiérrez.

"Perhaps if the king thought that France might be interested in our story—"

"It might hurry him?"

"At least it might call the matter to his attention. After all, Columbus went to France, you know. The French made a mistake in refusing him. They are not apt to make the same mistake again."

"It's an interesting possibility," Robles said, "but how—"

Gutiérrez arose.

"This hand was dealt to me," he said. "I'm about out of money. Drinking with Semplono is expensive. He likes fine wines."

Orellana took a handful of gold coins from his pouch and dropped them into Gutiérrez' hand.

"Drink the fine wine yourself, too, amigo," he said. "You are entitled to it. . . . Be careful you do not say I am going to France. Emphasize that France might be interested, but stop there. We are not purveyors of untruth."

"I understand," Gutiérrez said, and departed.

"Let's get something to eat," Robles said. "You are moping."

"I?"

"Yes. Cheer up. These things take time."

"I told Ana I would be back in a month."

Robles handed Orellana his sword and cape, and buckled on his own dagger.

"Sisco," he said, "Ana will wait. She will wait longer than you think. The way you are acting, you would think you were eighteen and she was thirty."

"I don't want to wait. She has me all stirred up. It is difficult for me to think of anything but her."

"It is obvious," Robles said. "She has you dangling like a fish on a line."

Orellana smiled.

"No, amigo, it is not as bad as that. I am a fool about her, yes; but not yet a fool. She sees these things so clearly. She is practical. I need her. It is when I see how good she is for me, and straightens me out on matters of which I know nothing, that I am most in love with her."

"That is all very well, but a man must be the master of his woman. You are not the master of Ana."

"No man is ever master of a courtship."

"Of the courtship, no; but of the woman, yes. There is a distinction. You have let her dominate you until now you cannot make up your mind about anything."

"Is it as bad as that, Alonso?"

"It is. You are a mooncalf. I am surprised at you."

"You think I should hit her over the head, then?"

"It would help—both her and you."

Orellana smiled.

"Perhaps you are right," he said. "Now that you have hit *me* over the head, let's forage for something to eat. A melon, perhaps, and a glass of wine."

They were crossing the Plaza del Campanillo toward a sidewalk café, admiring the fine Gothic structures for which the city is famous, when Robles stopped suddenly, stepped a pace back and put his hand on his sword. Instinctively Orellana also paused.

A grandee, tall and straight-backed and privileged in a cloak with the white arms and embroidered red cross of the Order of St. Iago, stood contemptuously before them, his immaculate beard belligerently jutted but with his long arms lax at his sides. He did not move, neither did he speak. He waited.

Robles also waited. Traffic on the street became quiet. Children stopped playing in the street. Women held their breath in windows and shop doors. Horsemen paused. The adversaries eyed each other.

Robles relaxed the grip on his sword under the towering contempt of the older man. The grandee smiled.

"That's right," he said quietly. "Not here. A better moment will present itself. I shall tell my sons that you are now in Spain. They will be glad to know."

He bowed to Orellana, turned his back, and walked away. Robles clenched his teeth, wheeled and strode rapidly in the other direction.

"My great uncle," he said aside to Orellana. "It was his sister's son who tried to kill me, and who died for it. I should have known that he would be in Valladolid, with the king."

39

THREE months passed, and nothing happened. The king prepared to depart for Italy. The betrothal of Philip and María of Portugal was announced. The five members of the Council of the Indies met many times in the church of Santa María la Antigua, but Orellana was not summoned. Juan de Samano remained silent. There was no word, either, from Seville. Perhaps afraid to trust his activities to a scrivener, Hernández wrote nothing. Neither did Ana de Ayala.

Orellana fretted. He could not risk the displeasure of Juan de Samano by seeking him out again. The word spread that he was in town, that he had discovered a domain larger than Peru, and twenty times the size of Spain. Men congregated before his lodgings to look at him, and to beg the favor of investing their fortunes and persons in his new enterprise to the Amazon. Women trussed their hair quickly as he passed, giggling into their lace curtains. The professors at the University of Valladolid invited him among them, and paid him the high compliment of listening to his dream of a world in which men should be measured by ability and energy rather than traditional privilege. The doctors of medicine were enchanted with the description of Carranza, whose medical wonders had kept the men alive and who had finally perished of the one ailment he could not cure. Orellana suggested that a chair of tropical medicine would enhance the University in this age of Spanish expansion, and the scholars were attentive until they discovered that Orellana would not himself endow such studies. All over town Orellana was lionized, followed, and praised—but he was ignored at the palace.

Gutiérrez had no better luck with Semplono. He and the barber were great friends. Semplono was so enthusiastic about the Amazon that he wished to invest money in the new enterprise, but he could not mention the matter to the king. Charles was engrossed in a new war with France, the betrothal of his heir, the uprising of the Protestants against Catholic rule in Germany. He suffered badly, also, from both gout and asthma. He had not mentioned to Semplono the discovery of the Amazon, and Semplono, burning as he was with fear that Orellana might be lured to France, had found no proper moment to raise the matter himself.

Robles was of no use at all. He did not venture out by day, and Orellana would not let him go abroad by night. Not that Robles feared the ultimate issue that faced him; rather he would have preferred to settle it at once; but Orellana decreed caution. Bloodletting by Orellana's men would prejudice his case at court. He did not want the king to become aware of him as a rowdy who fought with cousins of the great dukes of Medina Sidonia in the streets of Valladolid.

Fretting and idle, Orellana passed the summer in the capital of Castile and León, impatient more for Ana de Ayala than for his beloved river, desperate at Spanish indolence that ignored so great a decision as colonization of an empire.

Finally, late in September, he could stand no more. He was wild for Ana, intolerably oppressed by the frustration of all his hopes. More and more he crystallized his unhappiness in the person of Ana. If she accepted him, he believed, everything would be different. He would know how to act forcefully, as he had done in old times in Peru. He would find ways to reach Juan de Samano, ways even to reach the king. So long as his love remained unfruitful, everything was unfruitful.

Robles' words recurred to him: "A man must be master of his woman. . . . You should hit her over the head." And the philosophy of Hernández: "Dreams are too soft; like gold coins they rub thin in circulation." Ana's own words: "The one I marry must be a man, not a beggar." And the story told so long ago in the jungle by Juan de Illanes reared before him in a new light. "Women want exactly what you want; some of them just don't know. But once you teach them . . ."

The time had come to teach Ana de Ayala. Everything depended on it. This fire within him could not consume him forever.

Summoning his horse, he called to Gutiérrez and Robles.

"I am going to Seville," he said. "I am going to have things out with Ana, once and for all. With that off my mind, I will know what to do here."

"You are going alone?" Robles asked.

"I am."

"And if Samano summons you in your absence?"

"Tell him I have been called away on urgent business but return any day."

"Is that wise?" Gutiérrez asked. "It will be ill luck to have the whole matter come to a head while you are gone."

"It will be worse luck to have matters come to a head while my mind is reeling with doubts and questions. Four months, and I have heard nothing from Ana. I must settle that. Then I will know what to do here. I feel it."

"Bravo," said Robles. "Hit her over the head."

"With luck I will be back in three weeks."

"You will talk fast in Seville, then."

"I do not propose to talk. I am tired of doing nothing."

Gutiérrez brightened. The love sickness that had been upon his master was passing at last.

"I will get your horse, General," he said.

Orellana rode south in a fury. He hated the king. He hated Samano. He detested the king's barber. He abhorred the rooms in Valladolid that were empty without Ana. He hated the cold Gothic architecture of the University. He hated himself, himself most of all. In four months he had done nothing, and worse, he had not known what to do. It was one thing to settle a problem that was immediate and pressing: the threat of death in a cold mountain, the attack of Indians, the treachery of a Maldonado, the military insubordination of dying men.

Such things were concrete; always there was a clear settlement if one had courage to face it. Usually decisions of action are decisions of courage. Here in Spain there was nothing to face. The problems were elusive: the whims of a girl, the procrastinations of a court, the lurking death that stalked Robles. Against them there was no offense. Now suddenly and in fury, he knew that there was an attack. He was beginning to see the whole chain of conquest quite clearly. Everything linked together finally, but the first link would be the most difficult to forge.

This time he would take matters in his own hands, where they belonged, where they had belonged all the time. No more waiting. No more indecision. First things must come first. He regretted only that he had not been able to see his course earlier. He had required six months to acclimatize himself to the ways of civilization after the ways of the jungle. Oddly enough, the ways of civilization were the more barbaric.

He rode south. His horse, a rugged white Barb bred through many generations for endurance, carried him on swiftly, and he traveled light. A single change of clothing, a sack of emeralds around his neck, a dagger but no sword, these and his own hundred-seventy pounds were slight burden to a well-muscled horse. In Madrid he took a grudging ten hours, sparing the horse rather than himself. At Jerez he rested again, preparatory to crossing the rough Sierra Morena. Then on down into Seville, where he washed away the grime of his journey, but not the fury that was on him, before setting out for the home of Cosme de Chavez.

Seville slept as he entered, and still slept as he reached his destination. The little plaza of the common well whispered to its cork trees under a pale-starred sky. In an hour the roosters would begin to crow.

He found a foothold in the wall that surrounded the patio, and vaulted into the court. The ground floor rooms of spindle-shanked Chavez and his mountainous spouse were shuttered. Above them was the window of Ana de Ayala.

He furled his cape across his shoulders and fumbled for an ascent. He had noticed a flower box there before. Now he found it and cautiously tested its strength against his weight. A leap and his fingertips clutched the grille at Ana's window. He chinned himself to the sill level and listened. No sound. He swung over the ironwork and inserted a leg in the window, probing until it found solid floor. Then he was inside, holding his breath, listening. He waited until his eye focused in the vague gloom. The night was warm. He perspired a little. There was no air in the little room.

He saw the outline of her lovely figure upon a simple wooden bed. She lay, asleep like a child, innocent of the furies that intoxicated the man who looked down upon her and wanted her. Tears confused Orellana's eye. She was such a child sleeping thus, her body liberated from her inquisitive mind; a child, an innocent. Beauty in shadow, ecstasy in silhouette. He trembled. He had been right in coming. All doubts now were gone, all anxieties. She would be his, and everything else would fit in place, the torment in his soul would die, his mind would function again.

He stepped to the bed and knelt beside it. Her breath fanned his perspiring brow like a cooling wind. Now he saw the outline of those shoulders he had kissed, the gentle rise and fall of her chest. He could smell her hair, and her sweet breath.

His hands trembled as he fumbled with his gauntlets and lay them carefully on the floor, his dagger and cape beside them. Still kneeling, he reached out with an almost uncontrollably shaking hand, and placed it across her mouth.

At once she stirred, and his fever left him. He was ice now, his muscles sure, his brain keen at last. He had known it would be so. She opened her eyes, and tried to call out, but he silenced her with a whisper: "Ana, it is I, Francisco. Be quiet!"

She recognized the voice and stilled, drawing the sheet about her. She felt his face, the scarred eye socket, the wiry beard, with a quick hand.

"Be quiet, little pigeon," he whispered. "I had to see you. God, I have missed you. Ana, Ana!"

His fingers relaxed on her mouth, and she spat at him.

"What is the meaning of this? Do you want to wake the house? Do you want to compromise me? What do you want?"

"I want to talk to you."

"This is no time to see me. You are a beast."

"Yes." He crouched over her. She was not afraid. He bent to kiss her. She turned her head away quickly.

"Go away, before I call my mother," she whispered. "In God's name, go away. You don't know what you're doing."

"I know what I'm doing. Of all the things I have ever done, of this I am most sure."

"You must not."

"Yes, Ana. This I must. You know it, and I know it."

"I will scream."

"No, you will not scream. You love me. If you scream, we are both finished. I have ridden four hundred miles for this, and it is right, and you know it's right. Ana—listen to me."

"Then say what you have to say and go."

"In Valladolid—everything is wrong without you. The days pass like tombstones. The nights are an agony of wondering where you are, and whether you are alive or dead. Without you I am a dead tree branch, drying and ready to break off. I cannot do my work for thinking of you, or sleep for loving you. I must know that you love me, too. I must know before I can do anything else. Nothing is worth anything until I know that. Say you love me, Ana."

"Go away. Come tomorrow."

"No. Tomorrow will never dawn without you. You must love me tonight. Now. You have played with me long enough. I must know."

"Francisco—"

"Be quiet! I am speaking." He touched her shoulders, and she drew the sheet more tightly around her. He seized her then, unmindful of

355

her arms that pushed against him. His lips found her cheek, but she would not turn her head to him.

"Ana," he whispered. "Do you think I have ridden from Valladolid for nothing? With the horse hoofs beating out my love for you step by step I have come to you. I have waited long enough. If you did not love me it would be different. You do love me. I know it. Now you are going to tell me. With your own lips you are going to tell me."

"Beast," she said.

"A lover, my little turtle dove, not a beast. Beasts do not love, they only take. You and I love. Kiss me."

"No."

He kissed her, forcing her head to him. She struggled against him, but he ignored it.

"You love me," he said, kissing her again before she could answer or cry out. She began to weep, still fighting him. Her tears, falling upon his lips, enflamed him.

"You love me," he repeated fiercely. "Say it!"

He did not know exactly when she stopped beating him and began to clutch him. He was vaguely aware that she was whispering to him, but he did not hear her words. Now she met his kiss, and there was no doubt in his mind. Everything was right, and his way lay clear and broad before him, all the way back to the river. No longer was he alone.

Suddenly he heard her say, "You are right, Francisco. I do love you."

40

ORELLANA returned to Valladolid a different man. Gutiérrez observed it first. Orellana leaped from his horse at the door as though he had ridden half a mile rather than four hundred, and strode into the house with the clear eye of the conqueror. Gutiérrez stabled the horse quickly, and followed.

When he entered, Orellana was already undressed and laying out his finest clothes. Robles, a smile on his face, assisted.

"First, Juan de Samano," Orellana said. "This time he will see me. . . . Hernán, faithful Hernán, is your barber still here?"

"Yes, General, but the king leaves any day."

"Good. Tell your wine-loving friend that I am sick of waiting, and if I do not see His Excellency Don Juan de Samano today, I leave tomorrow for France. Can you find him on some pretext?"

"That is pretext enough, General," Gutiérrez said. "I will go at once. The barber will understand my anxiety."

"Good."

Orellana wasted no time. Over his bath he told Robles that Hernández already had recruited a hundred men who would sign on for an expedition to the Amazon, at their own expense. He was buoyant.

"And Ana?" said Robles.

"She will wait."

He spoke with conviction. Robles smiled and said no more.

When Gutiérrez returned, Orellana had bathed, dined and trimmed his beard.

"You told him?" he asked directly.

Gutiérrez sat down slowly, dejectedly.

"Yes, I told him," he said.

"You are not happy about it."

"No."

"What's the trouble?"

Gutiérrez looked long at Robles before saying, "I do not like to speak of it, but sooner or later you will know. We are friends together. Remember I do not speak for myself."

He organized his thoughts. The others could see that he was reluctant to speak at all. Finally Robles helped him.

"It concerns me, then."

"Yes." Gutiérrez looked up sadly.

"Then it is right that I should know."

"Yes."

"Tell us then, Hernán," Orellana encouraged him. "We have been through so much, we three—there is no blow we cannot take together."

Gutiérrez nodded, and sighed.

"The barber has been in touch with someone on the Council of the Indies. They are in favor of the enterprise, but will not let you lead it, or even go along."

"Because of me?" Robles said.

Gutiérrez nodded. "It is all very strange," he said. "Semplono was very agitated. He does not know now whether he wishes to invest his money, after all."

The two waited patiently. Gutiérrez said, "They say that what you really plan is a Lutheran colony in the New World, that you must be a heretic, otherwise you would not have a known heretic as your lieutenant. They say they have been informed most reliably that Señor Robles is an apostate, a protestant and such things, and that you and he are hiding the real purpose of your expedition behind idealistic words."

"My uncle!" Robles gasped.

"You denied it, of course," Orellana said.

"It is difficult to deny rumors, especially such sensations. Semplono seemed almost afraid to drink with me, lest he be accused of heresy.

The ears of the Inquisition are nowhere larger than in Valladolid, and even the king's household is not safe."

"Oh, the swine!" Robles said. "The filthy swine. It is one thing to attack me, Sisco—but to mix you in it—oh, the rotten, filthy swine."

"Do you know where the Council received these rumors?" Orellana asked. "Did Semplono know?"

"I asked him that. He said the matter came to their attention through a priest."

"A priest!"

"That's what he said, General."

"I have dozens of relatives who are priests," Robles said. "Priests, bishops, archbishops. The family crawls with them. Any of them could inform on me, on behalf of my cousin. I should have anticipated this, Sisco. I am a fool to risk your neck with my own."

"Your neck and mine are the same body, amigo," Orellana said. "I asked you to come. I should not have put you in such peril."

"It was sooner or later, Sisco. For me, I would get it over. But you —to cause you to lose all you have done, all you have dreamed—that I cannot do. I will go to my uncle."

"Don't be a fool, Alonso."

"I must. You brought me to Spain to help you. Well, I have been little help, hiding in dark rooms, going abroad hidden in a cape. You are not implicated with me. I will prove it."

"You must not."

"I must."

"I forbid you!" He put his hand on his dagger.

Robles sat heavily and covered his face with his hands. "Let us not fight, Sisco," he said. "Love of you is all I have left in the world. Let me preserve it."

Orellana placed his hand on his friend's shoulder.

"Don't take it so hard, Alonso," he said. "There are many windows in a house, and each has a different view. You said yourself, long ago, that your family could not turn you in to the Inquisition, because of the risk to its own property and prestige."

"Yes. That's why they tried to kill me."

"Well, then. What is there to fear? Take my horse; it is fleeter than your own. Ride to Seville, and return to the New World. Somewhere we shall meet again."

"And leave the wreckage of your life behind? The suggestion is unworthy of you, Sisco."

"Forget me for the moment. Once you are out of the way I can disavow you. I can say I heard of your sacrilege, and dismissed you. It will give me a good excuse to see Juan de Samano."

"It wouldn't work. Men are too suspicious. They would think you had sent me away until the fire died. They would have to see my dead body before they would believe you were rid of me."

"All right then. I would say that same family feud, of which I know nothing, had disposed of you, that thugs had kidnaped you from my house in the night. I would tell of the threat made by your kinsman on the street. Many witnesses could be found to prove it. Your family would gladly assist me in spreading the rumor that you were dead. Go, amigo, while there is time."

"I will think about it," Robles said, "but no one would believe it without the body. It is blood they must see in Spain."

Quickly Orellana diverted the conversation. A wily antagonist was at work before the Council of the Indies. A subtle antagonist, a man of the elusive stamp of Maldonado. Well, he had handled a Maldonado before. He could do it again.

"I am going to see His Excellency the secretary Samano," he said quietly. "Perhaps he will let slip some hint concerning all this. When you are cornered, attack. It is a good motto for Spain as well as Peru. Stay here until I return."

His fine clothes passed the scrutiny of the palace guards without question, and he crossed the elaborately sculptured door of the old palace and turned to the right along the inner court toward the apartments of the king's secretary. There he brushed past the guard with the confidence of one who is expected, and saw Samano talking to his scrivener beside a desk near the small window. Both looked up.

"Excellency," Orellana said, bowing. "I regret to intrude like this, but urgency compels me. If you have forgotten, I am Francisco Orellana."

Samano frowned, then made the best of the situation.

"Of course," he said. "I regret that I have had no news for you this long time. The king's affairs are very complex."

"But the Council of the Indies," Orellana blurted, "surely it has had time to consider my petition and act upon it?"

"The Council has had weighty matters of another nature," Samano answered smoothly, not taking the bait. "The situation in Peru is acute. Your friend Gonzalo Pizarro has organized an armed revolt against the king's viceroy and has publicly proclaimed disallegiance to the new code of laws the king has decreed for Peru. If you conquerors would work for Spain, sir, instead of for yourselves, we might have time to consider other ventures, and the stomach for them."

Was this a hint? Orellana answered carefully. "It is not my desire, Excellency, that the evils of Peru shall be repeated in New Andalusia. With such troubles in Peru, His Majesty should welcome a colony that enhanced his person and was a glory to Spain."

"It is a grave question whether His Majesty's person would be enhanced by your proposal for New Andalusia."

"I do not understand what you mean." Orellana waited tensely.

"We will not argue the matter here," Samano said. "I merely state that the Council has not made a decision on your enterprise. Many facets must be explored, many implications understood. These things take time."

The indirection annoyed Orellana.

"More time than a man's life can spare, Excellency," he shot back. "I could now be en route back to the Amazon with a fine expedition raised by the King of Portugal. I chose to be loyal to my king. But loyalty wears thin, sir. In France I might be better treated."

Samano, who had turned back to his parchments, now looked up

361

quickly, as though eager to turn the conversation from delicate ground.

"I did not dignify with belief the report that you would treat with our enemies. I trust it is a mere threat, Señor Orellana."

"It is now only a threat, Excellency," Orellana replied evenly, "but tomorrow it will be a conviction, and the day after that, a fact. Four months is long enough to wait."

Samano motioned him to a chair, and strode before him as he talked. "The difficulty," he said, "lies in Dr. Bernal, an eminent member of the Council. He does not believe that such a colonial enterprise should be entrusted to you. We know very little about you and your petition is—to say the least—unusual. What's behind all this? What is your real purpose?"

"A better world, Your Excellency."

The secretary's face was grave.

"Of what sort, Señor?"

"What I have outlined in my petition. No more. No less. Let the crown put over me a supervisor if there is any question. I do not fear inspectors."

"You would consent to that?" Samano appeared surprised.

"If it is done speedily. I am weary of waiting."

"The Council meets next week. I shall report this conversation to them."

"Next week I shall be en route to France."

"You do not mean that."

"I should hate to do it, but I am determined to establish a colony along the Amazon, and after four months of waiting, I am inclined to follow Columbus and seek help wherever it might be offered."

He had not intended to say this, but now an attack appeared his only hope.

"I see. I warn you that your case might be prejudiced by such impetuosity."

"A man who dawdles in miserable lodgings for a third of a year waiting for a promised summons that never arrives, is hardly guilty of impetuousness."

362

Samano smiled.

"Quite," he said. "I will see what is to be done. Do not be surprised if the Council tells you to go to France—or anywhere else you may desire."

Orellana bowed.

"I shall wait one week for your answer, Your Excellency," he said. "One week to the day."

"You will hear from me," Samano said.

Confidently Orellana returned to his lodgings. The difficulties were not insurmountable. The threat of France was greater even than the peril of Lutheranism. He turned into his lodgings calmly, sure of himself. Action accomplished all things. It had done so with Ana, he thought smiling.

Gutiérrez met him.

"General," he said quietly, pulling Orellana inside and closing the door. "Look."

On the bed lay Alonso Robles' sword and gloves. Casually, almost lovingly, Robles' cape was draped across the back of a chair as though its proud hidalgo owner had only that moment doffed it and intended immediately to pick it up again. Robles, however, was not there.

"Gone," Gutiérrez said. "He asked me to get him some buns and a bottle of wine. When I returned there was only this."

Orellana looked down gravely again at the scarlet-lined cape and said, "He will turn up. He must have stepped out for something."

"Stepped out—without his cape, General? When have you known Alonso to go abroad without his cape?"

"Never," Orellana said, frowning.

41

Don Alonso Robles, younger son of the youngest daughter of the indigent Marquis of Loja, legatee only of the flaming red hair of the illustrious Sidonias, walked calmly up the tree-lined avenue of La Concepcion, unmindful of his nakedness. Had any of his relatives encountered him at that moment, they would undoubtedly have recognized him; the fiery trademark of the breed was unmistakeable. They would hardly have acknowledged him, however, even in enmity, for he was bareheaded, uncloaked, and unarmed. His noble back and gentle walk distinguished him from the rabble about him. Even without the accoutrements of rank he looked the knight and gentleman: the mold-poured cast of breeding was upon him. Passersby eyed him sharply, deferential but amused that a knight should be abroad in bright daylight so indiscreetly clad. There could be but one conclusion. The young man had spent his siesta in a flesh house and, having taken too much wine, had left his gear behind.

Robles was cold sober. He walked with too much determination to be drunk. He knew where he was going, crossing the street carefully to avoid the open sewer in which a peasant woman was washing clothes, stepping thoughtfully around a group of playing children, turning a corner and entering the merciful shade of a splendidly tiled entryway. A stairs circled upward on the left. He took it bounding, poised on one foot at the top step. Then on as confidently as though this were his own house, through an open door into a paneled library. The gentleman writing at the secretary looked up. He did not have far to look, for he was very tall, white-haired and white-bearded, with the chiseled bleached face of the secure aristocrat. So unruffled and dispassionate was the venerable Don Carlos de Mendosa y Loja that it was said of him that nothing in all his seventy-one years had ever surprised him. He was not surprised now as he saw his nephew. He did not even put down his quill.

"A moment," he said, and went on writing. There was nothing ancestral about this room, Robles reflected. It mirrored rather the present state of genteel poverty of his branch of the family, than the inherited magnificences of furniture and trappings which still allowed the old Marquis to keep up appearances in Andalusia. This was a rented house, and looked it. The ceiling frieze was crumbling and had not been repaired; the Florentine lace curtains were baggy with decay; the Levantine floor runner was badly worn. With Charles back in Spain, and a glittering court functioning in Valladolid for the first time in many years, the presence of the Marquis was required, even though it cost him more than he could afford.

The family of the Marquis had built its fortune upon the Moorish wars. Rich plunder had balanced the household budget for many generations. Now the Moors were gone, driven finally and absolutely from Spain these fifty years, and the present Marquis had nothing with which to replenish the looting of his own capital by the dowries of three daughters each of whom had cost him a fortune, and by the perpetual greedy demands of the church. The Marquis, Robles reflected with gratification, was richer in only one thing than himself—pride—and the time fast approached when the aging grandee would be eating that, for he had little else left.

The old man wrote for a long time, often pausing to select his words or to contemplate what he had written. The manuscript was a letter, and from the care with which it was constructed, Robles thought, was probably a plea to some creditor to be charitable a while longer. The grape harvest this year was better. . . . The olives . . . the extra expenses incident to Charles' court soon would end. . . . In other days Alonso Robles, if kept waiting thus arrogantly, might have insinuated himself into the letter writing with red-headed insults. Today he was a supplicant.

At last the grandee lay aside his pen, precisely and deliberately, scanned his script a last time, and turned the pages face down upon the desk. He arose and leveled a mask-face at his nephew.

"Well?" he said.

Phrases carefully polished in his mind on the walk to his uncle's house ran like frightened mice from Robles' memory, scattered by the hatred that rose up in him at the grandee's coldness. He had to clench his fists tightly to keep from drawing his dagger. The Marquis noticed.

"Admirable self control," he commented. "It is a pity you did not learn this asset sooner."

"Likewise your youngest daughter's son, Excellency," Robles said. He had not meant to mention the matter at all. Sufficient that proud Castilians never forgot insult, without being thus goaded. The Marquis' frozen face revealed no trace of hurt.

"Why have you come to me?" he asked.

"To right a wrong, Señor."

The Marquis bowed a little, went to the window and sat in a throne-like chair with a very high, elaborately carved back, the pious faces of four ebony apostles peering over his white head. He did not invite Robles to sit.

"I have waited a long time," he said.

"Is it not enough," Robles said then, "that you should hate me, without spreading your hatred to include others who have done you no injury?"

The Marquis' mask dropped. "Others?" he asked, showing interest by a slight widening of his eyes.

"Yes, Excellency. I speak of the man whom I have had the great honor to serve in the New World, Francisco Orellana."

"I do not know him."

"The more reason you should not oppose his enterprise that might well be of great glory and enrichment to Spain."

"You babble. Say what you have to say."

Robles shifted his weight, aware that his tense body had made his legs ache.

"I have come to ask you to stop interfering in the affairs of Fran-

366

cisco Orellana, who knows nothing of my life, and concentrate your vengeance on me. It is beneath your dignity to involve outsiders in a family quarrel. I have come to surrender myself into your hands, in return for your word that you will undo the harm you have done my friend, and pledge me to impede him no further."

The Marquis was amused.

"I am grateful to this person, whoever he may be, for delivering you into my hands, but I do not know him, and have done nothing to him, and therefore cannot oblige him, much as I owe him at this fortunate moment."

"Come, sir," Robles said hotly, "it is not as though you had me in your power through any bravery of your own. I am the equal of yourself and all your sons. You know it, or you would have met me sometime during the past four months. I have come here voluntarily. At least show me the dignity of honesty."

"If I said I had ever before heard the name of this person of whom you speak, I should indeed be guilty of dishonesty. What am I supposed to have done?"

"Did you not cause to be circulated before the Council of the Indies the falsehood that Francisco Orellana proposed to found a Lutheran colony in the New World?"

"Sacred name!" exclaimed the Marquis. "Why should I do a thing like that?"

"Because I am Orellana's lieutenant, and by ruining him, you ruin me. It is a trick of which your sons would approve."

"You have ruined yourself, young man; we have only had to wait. But that is a different matter. You should know me well enough to realize that I would not concern myself with the murderers you choose as companions. I value my soul too highly to permit any contact with you except such as might be necessary to cause your death. I certainly would not disturb my soul with thoughts of heretics—Orellana or otherwise, yourself excluded. I have had no contact with the Council of the Indies."

"Nor your sons?"

"Nor my sons. Had they, I should know."

Robles was astounded. He knew his uncle spoke the truth. None of his family had ever been good liars.

"Then who is responsible for this fiendishness?"

"That is not my concern." The old man was icy again.

Robles had not addressed the question to his uncle. He had been thinking out loud. The evidence had been unquestionably clear. None but his family could possibly have known. Unless—merciful God, there was another. One whom Orellana could not possibly cope with alone.

He turned, thinking only of escape. The door was blocked by two men at arms. The Marquis rose quickly.

"I am afraid I must ask you to remain," he said. "There is a certain hospitality we must show you."

"Another time," Robles said, his mind on other matters. "Another time, I will give you your satisfaction. I pledge it. But now I—"

"I must insist," the Marquis said. He stepped aside as Robles drew his dagger and the men-at-arms rushed forward.

Robles plunged between them to the door and ran downstairs, the guards shouting behind him. The massive wrought iron doors in the entryway, so casually open when he had come in, now were closed. He turned swiftly, veering across a tiled court on which gave many doors and a long galley. He chose the galley, and bolted. The end was blocked by two more men-at-arms, one with a drawn sword, the other with a sword and lance. He flung himself at a door, opened it, burst into a gloom-hung salon and dashed for a door at the other end. Opening it, he erupted into bright sunlight. He was in the courtyard again, and the men-at-arms who had been upstairs were on him. The door at his back closed. He stepped backward into a corner, for there was nothing else to do, his dagger pitiful protection against the long blades of his uncle's men. Vaguely he saw a balcony that ran entirely around the court on the floor above and calculated his chances of scaling to it for a leap from a second story window on the street side.

He saw it too late. The guards who had been in the galley now rushed up and the lance was pinned against his chest.

"Hold!"

He looked up. His uncle stood on the balcony. The old man disappeared. A moment later he entered the court, two heavy Italian rapiers in his hands. One of these he extended to his nephew.

"I am too old a man to indulge in murder," he said. "I leave that to your generation." His tone was revoltingly contemptuous. "One murder in the family is enough. Let us see now whether you can die like a man." He extended a rapier, handle-first, to Robles. "Use your own dagger. These men-at-arms will not interfere. If I fall, the gates will be opened, and you will be allowed to go."

Robles took the blade. There was nothing else to do. The guards separated into pairs, blocking the two exits. Here on this tiled court the issue would be met, and Don Alonso Robles would live or die. The blade in his uncle's hand flashed, as the old man withdrew to the center of the quadrangle, waiting, rapier in his right hand, a dagger in his left.

Robles stepped forward, lynx-like, and in two passes he knew that the rusty joints of this seventy-year-old were no match for him, nor was the old man's skill. The Marquis was of the antiquated generation of the two-handed pole axe; the rapier was the product of a more modern day. He had no skill to cope with a heavy two-edged sword, nor the quick reflex required to manipulate a long and a short blade. What conceit, Robles thought, had possessed his uncle to choose a weapon so newly developed, a manner of combat the Spaniards were even then only learning from the Italians? The rapier was well known in the New World, and with it Robles had had long acquaintance. Not so, obviously, the uncle. Did the old man *wish* to die? Was he committing suicide? Or did he, in the passion of his pride, believe the Beloved Virgin or some holy saint would put strength in his brittle knees and suppleness in his feeble wrist?

Robles defended himself, but could not attack. The old man stood to him fiercely, chin beard at a defiant angle, cold murder in his eyes. Robles knew that at any moment, turning down his uncle's blade with his own dagger, he could sweep in and rake the Marquis' gullet from his neck, yet he did not do so. One death was on his head, necessarily but miserably. To kill the Marquis, too, in his own house, would set the remaining relations upon him in a pursuit so relentless that life would forever be a hell. Even more perilous was the threat to Orellana. To slay the Marquis in his own house would be to bring down upon Orellana the full vengeance of the family. At least now Orellana still had a chance. If the Marquis died, he would have none.

For a moment longer he postponed the issue of the combat, his eyes darting about the quadrangle for a means of escape, but there was none. He knew that he must die—soon, quickly, before the faltering hand of the Marquis dropped his heavy weapon. His next thought was for a clean death, quick and sure. In his uncle's blundering tactics there appeared a way.

His eye caught the cloudless sky, the flash of green from a tree outside. God will forgive my sins, he said to himself. Oh, Sisco, what my blundering has caused!

He stepped forward, exposing his heart to his uncle's thrust.

42

FOR TWO days Orellana and Gutiérrez waited for Robles to return. Two days of silence.

Finally Orellana said, "Help me dress, Hernán. I am going to pay a visit to the Marquis of Mendosa y Loja."

"Good," Gutiérrez said, jumping immediately to the task of outfitting his companion. As always he believed in direct action.

Orellana was scarcely dressed, however, before there was a worried knock at the door. Both men picked up their swords, and Orellana called word to enter.

The little barber, Semplono, poked his head through the door, spied Gutiérrez, bowed low to Orellana, and quickly closed the door behind him.

"My apologies," he said, addressing both men without facing either, "but the news of greatest import has just reached me. The king is incensed that four months have passed and no one at court has seen you. Mirabile dictu, what do you think of that? Of course I was only teasing when I said I might withdraw my investment. The king is leaving. I brought you the money. Five hundred ducats. The receipt now, please. I must hurry. We leave within the hour, the king and I."

No one took the gold.

"How did the king hear of me?" Orellana asked. He did not like the greasy manner of the little barber. He shot a glance of great admiration at Gutiérrez, appreciating his ordeals over many bottles of heavy wine.

"He has left orders for the prince to attend to everything. You will not be forgotten. He called Don Juan de Samano and such language! The king is very eloquent in anger. Ah, the beauty! What he cannot say in Spanish he finds words for in French or Flemish and when he is stuck for a filthy phrase that means everything—there is naturally Italian. The rhythm of it. Such name calling! I thank God I lived to hear it. I told him you were my good friend. Take the money."

"How did the king hear of me?" Orellana repeated.

"I cannot disclaim some of the credit, Your Excellency," Semplono said. "He asked who you were, and I was able to tell him. It was very impressive that I should know, while the court plowed their feeble brains for recollections. It was then that he called Semplono."

"What made him ask of me?"

"But you are the talk of the court today, Señor! Everyone enjoys scandal more than work, even kings. It is an old trick to spice information with gossip in order to reach the king's ear. But in this case it was no trick. The real article. A very great sensation. And of course it repudiated the horrid gossip some of us had heard about yourself. Everything is clear, now."

Orellana detested the little man the more. If this was a sample of the manners of the court, he wanted none of it. He controlled his temper.

"Señor Semplono," he said patiently, "I am afraid we are in the dark. Begin at the beginning, I beg you. What scandal could possibly affect us? Is it—is it—"

"But of course, Señor. What else? Everyone in Valladolid is talking about it. Why not the king, also? He is human."

"It concerns Señor Robles, then."

"Naturally."

"I must ask you for further enlightenment. We do not know what has become of Señor Robles."

Semplono's eyes illuminated with delight. Here was a chance to tell the story in all its glory, brightly burnished by a morning of ever-magnified retelling.

"You mean," he gasped, "that you do not know?" This opportunity was unbelievable.

"We do not know. We were just setting out to look for him."

372

Semplono found a chair and leaped into it eagerly. His open palms came together in delight.

"He is dead," he said. "Run through by no less a person than his own uncle, the Marquis Don Carlos de Mendosa y Loja. And in his own house!"

"Dead," Orellana said. "Alonso, my hot-headed brother. And for me." He arose and quickly turned his back on the barber. He pretended to look out the window. Gutiérrez sat stupefied.

"Dead," said Semplono. "He attacked the Marquis in his own house—his own uncle! There are four witnesses to it. He accused his uncle of hurting you, Señor Orellana, at court, and set on the old man with a rapier and dagger."

"It is not like him to attack an old man."

"There are four witnesses to it. The Marquis is in seclusion, made ill by the awful thing he had to do. But there was no help for it. Imagine, at his age, the strength to kill so young a man. Oh, he is a wonder, that Marquis. The feat has greatly set him up at court. The king may make him a general. It is all fantastic."

"No man, old or young, could have killed Alonso in an equal fight," Orellana said huskily. He saw Alonso, immaculate and big-bodied, fending off twenty savages at Machiparo. He saw his long blade flashing bloodily during many an ambush. He saw him sitting gently beside the fire in the camp of Gonzalo Pizarro, tactfully acquainting a Dominican friar with the heretical words of Martin Luther. He saw him, proud and purposeful, sharing with himself and Gutiérrez one cape, one pair of gloves, one pair of boots, at Cubagua. The boots, he remembered, were too large, and Alonso had said, "I cannot fill your shoes, amigo." A gentle jest of loyalty and devotion.

"Of course the story had to reach the court. You cannot hide a body, after all—and before witnesses. Blood must be explained, even by a grandee. That Robles was a Lutheran made the matter perfectly all right, of course. It is no crime to kill a heretic. One must expiate bad blood, the more so when it is one's own blood, so to speak."

Orellana saw his friend again leading him to his cousin's house, the excuses made to leave himself and Ana together. The interminable conversations he must have had inside the house with spindly Chavez and his fat spouse, so that Orellana might pursue his love. His protest that not even for love would he go with Orellana to Ana's house before a polite hour. His advice, to hit Ana over the head, that had turned Orellana's thinking into the secure channel of action that had accomplished so much. Robles, the clear thinker. Robles, the steady hand. He had counted on Alonso for so much—organization of the new expedition, at which Robles was so adept, and of which Orellana knew nothing. What would he do now for companionship and advice and impetuosity? To whom now would he confide his secret troubles? Into whose eyes would he look now for encouragement? Thank God he had Ana!

"Well," Semplono was saying, "naturally your name came into it, Señor. The motive for the attack had to be explained."

I will help you yet, Alonso had said.

"The king inquired who you were. When he discovered that the Council of the Indies had a full report on your discoveries, a land ten times larger than Peru claimed for his hand and he knew nothing of it—well, you cannot imagine the fury unless you know Charles. It is hereditary. He got it from his mother. 'It is no compliment,' he told Samano, 'that Spanish discoverers be treated in this way.' So you are a *cause célèbre*, as the filthy French say, and the prince will look into it. I should not be surprised if the prince asks to see you, even. What do you think of that? . . . I say, what do you think of that?"

"How?" Orellana said. "I'm sorry, Señor Barber, I did not hear you." He wiped his eye and turned from the window.

"And now you will take my investment, and give me my receipt?"

"I cannot take money now," Orellana said. "It would not be right. Leave it with Samano. If the expedition is ordered, he will turn it over to me. If it fails, he can give it back to you."

"But it cannot possibly fail now," Semplono said. "The king leaves orders; the prince carries them out. It is finished."

374

"Well, we shall see," Orellana said. "I thank you for coming to us."

"And you will take my five hundred ducats?"

"Leave them with Samano. If I return to the Amazon, you shall be an investor."

"That is a promise?"

"It is a pledge, Señor."

The barber bubbled to his feet and bowed.

"When we meet again we shall all be rich," he beamed. "Señor Gutiérrez—my felicitations and undying friendship."

"Thank you, Señor. God spare you on the king's journey."

Orellana turned back to the window. He did not want Gutiérrez to see his face.

He was summoned before the king's secretary that afternoon. Samano had before him a long report, attached, Orellana noticed, to his petition and, gratifyingly, to the Memorial of his services that had been drawn so long ago in Guayaquil.

Samano shifted the parchments irritably.

"The prince has requested a report on this matter," he said icily. "I do not appreciate your going behind my back."

"Any back that will bear the load, Excellency," Orellana answered with equal chill, "is good enough for me. Your own example has not been too inspiring."

Samano frowned.

"Nor yours," he said. "You humble me before the king's barber. You make me distrust you. There is a way to do everything. A little delay in the beginning may mean much speed later on. However—" he rattled the parchments.

"I did not ask my friend to die," Orellana said.

"The Council has been compelled to return an opinion, and if you concur in it, it will be laid before the prince." Pointedly he ignored the reference to Robles.

Orellana listened, excited that the stipulations closely followed the pattern of his own demands. The Council had even been more generous to himself than he had asked, no doubt in fear of the king's displeasure. Ana would be pleased. Only two significant variants from his own proposal were evident in the hasty reading. He must finance the expedition entirely by himself. No matter, there were ways of doing that. And his request for knighthood in the order of St. Iago was ignored. All else he had requested was approved.

He was excited, even in the chilly reading of Juan de Samano. All was here—Brazil, with himself the master, governor, and military commander with power to promulgate such decrees as he found necessary, guarantees of freedom for the Indians and all Castilians, assurance of property rights. He noted with gratification that the report mentioned Portugal—and France—which might also be interested in the great river. Indeed, the Council said there was a rumor at the House of Trade in Seville that Portugal actually was outfitting an expedition. Such reports must hasten official Spain. It was one thing to see the river, another to conquer it, as Orellana well knew. He was not alarmed.

Two minority statements were attached, and to these Samano paid closest attention. One was by Dr. Bernal, who doubted Orellana was a fit person to head a colonial enterprise. Trained in Peru, Orellana was apt to repeat the brutalities of Peru, he said.

"He does not know me," Orellana murmured.

Another member, one Gutiérrez Valásquez, emphasized that military force must not be used, and recommended that no fighting men be taken on the expedition. Instead, he proposed that a large inventory of barter goods be loaded aboard the colonial vessels and that a liberal policy of peaceful trade with the savages be initiated immediately upon arrival.

"I concur," Orellana said.

"Well—I do not," Samano said. "If you should meet an armed expedition from Portugal, how do you propose to defend yourselves?"

"The selva will fight for us," Orellana said. "We, knowing the wilderness, will find it friendly. They, not knowing it, will have an enemy even more deadly than Spanish arms."

"Scarcely a practical theory," Samano said. "However—you concur to everything I have read?"

"I do."

"You would undertake this mission on these terms, marking well the stipulation that it is at your own expense?"

"I will."

"You are aware that such an expedition will cost a great sum of money?"

"I am."

"You have such a sum?"

"I have some capital. I have met many men who are eager to invest in the enterprise."

"All of them are Spaniards?"

"No, not all." He thought of the king's barber, an Italian.

"I remind you that the laws forbid the financing or participation in expeditions to Spanish America of any persons other than Castilians."

Orellana thought of the Portuguese with Columbus, the Italians with Balboa, the Aragonese and Jews with Cortez, the motley riffraff of nationalities with Pizarro.

"I understand the law," he said.

"Very well, then," Samano said. "The matter will be put before the prince. You will stand ready for an interview." He paused. "I wish that I personally had more confidence in you, Señor Orellana. If this goes through, I shall be required for my own protection to appoint a crown representative to see that you live up to your contract. It is a pity you did not avoid that by leaving the matter entirely in my hands."

"I have nothing to hide," Orellana said.

43

HE SPENT the season of the Nativity with Ana, in Seville. She was as flushed as he with the imminence of his success, the rich vision of his future, with titles and authority and prestige and vast possessions in the New World.

She was tender, too. Tender as he had never known a woman could be. Even his most idyllic dreams of her could not approach the love she gave him, and the inspiration. She filled his heart completely, for now that Robles was gone, she supplied, as her cousin had done before her, the complementary qualities of boldness and shrewdness of which his own simpler personality was incapable.

Before the Christmas season ended and he set out once again for Valladolid to await his audience with the Prince, Orellana was as sure of her as he had ever been sure of anything in all his life. It was as though Robles, anticipating his own death, had bestowed upon Orellana a successor to himself who could supply all that he had supplied, and greedy, hungry physical love besides. All the affection that Orellana had given to Robles descended to Ana, and she enveloped him completely.

Gutiérrez and Hernández worried at her possessiveness, but were powerless to intervene. Instinct alone told them that all was not well. They discussed it together, but could not mention it to Orellana. They were not sure but perhaps their own feeling was one of jealousy. As she had absorbed him, his need for his old companions had shriveled. Now they were his associates, and only vaguely his friends.

Neither Hernández nor Gutiérrez went back with Orellana to Valladolid. Orellana wanted someone trustworthy to remain close to Ana, and for this task Gutiérrez volunteered. Hernández was busy with details. The news of Orellana's success at court had traveled fast.

Daily dozens of men sought him out, seeking favors, selling ships or stores, currying advantages. Bankers, none of them Spanish, proposed devious ways whereby the needed funds might be arranged. All these things bewildered Orellana. Hernández, with Ana's aid, looked after them.

Ana, Orellana thought proudly as he rode north, was capable of anything. She was everywhere, bargaining shrewdly, interviewing wisely, taking much and promising nothing. She would not yet marry him, however.

"You have me now," she had said just before his departure. "You have me more securely than promises made in church. It would not be well for you to marry a dotless female—and a cousin of Alonso's—before the prince has signed. I can wait."

Her self-sacrifice touched him. She was so right. The taint of Lutheranism must not be revived. Contact with Robles' house must at all costs, for the moment, be avoided. Yes, she thought clearly. And she loved him. Her childish rapture at the emerald he had given her at Christmastide returned to refresh his northward ride. The delight with which she had held the great stone, in its filigreed ring setting, to catch the long rays of morning light. She was a child who loved rich things. And he could make her rich. He thought of the ecstasy on her face when he had shown her the full contents of his vicuña pouch, the preciousness with which she had touched them—exactly as she had touched him. He wished he had been able to spare another emerald for her, but he could not. The men who signed on for his expedition would pay handsomely for the privilege. Investors would be found to buy the ships. Then when the time came to outfit the caravels with food and stores and barter goods and all other things mentioned in the Council's stipulation, the remaining emeralds would be sold. If he was careful, their worth was sufficient.

With an old, familiar gesture, he touched his shirt to make sure that the sack was still around his neck. He touched again, and reined up sharply. The sack felt differently than before. Less bulky, lighter.

Feverishly he tore open his shirt, ripped out the sack and spread its precious contents in his hands. The fish-eye emerald, the fourteen-carat water jar, a half dozen others, spilled out into his hand. But the seven matched emeralds, the precious roses each nine and three-fourths carats large, on which he was counting for twenty thousand ducats. Where were they?"

He turned the sack inside out. The seven rose emeralds were gone.

Prince Philip, burdened in adolescence with some of the most troublesome statecraft problems of his age, moved slowly to do his father's will in the matter of Francisco Orellana. Not until February did his vital affairs compose themselves to such an extent that he could deal with internal Castile. On February thirteenth he summoned Orellana.

Orellana knew little about the prince except that he was as pious as his sainted great-grandmother Isabella, without, unfortunately, the forthright qualities that had made her the sensation of her age. Schooled by priests, he spent too much time in prayer, too little in action, his exasperated courtiers said. Such matters as he undertook he dispatched with meticulous thoroughness and great attention to detail, presaging even at the age of eighteen the temperament that would lead him one day to send the mighty Spanish Armada against Elizabeth of England.

At eighteen, Prince Philip already had ruled his father's dominions in Italy for two years, and in a trial of his acuteness with Spanish ways, undertaken at seventeen, he had, in the eyes of philosophers if not of practical politicians, distinguished himself. He had studied the Spanish situation in the New World. Flanked as he was by priests, he had listened to the zealous exhortations of Father Bartolomé de las Casas and had been horrified at the Spanish treatment of the Indians in New Spain and Peru. Out of this horror had emerged a set of laws for government of the colonies, and out of these laws had emerged a new civil war, headed by Gonzalo Pizarro, in Peru. Logically, from the standpoint of his over-burdened father, Prince Philip was well equipped in background to consider the petition of Francisco Orellana.

Orellana's stubborn insistence upon the humanity of Indians, the sacredness of personal security, and the right of men to live as brothers under God, drew admiration from the church-saturated young man. He did not understand what Orellana meant in half that he said, but his feeling was kindred. He approved the project, drew up articles of agreement, and sent for its leader.

Orellana was received in a small chamber where the prince sat at an elegant polished table surrounded by luminaries. Prominent in the assembly was the Bishop of Carthagena, the prince's tutor, and the swashbuckling, hard-fighting sons of the Count of Cambria, Don Alonso and Don Pedro de Córdova. These Orellana recognized by sight. The rest were merely a foliage of faces, for in four steps he was before the prince and bowing low.

He straightened and saw a handsome youngster on whose face no trace of a beard grew, a boy of white ascetic countenance and the long, facile hands of a woman. The jutting Hapsburg jaw of his father was his also, but refined by the less concentrated blood of his mother, Isabella of Portugal. There was a smile on his face as Orellana looked at him, but Orellana did not like his eyes. They were too orderly, too pious, too hawk-quick, to be anything but those of a bigot.

They got on well. The prince was anxious that Orellana understand fully the new laws governing Spanish colonies, that he might adhere to them. Orellana readily consented; the enlightened theories of de las Casas were a joy to him. Other than on this point, the prince had little to say. His advisors summarized the articles of agreement that had been drawn, fixing the conditions for the exploration and colonization of New Andalusia. They were, in the main, the recommendations of the Council, which Orellana already had seen. Fear of Portugal and France was evident in one stipulation: namely, that he must take with him three hundred soldiers, of whom one hundred must be cavalry. Evidence of the prince's own nature was apparent in the requirement that he take, at his own expense, eight priests. The boy's intelligence in colonial matters knifed through the document in the requirement that he take with him the materials to build two small, shallow-draft boats with which to explore the Amazon. Orellana appreciated this touch.

To Orellana himself the prince was generous. The title of governor and captain-general for himself and his heir, a two-hundred square league fief for himself, to be selected from the colonized lands; five thousand ducats a year as governor, command of two forts which he would build, and as a reward for building them the sum of three hundred thousand maravedís a year for the life of himself and an heir; and the final staggering reward, one-twelfth of all revenues collected in New Andalusia, for himself and his heirs in perpetuity, up to a million maravedís annually, and exemption from the payment of import duties for ten years.

The prince could afford to be so generous, Orellana thought, with money which had not yet been made, for Orellana must collect this revenue from the fruits of his colony before it was his; how much more to the point to have offered fifty thousand ducats from the crown purse to help finance the expedition. Finances were acutely on his mind, now that the emeralds were gone. He had hastily dictated letters to both Ana and Hernández, immediately he discovered his loss, but Hernández knew nothing, and Ana's reply was vague. Somewhere he must find more money, and it was clear now that the prince did not mean to help.

He was an adelantado now, however, by command of the king. He was governor of a great, uncivilized world. In the face of this scroll of trust from his king, lesser men would invest the needed money. Of that there could be little doubt.

He agreed to the articles. Again the prince smiled, and wished him success. Orellana bowed.

"It is our express desire," the boy said, "to favor your enterprise in every possible way. We have therefore given especial charge to our father's secretary, Juan de Samano, to supervise for us the details of your mission and to ease such difficulties as you may encounter."

Samano stepped forward. Orellana had not seen him in the room previously.

"His Majesty's secretary," the prince went on, "pleads the need of assistance, that some representative of the crown remain with you, on our behalf, during your period of preparation, to insure your scrupulous adherence to these articles, to ease our mind that the required soldiers and horses set out with you, capably supplied for the long voyage and the period of exploration. The secretary tells us you have no objection to such a procedure."

"I have nothing to hide, Your Highness," Orellana said.

"Very well, then," the prince resumed. "It is our pleasure to appoint the most advantageous person possible, one who is familiar with the problems you will meet and who also knows at first hand the lands which you will populate."

He held up his hand, and a frock-clad body emerged from the faces. It was Friar de Vera.

44

BY SUPERHUMAN work, for which Ana de Ayala was greatly responsible, the Adelantado Francisco Orellana, governor of the as yet non-existent Spanish colony of New Andalusia, had a galleon riding in the Guadalquivir at the end of May, another ship and two caravels building, and three hundred men waiting in the hills of the Maestrazgo, in the fruity plains of the Almendralejo, in Málaga, Granada, Jerez, and in the County of Niebla from which Columbus had drawn some of his best men. Gutiérrez and Hernández had worked incredible wonders enlisting the crew, personally scouring the towns and villages of Andalusia and with the eloquence of St. Paul himself recruiting the needed soldiery. As laboriously, Orellana fitted out his ships, and Ana bartered with shipbuilders, tradesmen, bankers, brokers, and the gentlemen of the House of Trade. Money disappeared like wheat in a locust storm as the merchants, sensing Orellana's urgency, doubled and trebled their prices. The emeralds went one by one into the hands of the bankers, until finally Orellana's vicuña sack harbored only one, his favorite fish-eye stone which he had saved against some last unpredictable difficulty. And he was four thousand ducats in debt.

Had he been able to find the seven rose emeralds so mysteriously lost, the expedition might have been paid for during the month of June, and launched westward on the fine levanter that blew all that month. The recruits refused, however, to give in their passage money until the ships had been paid for in full, and Orellana had counted on the passage money to pay the shipbuilders. Thus he was at an impasse, and day followed day without any resolution of the difficulty.

Certain Genoese bankers were persuaded at the end of July to invest twenty-five hundred ducats in the expedition, and again Orellana took heart. Foreign investment, however, required the approval of the king's revenue collector, one Vicenzio de Monte, and he would not listen to the proposal. There was nothing in it for him, he implied.

Ana took him in hand. Obviously he liked her. When Orellana had gone to see him, his cadaverous eyes had remained on her the whole time. She had smiled at him, testing her strength, and he had responded. She had twinkled at him, and a flicker of his own cold eyes answered her. He was not very bright, a king's relation leeching a sinecure, and obviously his weakness was money.

After the formal interview, she returned to him alone. His Excellency was delighted to see her. The Genoese bankers might be persuaded, she said, to raise the amount of their bargain as an inducement to doing business with Spaniards. Orellana would get no more, but then he needed no more, while Vicenzio de Monte—and she—would profit. Vicenzio was sympathetic to her plea that the fiancé of an adelantado required silks and jewels to enhance her position and the matter was awkward for her because all her intended husband's funds were invested in the expedition. She in turn was sympathetic to his necessity. It was impossible, of course, for a man of de Monte's distinguished position to maintain his style on a salary. For one thing, he must support an extravagant house. He invited her to see it. There they could talk over, safe from prying ears, this matter of the Genoese and their money. She accepted.

Of course she told Orellana about it. He opposed it, particularly her visit to de Monte's house, but he was desperate for funds, and let himself be talked into it. After all, he could trust her. She was the very spirit of loyalty to him and his cause. And perhaps, she implied, the gifts of the Genoese to her would provide her with the trousseau she insisted on acquiring before their marriage. His new position demanded, she said, that his bride be worthy of him; otherwise men would talk, and the sailors who had signed on would lose confidence. He must appear rich and prosperous in everything he did. This was the essence of his preparations, the backbone of his flimsy credit, the stability behind his promissory notes. Now if suddenly he married a dowerless girl, his whole precarious house might collapse. There was wisdom in what she said. And because he fretted that they were not yet married, he consented to her connivance with de Monte. There seemed nothing else to do.

De Monte proved difficult. August arrived and he had not yet come to terms with the Genoese. He asked too much. Ana was often at his house, discussing new plans. Always when she returned, there was new hope.

In the first days of August, the largest galleon was loaded with hard tack, wine and cattle and prepared to sail downstream from Seville to San Lucar. At this news the soldiers and sailors slipped in from the hills, their passage money in hand. The funds thus gathered satisfied the payment for the second ship, and all but nine hundred ducats of the price of the almost-completed caravels. The Genoese bankers, seeing these assurances of success, came forward again with more liberal proposals.

Greatly cheered, Orellana set a departure date of September seventeenth and the news rippled with a thrill over Seville and all Andalusia. The end was at last in sight.

At this critical moment Friar de Vera turned up in Seville, and established an office in the House of Trade. He must inspect the fleet before its departure, he said.

A thorough inspection, as he well knew, would be disastrous. None of the ships had guns, as required by the stipulations of Prince Philip. Half the crew were foreigners, pretending to be Castilians. The masters of three of the ships were Portuguese, of the other a Ragusan, for Orellana could find no mariners in Spain who knew the Brazilian coast. That his navigators were Portuguese, Orellana knew; he had written two letters to Prince Philip begging that an exception to the interdiction on foreigners be made in their case. For the common run of recruits he had accepted their own word that they were Castilians, as Columbus, Cortez, and Pizarro had done before him, in order to muster sufficient force for his enterprise. A thorough inspection would reveal the truth of their nationality. This de Vera knew.

With de Vera's coming, insidious rumors swept through Seville. Orellana was in debt; he would never sail. He was a visionary without practical skill for so hazardous an undertaking. He was an heretical monster who would insist that every man who joined him renounce his Catholic faith. He was in league with the Portuguese. He was in league with the French. He was unlucky.

Seville burned with the stories. In the whole city there was scarcely a family unaffected by Orellana's enterprise. From every house a son was going; a bill lay unpaid, an order was unfilled, or an investment had been made.

Suddenly almost overnight, the enterprise that had set its departure date was deserted. Investors disappeared. Merchants cried loudly for payment. Shipbuilders made excuses. Half the men who had signed on with Orellana sailed to the New World with a commercial expedition. They had waited long enough, they said.

Walking into the House of Trade to salvage what he could of his labor, Orellana was met smilingly by Friar de Vera.

"A letter for you, Adelantado," he said, "from His Worship, the prince."

It was a categorical refusal for Orellana to take any Portuguese with him, no matter how badly he needed them.

Orellana rallied and went back to work. Again Gutiérrez and Hernández took to the hills in search of recruits. And Ana, after a day of temper, returned to the house of revenue collector de Monte for another conference.

Again the hopeless difficulties, the cries for money, the torrent of rumor. Doggedly Orellana went on, and slowly the work proceeded. In September, the second large ship, a galleon, was loaded in the river. The first ship went on down to San Lucar. One caravel, pert and graceful, was launched, christened and her loading begun. The other caravel was held by the builder pending full payment.

The first Saturday in October only twenty-five hundred ducats stood between Orellana and the open sea. Ana had gone again to Vicenzio de Monte. This time she returned as irate as a woman scorned. De Monte had made certain personal demands upon her now. Not enough that he receive twelve thousand ducats from the Genoese— he must have tribute from Ana, too, and not in cash.

Orellana would have rushed out and killed the revenue collector, had not Ana detained him by force.

"There is another way," she said.

Orellana calmed. They were in the patio of the house of Cosme de Chavez, where Orellana had been living for some time.

"You know," Ana said quietly, "that my mother wants to go with us to the New World."

"I have told you before, it is impossible."

"If someone paid twenty-five hundred ducats for her passage, would it be so impossible?"

"No one in his right mind would do that," Orellana said.

Ana smiled and kissed him.

"That's where you are very wrong," she said. "My stepfather Cosme would gladly pay—to be rid of her. He has an income. Certain rents, and of course this house. I heard him in anger tell Mama he would give all he had if she would just go and leave him alone, before he died of her appetite. I think he meant it."

"It is monstrous," Orellana said.

"And she—well, where there are three hundred men and only two women, and one of them the wife of the Adelantado, mother might be very attractive, don't you think? She would love to be with virile men. And—she might be good for the men, too, Francisco?"

"It is impossible," Orellana said. He saw Mama Ayala, fat legs exposed by a cynic breeze, standing like a commander aboard his flagship.

"But for twenty-five hundred ducats? With such a sum we could sail over the bar at San Lucar. What difference Mama then? Some soldier would claim her before we were gone a week, and your responsibility would be ended. Let me sound out Papa Cosme about it."

"Well—"

"Good. And don't worry. He will raise the money."

The sun fell. Mama Ayala hobbled from the house, kissed her prospective son-in-law on the ear with an excited giggle, and rushed to tell her neighbors the wonderful news. Cosme de Chavez went downtown. Ana and Orellana had supper in the patio as the first cool evening breeze descended off the Sierra Moreno.

"Ana," Orellana said when they had finished, "tomorrow I am going to ask Father Domínguez to publish the banns for us. I am not waiting any longer."

"But Francisco, you agreed with me—"

"I am weary of being prudent. When Cosme brings in his money, we shall pay our debts and sail. There cannot possibly be any damage done now. That dog de Vera scatters so many rumors to wreck us, there can be no harm in one more."

"But your position! Do you think I am going to damage you before all Seville? Do you think I love you so little that I will cause such embarrassment? No, Francisco. I will wait forever before I will do you such a hurt."

"You are very wonderful, little pigeon," Orellana said. "Your self-sacrifice only makes me love you more. What kind of a man do you think I am if I cannot own you publicly as the lady of my heart? Besides, we waste such valuable time. The little taste I have had of you sharpens my hunger. Tomorrow I will ask Father Domínguez to publish the banns."

"What will I wear, Francisco? What jewels? Do you want me to be shabby at our wedding? Not even a new dress for the wife of an adelantado?"

"You are beautiful as you are. No, Ana, I am through with excuses. It is time we posted the banns. Otherwise there might not be time, and I cannot take you with me if you are not my wife."

"With Mama along, everything would be all right."

"With Mama along everything will be wrong enough, without the other. No, it is on my conscience, as well as on my heart. Tomorrow, the banns."

"And I will be wed in tears because I stand almost naked to marry the greatest man in the world."

Orellana was silent a long time. Then he said, "I can find money to outfit you properly for your marriage. I would not humble you."

"Money?" she said. "You are already far in debt. No one will give you credit."

"I do not need credit," he said. He reached in his shirt and pulled out the vicuña bag. He opened it slowly, shook it. The fish-eye emerald tumbled into his rough hand.

"With the money from that," he said, "you shall be married like a princess."

She squealed and took the stone in her hands. He loved her delight.

"I was saving it," he said, "for a rainy day. It is the last."

She tried to keep it, but he took it from her.

"I will sell it Monday," he said. "There will be money for everything—the Mass, the priests, the carriages, everything."

"And a dress of silk and a manta of Sevillian lace?"

"Yes. A dress of silk and a manta of Sevillian lace."

She was soft and tender in his arms.

45

THE ANNOUNCEMENT was made in the parish church, the notice posted on the door. Friends and relations called on Mama Ayala all afternoon. Cosme de Chavez' best sherry, which was hid in the cellar to console him in his periods of great dejection, flowed until the cask was drained. Cosme, however, did not appear. He had been unable to sell his quit-rents for enough money to suit him in Seville, and had gone to Truxillo where, among Orellana's relations, he hoped for better luck. For three Sundays it would be like this: the announcement, the callers, the extravagant waste of sherry. Then the wedding, and on to the New World.

Late that night Orellana was roused by a ringing at the gate bell. In the absence of Chavez, he dressed and answered it. Hernández and Gutiérrez stood there, dusty and travel-worn. For a month they had been gone, scouring all Spain for recruits. Ruefully Orellana faced the friends he had neglected these past weeks, and invited them in.

Their story was not encouraging. Of the necessary complement they still lacked fifty men. They spoke to Orellana almost as strangers, they were so disheartened. He got them food and drink, and cheered them with his new hopes. The expedition, he said, positively would sail by the end of October. They had only to take men to the river and show them the three ships to prove it. This time there was no mistake. His own new father-in-law, Cosme de Chavez, was putting up the rest of the money.

Hernández and Gutiérrez were not cheered at this reference. Secretly, for a long time, both had hoped that Orellana would turn from Ana. She was jealous of the part they had once played in the adelantado's affections. She kept them from seeing him when she could, and

391

these days, when she was so much with him, her excuses were readily at hand. They brightened when Orellana proved to them that Chavez' funds, which might be looked on as a dowry, insured their success. Now at least, he would marry with dowered dignity, and further the expedition, too. Once again on the sea, they thought, once again started for that river which they knew Orellana loved more than he loved this woman, he would become again their great leader. The novelty would wear off once he was married. Perhaps, after all, it would be a good thing.

If—they could find the required men.

"Is there nowhere else to solicit?" Orellana said.

Gutiérrez looked guilty.

"We have not, for obvious reasons, gone near my old home," he said. "I think that in the mountains we might easily find fifty men among my own friends."

"No," Orellana said. "I cannot ask you to take that risk."

"I am not so sure it is a risk, now," Gutiérrez said. "I could go by night. If we are as close to sailing as you say—"

"We are," Orellana said with conviction. "I swear that we will be gone before October."

"In that case, then," Gutiérrez said, "I will go back to the mountains. If they pursue me, I can hide aboard the big galleon until we sail. It would not be long."

"No, please," Orellana said. "Send Hernández. You stay with me."

"He does not know the people. You must know the mountain people, or they will not listen to you. I will go."

"You're sure?"

Gutiérrez thought a moment.

"I will let you decide," he said. "I have wanted for a long time to tell you, anyway."

Orellana offered bread and cheese which both men took hungrily.

"You do not need to be told," Gutiérrez said wistfully, "that I was a poor man's son. All Spanish stories start that way. But we were not miserable. We had a fine little grazing ground on the side of a mountain where we raised pigs and were very happy. All the time I was growing up the count who owned most of the valley tried to talk my father out of his land. Our modest buildings and hogyard offended the view from his terrace across the valley to the mountains, and on warm days, it was said, the smell of our pigs offended his nose. Father would not sell. Where would a man with eight children go, once his land was gone?

"Then my father died. They say he fell from a horse over a precipice but it is not true. Drunk as a goat, my father could ride against any knight in Christendom. Besides, he did not own a horse. He died, nonetheless. Before even a Mass had been read for his soul the count appeared with a paper showing my father had deeded him the property, with possession at my father's death. Such a thing was incredible, of course."

He paused. The bleak mountains were in his eyes.

"What is a man to do?" he asked. "I was twenty, the eldest. There were five girls, two little boys. . . . I waited until the count had left, and followed, overtaking him at the precipice. He had two squires with him but I charged through them and the count went into the abyss, horse and all. The squires fled. I went into the valley and took the paper from the dead body and destroyed it. There was a great search for me, but I knew the mountains too well, and the mountain people hid me from the count's men. I do not know whether they have forgotten me now or not. But my mother and brothers and sisters still live on the hillside, that I know."

He smiled.

"If the paper had not been a forgery, the lawyers would have known, no? And my mother would not still have the farm? So I was right in doing what I did. Is it not so?"

"Yes, Hernán," Orellana said, "you were right in doing what you did."

"I am a simple man," Gutiérrez said, "but I know when something must be done."

"Yes, Hernán," Orellana said, "you do. I love you for the way you know what is right, and what must be done."

"I thought you had forgotten me, General," Gutiérrez said.

Orellana realized the anguish beneath the gentle reproach. Gutiérrez was his friend, and of late in the ordeal of fitting out the expedition, the maelstrom of creditors, the chaos of barter, the pandemonium of worry, the demandingness of love, Gutiérrez had been neglected, as a comfortable old boot lies in the closet waiting for the leisurely evening when it may be donned again. Gutiérrez had been the first man to volunteer in Guayaquil. Orellana had not known him very well then—a dependable young soldier who could be sent north along the coast to quell an Indian uprising quickly. The crier had not even finished his rounds of the market plaza, the square before the new wood church, the quay along the Guayas, and the stinking flats that flooded in winter, when the mountain man had appeared at Orellana's house.

"What is this you want me to do?" he had said. No haggling over terms; no quibbling over position. Clear-eyed, direct, as stout of heart as he was of limb, accepting the summons of his chief. Orellana had liked him from the start. At the council in the mountains when they were all near death, Juan de Illanes had described Gutiérrez as "small, wiry and dependable." The gambler Illanes was quick to size up men. Gutiérrez, first over the mountain; Gutiérrez first into Pizarro's camp; Gutiérrez, first ashore at Aparia, last to return to the brigantine at Machiparo; Gutiérrez, patiently cultivating the king's obscene barber, now for six months recruiting and holding together a rabble of soldiers and sailing men. Orellana could never have come this far from Guayaquil without the mountain man. These reflections were nothing in themselves, perhaps; but they epitomized much, each being a link in the chain of comradeship that joined the two men together. Now in the frenzy of complicated matters of which he knew so little, Orellana was weakening the chain.

The chunky, swarthy-skinned man looked at him through pinpoint brown eyes. Was he, too, thinking these thoughts?

394

"I could not forget you, Hernán," he said. "What we have done together has made us brothers. The blood you let gave me strength, and my spilled blood flowed into you. These past months have been difficult and we have not seen much of each other, but we are brothers, and brothers do not need to remind each other of kinship; it is the strong rock on which one stands. If I have neglected you, amigo, it is because now I need you most of all."

A happy light rose like a summer dawn in Gutiérrez' eyes.

"I am glad you said that, General," he said. "Until I served with you, I did not know that there were good men. I will go back to the mountains, and you shall have your fifty men."

"Be careful," Orellana said. "If there is trouble, send word and I will come at once."

Gutiérrez knew then that everything was all right. Orellana could feel it in the resolution with which his friend rose to his stout legs and buckled his gear.

"Night is best for traveling," Gutiérrez said. "Adiós."

"Go with God," Orellana replied, and let him out the gate.

Antonio Hernández did not go with him. He and Orellana returned to the patio.

"I'm glad you remained," Orellana said. "I have not had a good talk with you for a long time. I have missed our talks."

"You have been busy," Hernández said. "So have I. It is a little different from fighting the forest, is it not, Francisco?"

"Each day I spend in Spain, the more beautiful the forest becomes," Orellana said bitterly. "And the more beautiful are the savages. I live only to be back among them."

"I thought your passion for the river had been absorbed by other passions, perhaps."

Orellana looked up, startled.

"You think so?" he asked, thinking over the matter himself. "No, no. My mind is absorbed with greedy men and hopeless difficulties, but my heart is still along the Amazon, and there it will be until I die."

"Ana has not detracted you?"

"Ana has filled in my heart that empty corner the river could not fill. But the heart itself—no, Antonio, I know what you think, but it is not so. I have suffered humiliation and shame and misery here in Spain. Do you think I would take such humbling if I was not determined that nothing shall interfere with my return to the river?"

"I had wondered."

"Then wonder no more," Orellana said. "I have sunk so low that I despise myself. I have let Ana connive with bankers. I have even agreed to take Ana's mother—that detestable fatbelly—back with us. I have haggled like a peddler, groveled like a beggar before the merchants, until there is no longer any pride in me. Would I do that if the end was not worth anything—anything at all, even the worst kind of self-abasement?"

"I am glad to know."

"Don't worry yourself, old friend. The river has become a passion with me. In everything that happens there is a reminder of how wonderful the world might be, if it were not for men. How God must suffer, watching the despicable things His children do! A new world must be made, Antonio—a world for good people, the world of Carranza, and Gutiérrez, and you. Man is the real beast; the animals of the jungle are noble beside him. I am more convinced of it each day. And I tell you, Antonio—there is nothing I will not do to succeed. Nothing! Even Ana is nothing to me in comparison with this dream."

"You are sure of that?"

"Yes, I am sure. If I had to choose—and may God never make it necessary—between Ana and the river, I would take the river."

"That is a strong statement, Francisco."

"It is true. I have used even Ana to get done what must be done. I would do it again."

"Good. It is what I hoped you could say. I'm glad you said what you did to Gutiérrez. I understand why we have not seen much of you—but he does not think the same as either of us. Simple words of praise are the food on which he lives. Remember that, Francisco. There is nothing he would not do for you."

"I know that. I will do better."

"Good. I have been able to take care of him these past months. We have been much together. But you must do it alone from now on. That is why I tell you."

"Antonio!"

"I'm sorry, Francisco. I had hoped to go back with you to your New World. Only the despised can appreciate the magnitude of your dream. I wanted to share it. I wanted to be able to look this ugly world straight in the face when I died and say, 'There. What I have done is not much. But it is a little. And a little good counts a great deal, since there is so little of it.' I wanted to go back with you, because what you are doing will start something fine that will endure even though you yourself fail."

"We shall not fail, Antonio."

"As you vision it, Francisco, you will fail. I know that. But in the end, long after you are dead, what you plant will grow."

"It will come in our lifetime, Antonio. God wills it."

"I hope so, but I cannot see it. Men are not ready for God's will to be done on earth. But the seed must be planted anyway, and that I would like to help you do. The tree that cuts best has grown a long time. . . . But I must leave you now."

"Why, Antonio?"

"A certain merchant of your native city is on my trail. I made the mistake of going to Truxillo, hoping that among your own people I might find recruits. The merchant recognized me, even though I had taken the ribbon from my hair."

"You should not have risked it."

"What's done is done. Even now the merchant, and two strong sons, pursue me. I must disappear before they involve you, too."

The clatter of hooves echoed in the night. Excited words rumbled over the patio wall.

"It is too late," Orellana said. "Go in my bedroom and hide."

The silver gate bell rang. Orellana went slowly to answer it.

"Francisco Orellana?"

"The same. And you are Carlos Sánchez."

"I am. I seek a thief who, I have reason to believe, is in this house."

Orellana noticed the old man's two sons. They were formidable fighting men, heavily plated and carefully armed.

"Come in," Orellana said. The merchant did not move.

"And have our quarry slip over the garden wall? I am not a fool, Señor. With your leave, my sons will search the house, while I remain here."

"I am unable to give you such permission," Orellana answered evenly. "The house is not mine. Its master is away, and two women are inside asleep."

"I should regret forcing a passage, but I mean to have the thief."

The merchant put his hand upon his sword. His sons did likewise. Orellana's arms were in his bedroom, across the patio. He shrugged.

"And if you should find the man you seek?"

"He shall hang."

"What good is he to you dead? Blood will not return your money."

"Blood is better than nothing."

"His life might be bought, then."

Hungrily the old merchant beamed. "The price is dear," he said.

"How much?"

"That which he stole, with reasonable interest for these fifteen years."

"What is the principal?"

"Five thousand ducats."

Orellana laughed.

"Your memory is faulty, Señor. The amount was but half of that."

"You cannot prove it."

"I saw the money. Sebastian was my uncle. Your gold financed our voyage to the New World."

"Incredible."

398

"The truth is often incredible. I will buy the thief's liberty with twenty-five hundred ducats, not a cent more."

"Plus interest compounded at seven percent."

"Twenty-five hundred ducats. No more, no less."

The merchant Sánchez understood that with this conquistador there was no bargaining.

"Let me see the money," he said.

"First you will write and sign a paper, completely discharging the debt." He brought quill, ink, paper, and a sand box from the house. A son wrote; the merchant signed.

Orellana took the paper, and from his blouse drew a limp vicuña sack. The fish-eye emerald that was to finance his wedding to Ana de Ayala fell into his hand. He extended it to the merchant.

"The House of Colombo will give you twenty-five hundred ducats for the stone, Señor," he said. "They have already appraised it."

Sánchez bowed, and held the emerald before the candle, searching it with a practiced eye for cracks and flaws. He smiled.

"Your servant, sir," he said.

46

GUTIÉRREZ returned on the eve of the wedding. He had found his fifty men. They would come down from the hills on Sunday, the eve of sailing.

The last caravel was paid for in full, from money provided by Cosme de Chavez, who had sold everything he possessed except the roof over his head. At the last moment, he could not part with his house, and had instead mortgaged it for the last hundred ducats required to pay his wife's passage. Orellana had not held the money very long; every cent of it paid some bill or pledged a further debt. With the ships unencumbered, however, the merchants were again tractable. Provisions, naval stores, livestock went aboard the ships. On the last Saturday in September Orellana had only one item of unfinished business prior to sailing on the following Monday. That business was his marriage.

Orellana was proud of Ana. She had taken bravely the news that there would be no expensive wedding, no carriages, no silk dress or lace manta. He had waited until a most opportune moment to tell her—when he knew definitely that on Monday the expedition would sail, and she was weeping as women will in the anticlimactic moment of assured success. At such times, having had their way, women will give away everything they possess except their triumph. Orellana sensed this, and told her what he had done with the fish-eye emerald.

She drew back and stared at him a moment in disbelief. Then her face softened, she kissed him firmly on the mouth, and smiled. "Don't worry," she said. "I will make out."

Now the wedding eve had come, and Gutiérrez was in from the hills, alive and with fifty pledges. There had been no hint that anyone remembered the old count or his murderer. The sailing time was posted with the House of Trade. The scoundrel de Vera and the king's men were at that moment at San Lucar de Barrameda, inspecting the two ships and caravel that waited there, fully enough laden to get away, and on one ship, newly mounted, were four culverins, gifts of Prince Philip, to protect the fleet from attack by French or Portuguese. True, certain stipulations had not been met, but all might easily be remedied at islands on the outward crossing; and de Vera could not examine the crews, for they had scattered throughout Seville at the approach of the inspectors.

Even the Genoese bankers wanted to come in, now, on the terms laid down by Ana and the revenue collector de Monte. Ana had gone to de Monte's house to procrastinate. In the New World, Orellana said, he would soon find the means to buy her the gifts the bankers offered: a dress of the finest Chinese silk, a manta and shawl of Bohemian lace, vials of rare scents from the Levant. Prudence directed that the offer not be turned down at all—just left dangling against some last-minute default in the plans. Ana would know how to handle that, Orellana thought.

He regretted that she was marrying without the fine clothes and jewels which she thought so important to his position. That would soon be forgotten in the New World. There man would be what he was, not what he had. Soon he, and everyone who shared this enterprise with him, would have more than enough: plenty, and peace, and peace of mind, in a blessed simple land far from greedy Spain.

At the church, Gutiérrez and Hernández, who were to attend him, did not appear. There was no explanation or message. In the vestry with the priest, the acolyte, and altar boy, Orellana was sure they could have made no mistake about the church. Ana had arrived in a carriage, attended by her portly mother. Orellana was sure he had told both his friends, in Ana's presence, that the marriage would be solemnized in the Church of St. Mary the Virgin. If she had not mistaken the place, how could they?

The priest waited until after the appointed hour. The guests had assembled. Even Cosme de Chavez was there, a little drunk and across the aisle from his wife. Orellana dispatched the sexton to the church steps in search of his friends; perhaps they were there, but did not know where to go.

The sexton returned. With him was a gentleman, well dressed and handsomely groomed, with a rogue's head that Orellana identified even in the cathedral gloom of the old church.

"Never let it be said," the newcomer said smiling, "that I let my old leader go unaccompanied to the altar. In the absence of better men, I shall be glad to serve."

It was Juan de Illanes, the gambler.

Hastily Orellana thanked him as the priest began his processional, and then, for he could not restrain his curiosity, he whispered, "I thought you returned to Peru, to marry a rich widow."

Juan de Illanes shrugged and fell in line behind his old chief. "Peru is overtaken with civil war," he replied over Orellana's shoulder. "The widows of Peru are no longer rich, so I returned to try my luck in Spain."

There was time for no more. Orellana stepped forward, searching for Ana, and suddenly he saw her, blinked his eye to look again, shook his head and faltered. He would have stumbled had not Illanes, coming up swiftly, touched his arm and whispered, "Steady, man; you've been through worse than this."

Orellana, however, was not sure.

Standing smilingly, confidently, serenely at the altar was his bride, in a Genoese-cut dress of the finest Chinese silk, on her head a manta of Bohemian lace. Worst of all, at her dainty throat, dancing out with the brilliance of a thousand stars, was a necklace of gold into which was set Orellana's seven matched rose-cut emeralds.

He closed his eye. He did not hear the ceremony. He did not know that he knelt, or rose, or that he walked away, leaving his bride to be escorted out by Juan de Illanes. He found himself on the steps of the little church, in the bright sun. Gutiérrez and Hernández were there,

402

wringing their hats in their hands, dressed for shipboard rather than for a wedding.

"Mother of God," Gutiérrez said, seizing Orellana's arm. "Mother of God, we could not help it."

"It is no matter," Orellana said, dazedly.

"All night we have worked with the dogs, but they are adamant. De Vera has stopped us again."

Orellana leaped from his daze.

"Why now?" he asked.

"The big galleon, our largest ship," Hernández said, "the flagship."

"What is the matter with it?"

"Condemned. Unseaworthy. De Vera insists it is so, and the inspectors agree to whatever he says. We must abandon the galleon, and there is no other ship. We cannot sail tomorrow."

Orellana crept back into his haze.

"No matter," he said, "no matter at all. Give me your arm, Antonio. I cannot see the church steps."

47

A NA FOUND him aboard the caravel in the river. She had changed her clothes, and was dressed in the white blouse and red-flowered skirt that were among his favorites. The Giralda tower was blushed with sunset as she put out from shore in a long boat rowed by Juan de Illanes, who had not left her all afternoon.

Orellana stood alone on the afterdeck, watching the receding tide that raced downstream toward the bay of San Lucar, where the shattered remnants of his dream, three hulks heavy with provision, itched expectantly at their anchors, awaiting the morning tide to be off across the sea.

She went to him, prudently leaving Illanes in the long boat. She was afraid to touch him, or to speak. She stood beside him a long time.

Then he said, "Why did you do it?"

"For you," she said, that and no more.

"You have odd ways of serving me," he said, after another silence.

"No," she contradicted, "not odd. For a year I have been consistent in one thing: not to shame you before the world. For a year I have postponed our marriage until it could be worthy of you. You should have known I would not disgrace you, not even to be your wife."

"So. In order not to disgrace me, you took a bribe from the bankers, knowing we would not take their money."

"On the contrary, I knew we would have need of them. At de Monte's house I learned that the galleon had been condemned. Where else would we get money to replace it, except from the Genoese? If, in return for my prudence, they give me a few wedding gifts, what disgrace is that?"

Orellana trembled at the realization that there was still hope for his enterprise. If a ship could be procured, they might still be under way tomorrow! The hope struck and passed like a lightning flash, for a moment clearly illuminating the horizon, then blackening the world with night.

"And the emeralds?"

"Yes, I took them. I knew you would not give them to me. And I was right! You are ready to sail without losing them, and tonight in Seville everyone is talking about the priceless gift you gave your bride. They say, 'That adelantado must be very rich to afford such a gift.' Your credit will be unlimited. Ask anything, and the merchants will grovel. . . . You see, it was for you, beloved. In some matters, as you have often said, my intuition is better than your reason."

"With the emeralds, we might have sailed last May. That is all I can think of now—that we might now be on the Amazon and are not. And that you are a thief."

"Not a thief, my husband. Rather, I am a girl who is so much in love that she will risk her husband's displeasure, risk anything, that he may be a great man and realize his great enterprises. Even as you would risk anything—risk even me. You sent your betrothed to the house of the lecher de Monte to do what you could not do yourself. Do not speak to me of honor, my husband. We have both chanced it, but for a stake well worth the risk. What I have done I have learned from you, and done for you. And for such a love what have I gained? Desertion on my wedding day."

She wept, her head thrown back into the wind. He did not look up even at this.

"If you knew yesterday that the galleon was condemned, why did you not tell me?"

"Have you forgotten so soon that I was a bride?" she flared at him. "A girl must not see her betrothed on the eve of the wedding. Besides, there was too much to do. The galleon was not condemned because it was faulty—that was but the excuse. The real reason was that Friar de Vera was goaded into it by a friend who had just come from Portugal."

"Maldonado!" Orellana exclaimed.

"That was his name." Ana's voice was hopeful. Had she at last found the unguent to his terrible wrath?

"Why should he want to delay me?"

"Because he is leading the Portuguese expedition, and he is not yet ready to sail. If he beats you to the river, with four heavily armed ships—"

"Oh, the dog!"

"So you see, husband, I had to hold the Genoese, make the best of our situation, bargain, accept gifts, anything, until I could see you!" Her voice softened. "And for doing my best, am I to be cast aside on the day of my marriage? Is this my reward for believing in you?"

To her surprise, Orellana's face hardened again.

"The emeralds."

"The best thing I ever did for you was to take them," she struck back. "You—irresponsible dreamer that you are, would have sold them for half their worth. Now they would be gone, instead of security such as has set all Seville on fire with admiration. You can have no better credit than a fortune around your wife's neck, nothing! But you cannot appreciate such things. You know nothing of the world, only of Indians."

Orellana thought of the clear-eyed Indian girl Lalah whom Robles had so much desired. "What has your world to offer her?" he had asked. What, indeed, had civilization to offer anyone whose eyes and heart were clean? Yes, he was an irresponsible dreamer. In Spain, man's security was a fortune in emeralds at his wife's throat. The Indian girl would never understand that. Her security was the strong arm that stroked beside her own, upstream to a hut in the wilderness where children played at the door and the only menace was the civilized man who might come again.

He recalled his talk with the Negro slave, Nogal. "As long as men are slaves, I must be with them, and you, too." "But I am not a slave." "As much a slave as I, master," Nogal had said. "Forgive me, but is it not so?"

Nogal, with only one master; Orellana with many. Orellana's masters, however, were not human. They were inanimate, traits that were worse taskmasters than human beings: avarice, greed, cupidity, prejudice, hate. And Ana. He was her slave, too.

Was this what he had meant when he had pledged Carranza a world without slavery? Did he seek freedom from the slavery of human character? Was it possible that, divorced of the environment of Spain, among lands so vast as to overwhelm greed, among people who asked nothing of life but life itself, men themselves would change? He himself had changed. He was not the man who had started down the river, scorching with the ambition to be a privileged grandee in Peru. Somewhere, he had been turned aside. He, and Robles, and Gutiérrez, and Hernández. He had been clean, then, and close to God, and God had favored him. Only in Spain was the slave taint upon him. He had not thought much about God, lately. Only in Spain was he guilty, as Ana had said, of chancing his honor.

Well, what had been done once might be done again. Gutiérrez, Hernández and himself. What the river had done once, to three, it might do twice, to many; unless Maldonado got there first.

"I must go back," he said, "quickly." He did not mean to say it aloud. He, the slave, would lead his masters back in the bodies of many men, and let the river itself make freemen of them.

"And I with you," Ana said.

He was again conscious of her presence.

"Yes, you, too," he answered. "You, above all."

48

Eight months later, on the tenth of May, they were ready to depart again.

Ana and her mother had been for some time aboard the flagship at San Lucar, watched over by Juan de Illanes, who had taken Ana's welfare as his special charge. Gutiérrez had gone back to the mountains for his fifty men; they were still anxious to go along. Eight priests, as required by the Crown, waited in a monastery in Seville. The crew and soldiery were under orders to attend their Sunday Mass well, and to be in San Lucar at Monday dawn, for the tide was full at ten o'clock, and a harbor pilot had been chartered to lead the fleet across the bar.

Orellana was not pleased with his ships, but he was past pleasure at anything. His flagship was a small galleon, that carried a crew of sixteen. Next, then, was the *San Pablo*, a Galician ship manned by twenty sailors, and burdened with Prince Philip's culverins. Slightly smaller was the coastal sailor *Bretón*, twenty years old but presumably seaworthy, in whose crew of eighteen there were only two Spaniards. Last in line, but first in importance, was a light caravel, the *Guadelupe*, with ten crewmen, and piloted by the only man who knew anything of the Brazilian coast, and he not much, one Gil Gómez, a Portuguese. Orellana hoped, but he could not be sure, that the two hundred foot soldiers and one hundred cavalry he was under bond to take with him, would appear at sailing. They were signed on; that was all he knew.

Orellana had heard nothing more of Maldonado, though agents in the House of Trade informed him that the Portuguese expedition had not yet sailed. Ever since Maldonado's stealthy visit, however, Friar de Vera had been acting like a man of definite purpose. He had sent weekly reports to Prince Philip, in which he lay upon Orellana the blame for every delay, magnified every difficulty, insinuating into the prince's mind, by constant reiteration, the idea that Orellana was no fit leader for so vital an enterprise.

So great was de Vera's prestige with the King's secretary, Juan de Samano, who relentlessly remembered that Orellana had embarrassed him before the monarch, that Orellana was powerless to intervene. Even when de Vera made a hurried trip to Valladolid to see the prince, Orellana could not follow to plead his own case, lest new conspiracies break in his absence. The burden was his now; Ana helped no more. Evicted with her mother from Cosme de Chavez' house, she reigned upon the flagship, consorting openly with Illanes. Orellana needed no two eyes to see the motive behind Illanes' attentiveness. Having seen her on her wedding day, with a fortune in emeralds about her neck, Illanes the gambler knew how to wait. Orellana did not even care. Indeed he welcomed Illanes, for the gambler kept Ana occupied; but he could not discern why she should be attracted to him.

Orellana dressed carefully for his last church service ashore. Hernández was with him, in the house of Cosme de Chavez. They were leaving the house when Gutiérrez appeared, afoot, and hurried to them at the gate.

"The fifty mountain men are at San Lucar, General," he said triumphantly. "Fifty men, and every one known to me from my youth."

"That's magnificent, Hernán," Orellana said. "Now come with us to church, and then we will go aboard our ships."

Gutiérrez cast a restless eye over his shoulder.

"I am followed, General," he said. "The new count has discovered me at last. Even now he trails me with sixteen cutthroats, bent on vengeance."

Orellana smiled happily.

"Sixteen men?" he said. "Well, now, that is like the old days— sixteen against three. Come on to church. They will not attack us there. If we meet them later, we will show them what three men of the New World can do against the Old."

Gutiérrez laughed, and fell into step with them.

"When you speak like that," he replied, "I know that good times have returned. Now we shall sail, surely."

They made their Mass at the new cathedral. The church was crowded. Among the worshipers were scores of their own company. The chapel of St. Iago, patron of Spanish soldiers, was crowded with women who bought all the vigil candles available. The priest read a special prayer for the safety of the expedition, blessed it, and dedicated it to the greater glory of God and His Most Catholic Majesty, the Emperor Charles.

Orellana, Hernández, and Gutiérrez emerged from the cathedral glowing with well-being, and sniffed at the air from the river for a sign of tomorrow's weather. The men agreed on the verdict, and a smile passed between them.

They had not gone two steps onto the plaza when their way was blocked by a swaggering figure that they had not seen for two years.

Maldonado, the former equerry, stood before them, dashing in a new cape and a plumed hat.

"My felicitations, Adelantado," he said, bowing with great gentlemanliness.

Orellana nodded but he did not bow. Gutiérrez fingered his sword so obviously that Hernández softly put out his hand to stay the hatred of the mountain man.

"I need not inquire what brings you to Spain," Orellana said. "Spying has always been lucrative for you."

Maldonado laughed.

"I might have saved myself the risk," he answered lightly. "I shall outnumber, outgun and outsail you—and when we meet, there will be no doubt of the outcome. My men are sailors, Señor, not fishermen; my soldiers are fighters, not scum from the prisons and brothels of Spain."

"Swine!" Orellana said, brushing past him.

"Quite right," Maldonado admitted breezily, "but a very fat pig, well-fed by the Portuguese king—not a starved shoat like yourself."

Again Gutiérrez placed his hand on his sword, and again Hernández seized his arm and pressed it hard.

Orellana, however, needed no assistance. He walked on, slightly brushing Maldonado aside. This Maldonado could not stomach. The interview was not ending to his liking.

"Stay!" he called. "I have not finished with you."

"I have with you," Orellana said coldly, without breaking his stride. Maldonado followed and touched Orellana's arm.

"You need not be so arrogant with me, old goat," he said. "I know it for the bluster that it is. I know you will not sail tomorrow. Friar de Vera is aboard your ships right now, making another inspection."

He laughed at Orellana's anxiety, enjoying the sensation.

"I know much more than that," he said. "Will you listen?"

Orellana stopped. It was best that he know the worst, and his former equerry boasted only when he was sure of his facts.

"Friar de Vera has a secret order from the prince, naming himself your successor—in the event of your untimely death."

"There you are wrong," Orellana said. "The friar is not even sailing with us."

"He is sailing, all right," Maldonado said. "The prince has appointed him inspector general of the expedition, for the Crown. He carries the order in the secret hollow of his crucifix. I know, for he showed it to me."

"He showed it to you?"

"Why not? When he and I reach the Amazon, why should we fight each other? The country is large enough for us both. It is just too small for us—and you. And I shall be there before you, for I leave next week."

"And I tomorrow. We shall see."

"No, Your Worship, you will not leave tomorrow. Why do you think I came to Spain? Friar de Vera is most obliging. There is the little matter of an unpaid provisions bill you owe a certain merchant of San Lucar. The sails of your flagship were taken off this morning, to be held until the note is paid."

"He could not do that."

"You forget that the Friar speaks for the king. It was de Vera who suggested the security to the merchant, and permitted the sails to be moved. By the time you redeem them, I shall be well at sea."

"Such baseness is worthy of you, Maldonado," Orellana said.

"Oh, it was de Vera who thought of it," Maldonado answered lightly. He was ready to leave now. One more sensation, and he would have humbled the adelantado enough. "Just—" his voice assumed confidential significance, "just as, at my request, he thought of the way to keep you from sailing last September."

Orellana did not satisfy him by asking for details, but Maldonado could not stop now.

"You thought it was your wife, didn't you? Well—it was, in a way. A beautiful little wife you have there, my friend. Beautiful to deal with." He laughed. "But the credit really belongs to de Vera. He put it into her head that to condemn the galleon would force you to borrow from the Genoese, and guarantee her own rich gifts. She is a tractable woman—your wife." He bowed, and lifted his hat. "To our meeting in the New World, Adelantado."

Orellana stood still until he was out of earshot, then turned quickly to his friends.

"We must sail at once," he said. "We must get the sails and go. Antonio—go to the merchant. Give him back all his provisions, but get the sails."

"What will we do for food?" Hernández asked.

"We can sail with empty stomachs, but not with empty spars," Orellana said. "Hurry, there is no time to lose."

"Very well, then," Hernández said, "but it is dangerous."

"And Gutiérrez—scour the town and get together the men. Send word quickly. Everyone aboard the ships. But quietly. Do not alarm de Vera, and do not send word to the monastery. The priests would tell de Vera. We must sail without them."

"Yes, General," Gutiérrez listened, but his eyes were on the retreating figure of Maldonado.

"I will meet you both at the long boat in front of Velásquez' sailyard in San Lucar. We will go out to the ships together. Hurry!"

"Think twice, Francisco," Hernández said. "If you sail without leave from de Vera, your charter, your titles, your whole contract with the prince is void."

"Let it be voided, then," Orellana said. "Nothing succeeds like success. A new Spanish empire along the Amazon will silence all the critics. Remember Cortez, and Pizarro. One must be in ill repute, it seems, in order to win success. Hurry!"

He rushed off across the plaza. Hernández sped toward Chavez' house to get his horse and gallop to San Lucar.

Gutiérrez alone was left in the plaza. He watched Maldonado swagger down the street. His eyes were not on the retreating figure, however, but upon the little deck of the brigantine *Victoria*. He, Hernández, Carranza, and Robles, were urging Orellana to take command of a company of dying men. "And Maldonado?" Orellana had asked. Gutiérrez remembered well his own answer to the question. "From this day, Captain, Maldonado is my special charge."

Maldonado turned a corner, out of sight. Gutiérrez loosened his sword in its scabbard, and followed quickly.

49

GUTIÉRREZ did not realize that he himself was followed. He had eyes only for Maldonado, and he stalked him a long time. The Sunday crowds were everywhere. Now and then Gutiérrez paused long enough to speak a quick word to a group of sailors and assure himself that they hurried away before he continued after Maldonado. His quarry's route took him circuitously toward the House of Trade. This was odd, for no business was transacted there on the Lord's Day.

He caught up with Maldonado in the ground floor arcade of the ancient Moorish building, a long avenue flanked on one side by the Guadalquivir, on the other by many doors leading off to business apartments. Maldonado strode toward the door of de Vera's office. Gutiérrez hastened forward and spun him around.

"Not so fast, bloated viper," he said, drawing his sword. "You have done harm enough. The time has come for you to die."

Maldonado's long blade whipped from its scabbard, and he drew his dagger, too. Looking quickly around, he put his back against the fluted columns that opened on the river side, so that Gutiérrez would have the sun in his eyes. He was not alarmed; he knew his strength with the sword. And he had two weapons that the mountain man did not own, his dagger and his cape.

"Think twice, little man," Maldonado said. "You are no match for me. What have I done to you?"

Gutiérrez' answer was an aggressive attack. His sword was much heavier than Maldonado's, and he had the advantage of mobility. He could turn on an arc. Maldonado must stand and fight, or face the blinding sun. Gutiérrez had serious trouble, however, with Maldonado's dagger and cape. One moment of delay, and the cape would be around his blade, snagging it, and he was finished. He could not reach Maldonado's throat; the dagger parried him. He thrust, probing, watching his opponent's eyes rather than his sword, pivoting to the left, to the right, the cape ever in front of him.

"You had better stop, little man," Maldonado said. "I might get angry and hurt you."

Maldonado was the better swordsman. Gutiérrez knew that at once. The mountain man's only resource lay in his strength. He must beat Maldonado down. And although the sun was in his face, he had one advantage of position. Maldonado's right foot was anchored to the pediment of one of the arches that held up the fluted ceiling. He had pushed his boot into a corner to brace himself and give greater facility to his hip motions. In a fight where a man must stand or die, thrusting with sword and parrying with dagger and cape, the axis of defense is his hip bones. The anchored foot strengthened that defense; but did it also open a weakness?

Gutiérrez risked the fatal envelopment of the cape to test the weakness. He took a quick step to the right, thrusting obliquely at Maldonado's left breast. The thrust was short of its goal, out of respect to the cape, but it proved the weakness. Maldonado could not step away from the attack without stumbling over his own right knee. Gutiérrez parried Maldonado's long blade, watchful. Maldonado's wrist must turn now, giving him the opportunity. There would be only one chance.

Maldonado's wrist flipped. Gutiérrez threw his weight hard over to the right, his heart side completely exposed, and drove forward through the enveloping cape with all the strength of his broad back, his mountain legs, and his ox-like arms. Maldonado's long blade passed under his left shoulder, as Gutiérrez' sword found flesh, then rib and then, long-lunging, the wall at Maldonado's back.

Gutiérrez withdrew his sword from the dead body and stooped to wipe it on Maldonado's cape. As he did so, he became conscious that he was not alone. Standing in the arcade, blocking the exit, sword in hand and many men at his back, stood the young Count de Montana.

"Very good," the count said icily, "but you are not yet finished."

415

Gutiérrez backed cautiously away. The count advanced alertly, respectful of the swordsmanship he had just seen. Between two of the fluted columns, Gutiérrez saw the river only ten feet below. He doubted that the count could swim; it was an accomplishment of the New World.

The count advanced another step. Gutiérrez raised his blade, but he did not engage. Instead, he drew his arm back suddenly, and threw his sword into the count's face, at the same time leaping from the arcade, between the Moorish columns, into the Guadalquivir. He struck out with powerful muscles for the farther shore, and he was out of the water before the count's men could reach him in a boat.

Now he had only one thought—he must get to San Lucar. Without him, the fifty mountain men would never go aboard. He pulled a man from a horse, and fled galloping. He had a start; but the count would know his direction, and follow. Somewhere along the way he must cross the river, before it became too wide.

He reached the town at last, dismounted, turned the spent horse in the direction of Seville and slapped its rump, then made for the waterfront. At the wharf of Velásquez, the sailmaker, the Sunday afternoon was lazy. Peering cautiously around a corner of the building, Gutiérrez saw three old fishermen mending their nets by the water's edge. The tide was outward. Fishing boats tugged at their painters with guttural coaxing sounds. A lazy gull was settled on a pile as though he meant to spend the night there. Off in the harbor were the four ships at anchor. There was not so much as a long boat around them. Whatever inspection de Vera had made was now finished. Gutiérrez squinted closely at the silhouette of the flagship. If she possessed sails, they were not in evidence.

The clatter of hooves on cobblestones startled the old fishermen to their knees. Taking advantage of their distraction, Gutiérrez slipped up the steps of the sailmaker's loft, and flung himself down like a mole, burrowing under canvas. He could see the edge of the wharf, the harbor and the ships beyond.

The Count de Montana questioned the fishermen. Gutiérrez could hear their voices, swearing on the Holy Virgin that no man within the hour had passed out to the ships. The count ordered his horses to be tied. He could afford to wait.

Now Hernández came, and went out to the flagship on a barge. He was gone a long time, returned gunwale down with casks, tubs, and meat. He did not unload the barge. Rather, he roused the three old fishermen, and on their yawl hurried to the flagship, bearing with him the precious sails.

Again he returned, towing a long boat. Gutiérrez could see the tip of it tied to the dock, and Hernández' head above it. The count strolled casually onto the wharf and sat down.

Orellana came, at dusk. He conversed with the Count de Montana for a long time. Once or twice Gutiérrez heard Orellana's voice raised angrily, and the count's gay laughter which was answered, like a rumbling echo, by his men. Gutiérrez did not move.

Many men now appeared on the wharf. Many boats came down the river from Seville to unload human cargo at Orellana's fleet. The three old fishermen made a great catch that night, transporting soldiers and sailors down the bay.

Orellana remained by the long boat, Hernández with him, keeping the count's vigil. At each new group of arrivals, the count's guards blustered, holding a lantern to the face of each man before allowing him to climb into the fishing boat. On the wharf beside the long boat, the count watched but did not move.

Dawn silvered the rippling water of the bay. The wind blew outward. A rider, pompous in the king's colors, spurred his horse to the edge of the wharf.

"In the king's name!" he shouted. "The Adelantado Francisco Orellana is commanded to stay his departure until the arrival of His Majesty's commission, on peril of a fine of ten thousand ducats and cancellation of his commission."

"You do not need to bray," Orellana said. "We are blind of an eye, but not deaf of an ear." In the sailmaker's loft, Gutiérrez chuckled. The adelantado was himself again.

"His Majesty's commission will arrive within the hour," the horseman said.

"Then I guess, Antonio," Orellana said, "that we had better go. We cannot wait any longer."

"I have warned you!" the horseman said.

"Yes, indeed. I am very grateful," Orellana replied. "My compliments to Friar de Vera, and may he enjoy a long life ashore."

He and Hernández leaped to the boat and cast off. Now, Gutiérrez thought, it is now, or never.

He burrowed up from the canvas, but a glance at the waterfront was enough. The count's men were everywhere. He would never reach the wharf. And if Orellana and Hernández returned to help him, they would never get away, either. For himself, he might have chanced it, but he could not jeopardize them.

He lay down again. The long boat, stroked by two sets of oars, plowed to the flagship. The adelantado's flag immediately went up. Sails broke out on the halyards of the four vessels. The little caravel *Guadelupe*, with its Portuguese pilot, led the fleet across the bar.

De Vera arrived at the wharf in a four-horse coach as the heavy *San Pablo* swung on a close tack outside the bar. The four ships of the expedition to New Andalusia were under sail at last. Gutiérrez could see them clearly from his vantage in the loft.

"The dog has sailed without me," de Vera said to his companions. "He is finished. He does not have water enough to reach Tenerife, and he will starve to death before he raises the Cape Verdes. He lacks at least a hundred men, forty horses, and there is not a mariner aboard capable of taking him across the Ocean Sea. And note that he left the eight priests behind. I told you he was a heretic. You have seen it with your own eyes. I will need you as witnesses when I report the matter to the king."

He departed, but the Count de Montana remained. Gutiérrez' eyes were on the ships. Safe over the bar, they anchored in the roadstead, and there remained. At noon they were still there.

"Why do you suppose they do not go?" the count asked one of his men.

Gutiérrez knew why. They waited for him. Waited in the hope that somehow, some way, he would get out to them.

"For the love of God, General," he prayed, "be on your way. Don't wait for me." And thinking of Maldonado, dead in the arcade of the House of Trade, he added smilingly, "My work is done."

The ships remained in the roadstead until late in the day. The sun, falling behind them, drove into Gutiérrez' eyes so that he could hardly see them when finally they made off westward after the sun. They grew smaller as the sun went down, and finally the sun alone was on the sea.

Hernán Gutiérrez buried his head in the canvas, and wept.

50

AT TENERIFE, Orellana took on water, but was unable to procure food supplies. For three months he negotiated with the merchants without success.

Finally he went aft to Ana's apartment on the poop. Illanes was with her.

"I must have one of the rose emeralds," he said. "There is a long voyage before us, and you as well as I will starve to death unless we can buy provision. I do not ask for the whole necklace, just one gem."

"What good is a necklace with a gem missing?" Ana replied. "In the New World I shall need the necklace, to impress people with your authority and dignity. You have gotten this far without it, why spend it now?"

"In all our despairs, we have not faced a time like this. In Spain at least there was credit. Here there is none."

"I cannot help you," she said. "I knew you would demand the emeralds if I brought them, so I left them, for safe-keeping, in Spain. Later, when we are established, I shall send for them."

He knew she was lying, but he could do nothing. If he tried by force to search her luggage, Illanes would interfere. He did not fear an encounter with the gambler, but the morale aboard his ships was tottering, and a brawl upon the poop of the flagship might end the enterprise. The men already were talking about Illanes and Ana. If now Orellana made any issue, the men would surely believe him a cuckold, and contemptuously desert him.

Orellana returned to his quarters. "Raise sail," he said to the shipmaster. "We shall have better luck in the Cape Verdes."

Weak from hunger, the expedition reached the islands and Orellana humbled himself again before the merchants. They wanted money, and Orellana had none. Worse still, a pox raging in the islands struck Orellana's weakened crew and ninety-eight persons died, including Ana's mother.

On the morning that they took Mama Ayala ashore and buried her in the little cemetery overlooking the roadstead, Orellana went again to Ana.

"Now, for the love of God and your mother's memory, and to save us all from death, give me the emeralds. I must have them."

Ana shook her head. She had not wept at her mother's death.

"I do not have them," she insisted. "I told you that. And if you dispute the matter, Illanes and his friends will defend my person."

Orellana looked contemptuously at her guardian.

"I do not see," he said, "what charm you find in this gambler."

Ana smiled.

"Illanes has a great fortune in gold hidden in Peru," she said lightly. "The secret was given to him by an old man who died on the Amazon. Perhaps we shall go there one day, and dig it up."

Sorrowfully Orellana turned away. The hidden treasures of old Soria, Carranza's friend! He had not recalled Soria for many months, but he had not forgotten Carranza.

The memory of the physician was strong upon him as he turned from Ana and hailed his shipmaster, and gave the order to depart.

But now the ship captains refused to leave. In the stormy roadstead they had lost all their anchors, their cheap ropes and hawsers were disintegrating. Only madmen, they said, would put to sea with such equipment. They packed their belongings and went ashore.

Orellana turned to Antonio Hernández.

"We have not come this far to die," he said. "Get what men are still with us, abandon the galleon and use her fittings to repair and outfit the other ships. Dismount His Majesty's cannon and attach them to the anchor chains. We are going on."

The three ships sailed, but fifty men joined the captains ashore, preferring the pestilence of the islands to the open sea.

Four weeks of open water, and the drinking casks were empty. As often as a horse died of thirst, his body was seized for meat.

"We can go no farther," the coastal ship *Bretón* signaled one evening. "We perish for water."

"Onward," Orellana said. "There is only one destination left us—the Amazon."

In the morning the *Bretón* was gone, swallowed up in the sea with seventy-seven men, eleven horses and, worst of all, the brigantine that had been built in Spain to explore the Amazon.

"God punishes us, Antonio," Orellana said to Hernández, "but we must go on."

"We could raise Hispaniola in a day from here," Hernández said. "Put in, Francisco, and let the men rest and get fresh water."

"What good is Hispaniola without money? No, Antonio, the Amazon is the only place where money is of no value. Sail on."

They saw the river on the twentieth of December, feast day of Saint Mary of the O and dropped the cannon that served as anchors in the lee of two islands. Indians swarmed toward the two ships in dugout canoes, and the hundred and twenty-five survivors of the original company of three hundred and fifty turned in fear toward their leader.

Orellana had come home at last. The sadness of a year dropped from him as a shadow vanishes at sundown. He strode to the high bow of the flagship, visible to every eye, both European and savage, calm and masterful, as assertive as a husband entering his own house.

"We come in peace," he called clearly across the water in the Carib tongue. "We come in peace, with rich gifts to exchange for food."

They understood. They brought food abundantly, and water, and fiery native drink. That night there was gayety aboard the two ships, a great feast to Saint Mary of the O, thanksgiving for salvation from the sea, toasts to the colony of New Andalusia which would be born tomorrow. Toasts also to Francisco Orellana, who had led them through, over the fevered body of death itself and who, now that he was home, was great in leadership. He could talk to these savages like a brother. He could secure food and drink, could barter, coax, cajole. Now they understood why he had come to the river. In Spain he might be indecisive, but not here. Here he was at home. "A toast, gentlemen. To New Andalusia. To the adelantado, who will make us all rich!"

Next day they were off upstream.

"I know the place," Orellana said. "We named it Porcelainville on the way down river. There are tilled fields there, kind people, good roads to connect the forts that we will build, abundance in everything, and close by is Prince Cuenco and Lalah his wife, my friends, both. We must go there and build a city in the new land. First things first."

They cruised up the river with high hopes, one hundred twenty-five men and a woman. Orellana could not find Porcelainville.

"I do not understand," he would say to Hernández. "It should be about here." They had come five hundred miles upstream.

"You will find it, Francisco," Hernández said. "Have patience."

On again, up the river, exploring the many channels that hid among the uninhabited islands. Where there were no savages there was no food. Men began to die. January and February fused with March. Fifty-seven men died.

"We must find it soon," Orellana said, and kept on.

Now the men had no stomach for it. Too many of them were dying. To keep them busy, Orellana put in at an island, broke up the flagship and from her planks built a smaller vessel. Big ships were not needed now. Sixty-seven men and a woman remained, aboard the caravel and the new brigantine.

In the night, fighting a strong current, the caravel broke her moorings and smashed ashore.

"Well," the men said. "God has picked for us the site of our city. Here we must build. There is no other choice."

"No," Orellana said. "In these mangrove swamps we would all die of malaria. God makes things difficult only that we shall appreciate our new civilization the more. What we are to build, gentlemen, will be worth our sufferings, not only in our lifetime but forever after. Think what we shall build with our own hands and our own hearts. We may be a little company now, but think what is to follow! Courage now, just a little longer. Then a life such as you could never have in Spain."

The men rallied. Leaving twenty-eight of them on the island to build another brigantine from the wrecked caravel, Orellana took the remaining men, and Ana, and set out again to search for Porcelainville.

Ana was constantly with Illanes now, but Orellana still had hope. The river had changed him. Twice it had done so. First on the long voyage down. Now again the clean air, the simple savages, the vast stretches of pure jungle, calmed and strengthened him. Here on the river he could do anything. And perhaps, here on the river, he would find Ana, too. The air itself would purify her, that and the humility born of such vastness in space and time. If she were not meant for him, she was still precious and must be preserved. In her, and in her alone, was concentrated the motherhood potential of the new colony. In her, and in her alone, was the future generation of New Andalusia at that moment placed. Her emeralds were of no account now. Her future was her womb, the nursery of the future of a great new world. She was not now with child, but she was a woman, one Spanish woman alone in a New World, the beginning of a new generation. He could not leave so precious a burden. She must not die.

The malaria struck him on the twentieth day of exploration. He had not found Porcelainville. With tears in his eye he gave the order to turn back and join the men who remained on the island. Better that they all stick together, he said.

They reached the island on the twenty-seventh day. Orellana was flat on his back, tortured with disease. Hernández came quickly to tell him the news, but he did not return as quickly with the discovery that those they had left behind were no longer there. That they had built a boat was evident, but if, or where, they had gone, there was no sign.

Forty-five men and a woman.

"There is now nothing to stop us from going farther upstream," Orellana said. "We must hurry. There are so few left, to do so much."

He insisted on coming on deck, scanning the shoreline in the torturing sun, unmindful of the swarms of insects, his chart stretched before him in chill-trembling hands.

"You must lie down, Francisco," Hernández said.

"If I lie down I shall die," Orellana answered. "I am not yet ready to die."

A week later, when everyone aboard, including Hernández, was begging him to turn back while there was yet hope of getting out of the river alive, Orellana's face lit up like a starry sky.

"To the south bank," he said.

They cruised for an hour along the shore, Orellana's fingers following on his chart the contours of the river. Forgotten now was his illness, in the excitement of familiar shores. He recognized the trees, now—the giant jacaranda and the low plain beyond, the triumphant surge of the rising hills. The gurgling water quickened its chatter beneath the brigantine. The oars creaked with purposeful firmness. He even thought he could smell the pungent Indian fires of Porcelainville, although he could see no smoke.

"The next bend and we are home," he said. "We have made it, Antonio. We have made it!"

They carried him ashore and laid him in the shade of a giant tree, where the Indian road met the water. Stretching behind was the white avenue that led through the town to the cultivated hills. The oats were tender green in the fields, and smoke scurried from the porcelain kilns outside the neat huts. An Indian, accompanied by several others, approached. Orellana raised himself with great difficulty and met the chief standing. The gift of tongues was upon him still. The chief understood his wants, but said the food stores had been moved inland after the last visit of white men.

Orellana sent thirty men up the white road to bring back food. They left buoyantly. They had arrived at last. Some of them found strength to cast about among the curious villagers, searching hungry-eyed among the females, exchanging the ribald humor of soldiers who, after long continence, know the time has come to relax.

Watching them go, Orellana smiled. The land was not without women, after all. The races would intermingle swiftly. He thought of Carranza, lying somewhere under a tree not far upstream. Carranza should be here now. He would appreciate, more than any other, the implications of this fusion of blood that soon would take place, ameliorating both the Spanish and the native peoples. The beginning of the dream! Here it was now, before his eyes. Forty-five men, and Ana, and a native village. And beyond, the cultivated fields. And that knoll there at the bend of the river would be the site of the first fort, the first protection of New Andalusia against the encroachments from without that were all they had to fear. The dream was coming true. No lawyers, no poor, no priests. Forty-five men and a woman, and a New World.

Hernández came to him anxiously.

"You must rest, Francisco," he said gently. "In God's name, husband your strength. This is only the beginning."

Orellana knew, however, that for every beginning there must be an end, too. Coming down the river he had made his beginning, in his resolution to return to the river, and in that beginning, Carranza had died. He knew now why Carranza had died. He himself would never have seen everything so clearly, and so fixed his determination that nothing could divert him from his North Star. New Andalusia was fulfillment for Carranza, rather than for himself; for Carranza and Nogal, and the millions who would come after them. Yes, and for Robles, too. And for Gutiérrez, wherever he might be. And for Hernández, who was a beginning, too.

Now in the hot clarity of fever, he knew that he had come far enough. He had come home.

And then of a sudden he was jolted by a realization that brought him to his knees. He was sharply aware of the truth, a truth he had not been able to see before: that this home, this vast and serene and magnificent jungle that held in its bosom enough for all men, this giant land that nature had given the power to destroy man himself if man was not worthy of such an inheritance, was too great a legacy for the men he knew.

Man could not appreciate what he had here. Man must grow to the stature of the jungle before the land would open its womb to him. Not in Spain, or anywhere in Europe, was there a man worthy of this jungle. This was God's world. And here it would remain, serene, grand, noble, until man too was of the stature of God.

How long would that be? Tears came to Orellana's eye. He could not even guess what centuries! God was patient; He would wait. The jungle was patient; it would wait, while base men strove to wrest its treasures into their greedy hands. They would try to conquer the jungle but they would fail. No matter in what numbers they came, or with what conquering weapons, they would fail. The jungle could not be conquered; it must be won, and that could be done only with love. Greed the jungle would always overcome, and lust, and avarice, and jealousy, and pride of empire. Hate, caste, discrimination, exploitation, cruelty. In other words, man. What chance had such a man against the jungle? None at all. The jungle was here, waiting like a good and fruitful woman, waiting with God, for love.

And on that day when man, in love, walked hand in hand into this wilderness with Everyman his brother, the jungle would receive him.

Hernández came to tell him that the food party had been ambushed and seventeen of its numbers slain, but Orellana did not hear. He was gone, not far upriver, to join Carranza. He was smiling, and there was a tear in the corner of his eye, deep in the heavy socket.

Antonio Hernández saw the tear there, and he did not wipe it away. He stood beside the body of his friend for a long time.

Then he called the others. Twenty-six men and Ana, counting himself.

Ana looked down at the body of her husband. Juan de Illanes moved closer to her. She observed the movement, and looked at him.

"Well," she said, "there is nothing to keep us here any longer. We had better go, before we are all dead."

She glanced again at the body, and again at the gambler Illanes. Her hand fumbled to neaten the stringy wisps of her jungle-matted hair. The sunlight clung to her. She straightened her shoulders and primped a little.

"I am a widow now," she said.

Juan de Illanes smiled.

Hernández buried the body after they had gone. He buried it carefully, wrapping it in a blanket that he found in the village. He buried it as Carranza had been laid to rest, at the foot of a jacaranda tree, above the floodmark of the river. The low mound of freshly turned earth overlooked a great bend in the Amazon. To the north, the far shore was faintly visible, enveloped in sedate blue haze. Two lazy birds spiraled overhead soundlessly, watching the fish splash in the water. The birds did not swoop upon the fish. Their craws were full of berries from the abundant shore; there was plenty here, without killing.

Antonio Hernández sat down beside the fresh earth, and looked upstream.